READER'S DIGEST

CONDENSED BOOKS

FIRST EDITION

Published by

THE READER'S DIGEST ASSOCIATION LIMITED
25 Berkeley Square, London W1X 6AB.

THE READER'S DIGEST ASSOCIATION SOUTH AFRICA (PTY) LTD.
Nedbank Centre, Strand Street, Cape Town

Typeset in 10 on 12 pt. Highland Lumitype Roman
and printed in Great Britain by Petty & Sons Ltd., Leeds

Original cover design by Jeffery Matthews A.R.C.A.

ISBN 0 340 179 457

READER'S DIGEST
CONDENSED BOOKS

THE KAPPILLAN OF MALTA
Nicholas Monsarrat

LA BALSA
Vital Alsar with Enrique Hank Lopez

THE SHADOW OF THE FALCON
Ewan Clarkson

THE TOWER
Richard Martin Stern

COLLECTOR'S LIBRARY
EDITION

In this volume

THE KAPPILLAN OF MALTA
by Nicholas Monsarrat (p. 11)

"Kappillan" is the Maltese word
for *priest*. When, on the first day
of the war against Italy in 1940,
Father Salvatore went with his
sacristan to the catacombs that
were to shelter his flock in the
terrible years of aerial bombardment ahead, he took with him his
ancient altar stone as symbol of
his faith: faith in God and in the
indomitable spirit of the Maltese
people.

He was a man of complex
allegiances: to his mother, the
Baroness Santo-Nobile in her
palazzo on the heights of Valletta;
to the simple people in his care;
to his sister and to his beautiful
young niece so soon to suffer the
joys and agonies of wartime love;
even to his brother-in-law, a
known Italian sympathizer. . . .

His strength, like Malta's,
faltered but never broke. To this
extent his story is Malta's, a story
of human courage, and endurance, and final victory.

". . . an inspiring book . . . really
superb immediacy and vivacity
. . . in my opinion a better novel
than *The Cruel Sea*."

—*The Sunday Times*

LA BALSA
by Vital Alsar (p. 263)

The voyage by sea from Ecuador to Australia traverses some 8,600 miles of the most treacherous weather in the world. Yet four men and a cat, led by the cheerful Spaniard, Vital Alsar, determined to make the journey on a crude balsa wood raft. Courageous men, their tribulations make hair-raising—and sometimes hilarious reading.

THE SHADOW OF THE FALCON
by Ewan Clarkson (p. 351)

The peregrine falcon inhabits distant, desolate places, safe— so it might be thought—from the insidious spread of human civilisation. Today, however, no living thing is safe from man's meddling, and Ewan Clarkson, in this vivid story of Freya the falcon and her mate Frika, paints a picture of the imperilled world about us that is both poignant and ultimately hopeful.

THE TOWER
by Richard Martin Stern (p. 419)

The Tower's dedication ceremony was to have been a memorable gesture of civic pride. Dignitaries from all over the state came together with due pomp on the topmost floor of the tallest building in the world. And above the clink of martini glasses the sound of a fire alarm shrilling far below passed almost unheard. . . .

THE KAPPILLAN OF MALTA
Nicholas Monsarrat

THE KAPPILLAN OF MALTA

a condensation of the book by Nicholas Monsarrat

Published by Cassell, London   Illustrated by Pino dell'Orco and Ivan Lapper

The Maltese are a proud and determined people. Proud of their heritage, their nationhood, their language, and determined to preserve these against all attack. They were never more determined than in June 1940, when the savage power of Germany and Italy was first unleashed upon them. Throughout the island priests became the symbol of that determination. With God's help they would survive, as they had survived before, down the troubled years of their history.

Father Salvatore was such a priest—a simple, loving man. Some might say it was the simplicity of his love for his flock that finally defeated him. But he was a Santo-Nobile also, son of the indomitable Baroness, his faith and courage growing from subtler roots than simple acceptance and obstinacy. Possibly it was this very subtlety that defeated him. Possibly, indeed, he was never defeated, but won his own battle, in his own way.

Certainly he helped Malta to win *her* battle. Through her terrible years of bombardment, of starvation and death, his example never failed; neither did his message of hope, the stories he told of her brave past, of the nation that survived and grew to Christian dignity and manhood and would not be cast down.

Once again Malta held firm. And Nicholas Monsarrat, in a book that surely surpasses even his triumphs of *The Cruel Sea* and *The Tribe That Lost Its Head*, shows us how—in warm, human, day-to-day terms—this came about.

Prologue

Memoirs of a Day-Tripper 1

The man in the bar of the Phoenicia Hotel, by the main gate of Valletta, gave me more misinformation, in the space of two hours, than even six gins-and-tonics could really justify. He was a fattish, pinkish man in bulging blue shorts; a man on a long lazy holiday, but discontented none the less.

He was looking round for a decent place to settle, he told me. He'd already "done a recce" on the Bahamas, the Channel Islands, Jamaica, and Capri. Now he was in Malta. Among the Malts.

"Don't get me wrong," he said, popping salted peanuts into his mouth one by one, like a man on a very strange, measured diet. "I *like* the Malts! But you know what their trouble is? They're not organized. You can't even get a decent mixed grill here. Well, I mean, that's no bloody use, is it?"

He droned on until finally I told him that I must leave because I was crossing on tomorrow morning's early ferry to Gozo, the next-door island, for a day trip.

"Well, I wish you joy, old boy. A day's about enough. . . . There's nothing on Gozo. Talk about *quiet!* If you draw a cork they think the revolution has started. . . . But at least you've got one good thing going for you. There'll be no one on the boat. Not at seven-thirty in the morning."

11

By seven-thirty in the morning, as I might have guessed, there seemed to be more people on board the boat for the three-mile trip than there were in Valletta itself. All the lower-level benches were close-packed with humanity, and it was standing-room-only even on the upper deck. Almost all the passengers were Maltese and in black, except for children who carried bunches of flowers. There were many priests; many men in dark business suits; quite a number of old people in wheel chairs. There was a group of nuns, either pious like pictures or jolly like housewives Bingo-bound, near one of the lifeboats. Now, at some reverent signal, they started to pray out loud, and people near them joined in. At the end they all crossed themselves in unison. The whole boat-load had a pilgrim air which I could not quite place.

Suddenly a violent flurry of activity erupted from below, preceded by a tumult of shouts and cries. Laughing people pushed their way up the ladder in support of an enormous, labouring old man, who was himself carrying, bodily, a battered wicker wheel chair. Enthroned on this, clinging to its fragile sides, seeming to laugh and to weep at the same moment, was a crippled dwarf.

This strange pair was swept upward on a wave of strong arms and gusty goodwill. Where a moment ago there had been no room at all on the deck, there was suddenly plenty, and the dwarf and his wheel chair and his huge attendant were set down in a prime vantage-point. They began to hold court immediately.

Everyone seemed to know them, and to crowd round. Food was pressed upon them—crusty horns of bread, gleaming segments of fresh sheep's-milk cheese. Throughout the voyage the old man stood sentinel, behind the wheel chair, head and shoulders above everyone round him. He was an extraordinary figure: a rusty black frock-coat covered him from his shoulders to his calves; a coat seemingly as old as the man, and both of them well into their eighth decade. But it was the tiny dwarf who was the centre of this stage.

He was about fifty: beak-nosed, deeply lined: above his burnt-olive face was a shock of black hair, the last evidence of virile, vanished youth. He had a tattered rug over his knees—or rather his knee; for a chance movement showed that his left leg had at some time been severed at mid-thigh; even this pitiful body was maimed and incomplete.

What on earth was it all about? There were plenty of clues, but absolutely no answers.

The ferry passed the small island of Comino. It was a moment of rare beauty. There was the view of Malta astern, with its rocky cliffs and pink-turreted police station, and then of Gozo ahead, its ridge of honey-coloured houses broken only by the spire of a church. Presently the boat tied up at Mgarr harbour on the island's southern corner.

Within the small haven, guarded by a fort and crowded with visiting yachts, a fishing-fleet of Gozo *luzzus* swung peacefully at anchor, their garish colours reflected in water of clearest blue. The dwarf and the giant quickly vanished, borne down from the upper deck by the same willing hands. Lazier passengers such as myself held back from the press, but, within half an hour, I was in Victoria, the Gozo capital. The hotel there promised me "a real English breakfast", and the waiter inside confirmed the offer. "There's a choice of fruit juices," he began, "then porridge or cornflakes, fish, eggs any style, bacon, ham, grilled tomatoes, grilled sausages, grilled kidneys." He paused, but only for breath. "Toast or rolls. Honey, marmalade, or jam. Tea or coffee."

Breakfast was not a meal I counted on to sustain me for the whole of the working day. "What sort of fish?"

"*Dentici*, sir. Caught new this morning. Like a dog-fish. Or a salmon."

"I'll have that."

When he brought it—it was actually like a cod, and very good— and saw me settled down, he returned to gossip. The news that I might write a book about Malta filled him with enthusiasm.

"Is that why you're here? Have you come for the *kappillan's* funeral?"

"I beg your pardon. Whose funeral did you say?"

"The *kappillan*. It means a priest. The priest who is dead is Father Salvatore. He was a famous good man."

The *dentici* was finished; now there was only toast and honey, which didn't matter. "Tell me about him."

The waiter shrugged. "He was a priest in Malta during the war. He had a church in the catacombs, near the Cottonera Lines. That's what they called him then—the priest of the catacombs. He looked after all the people. They lived there because of the bombs. And do you know something—" suddenly his eyes were shining, "that's where I was born! I was the first baby to be born in the catacombs! He baptized me with his own name. Salvatore. That's my name."

The moving little story invited many questions. I could only think of one. "Why is the funeral here?"

"He lived here, ever since then. In the monastery where his body lies and where the funeral begins. They say he was sent there, or something, but it was never properly told. Anyway he died yesterday. So all the people have come to Gozo for the funeral. Everyone is going."

"Are *you* going?" I asked.

"Oh, yes!" The young waiter straightened up. "One thing is for sure—I'll be there, even if they give me the sack!"

"You said the funeral starts from the monastery," I began after a moment. "Is there a procession? Where does it go to?"

"To Marsalforn, a village on the north coast. I am going straight there in half an hour. There will still be a bus, if it can get through the crowd. If not, I will walk." He looked down at me. "Will you go?"

"I don't want to—" I was not sure how to phrase it. I didn't want to treat it as a tourist excursion—something like that. But he read me, clear as a bell.

"This is a very holy day," he said. "I think you understand. . . . Come with me."

At Marsalforn I lost my friend, who as a baby had been christened by Father Salvatore. But by the greatest stroke of luck I exchanged him for another, who had know the *kappillan* even better.

Though Marsalforn had a ridge of garish new flats and holiday villas, its small and simple fabric remained intact. It was still a fishing-harbour, tucked into a corner of a perfect bay. Today, however, people were here in the mass: street-corner crowds, quay-side crowds, sad crowds (for a good man was dead), happy crowds (for such a man must be near to heaven already); crowds which had become important, being like myself, part of the funeral. They *were* the funeral.

As we looked up the dusty hill towards Victoria and the Capuchin Monastery, a vast sigh, like the breath of heaven itself, suddenly engulfed the whole throng. Far away the glint of a cross caught the sunlight, and the first thin thread of humanity came down the valley towards us. Two miles away, the procession had started.

It was at this moment that I found myself next to a wicker wheel chair, and to the dwarf from the ferry and to the grotesque giant who was his escort. Either by accident or by the strange design of their friends, this pair had been left almost alone and now I had invaded their curious isolation. But within two minutes—such was the welcome of the Maltese for all strangers—the dwarf was answering every question of mine, and sharing every feeling, even his grief. He spoke excellent English, and gave me all the benefit of it. "Have you not heard of Father Salvatore? I thought that all the world knew his name. Dun Salv we used to call him. . . . During the war he came to our help when we needed him."

"What did he actually do?"

After a long pause the dwarf answered: "He gave us heart." Then he turned away and looked up the hill. His face, which had been brooding, grew animated again. "See there! He comes!"

The river of people was now in full flood, a giant cross—the same which had flashed the first distant signal—borne at its head. Then there came the clergy and the choir. Then the hearse, separate from all else; and then the vast following of the mourners. Far away up the hill, church bells were tolling faintly, in the five-note descending sequence which by its very repetition seemed the saddest voice with which any bells could speak. They were answered from near at hand, by the thin dialogue of the Marsalforn bell-tower. The place of death was now linked, by grievous music, with the place of burial.

Now could be heard a swelling tide of prayer from the mourners, and it was answered here and there among the crowd: no more than a private muttering of responses, yet loud enough to reach the sky and to rend the heart on the way.

Suddenly there was a cry, a woman's cry, among the crowd a little way off. It was one of many such cries. The dwarf looked towards the noise. There were beads of sweat on his brow. The stump of his thigh was twitching, and he calmed it like a fractious child, a child with toothache or a high fever. He spoke now with difficulty.

"We loved him always. We can never forget him. Some believe that he will come again to Malta, when we need him. He used to say that himself, of other men, old dead men. That was what he taught us in the catacombs." The swaying cross appeared at the corner of the street, upheld by a sandalled friar, whose knotted hempen girdle swung in unison; and a loud voice was heard in prayer. In extreme agitation, the dwarf ended: "I am sorry. I cannot speak now."

After the cross and the priests, the ancient hearse, drawn by a black-plumed horse, came into view. It was black and creaking and shabby, yet with a moving majesty about it—the last majesty of all. Its top, buried under mounds of flowers, rocked crazily as it rumbled onward. The horse which drew it, caparisoned for this dread assignment, strained against the weight.

People fell on their knees as the shadow of the black nodding plumes touched the ground in front of them. When the hearse drew level with the wheel chair, the giant behind it seemed to crumple earthward as he knelt, while the dwarf shrank away, and then recovered himself. But it was only to let out a terrible cry, as the shadows slid across his single foot: "I cannot march, Dun Salv! But I follow you always!"

The Feast Day of Father Salvatore
11 June 1940

Father Salvatore hated his boots. They were black, thick-soled, awkward, and ugly; when they grew shabby, as they always did within their first year, the toe-caps reared up like swollen fists. Once, long ago, as a young seminarian in golden Rome, he had bought himself a pair of elegant Italian shoes, and earned a fearful rebuke from the Vice-Rector. "*Shoes*, Santo-Nobile?" the voice of authority had thundered, making "shoes" sound like "fornication", and his honoured Maltese name like some coarse country joke. "Dancing-master's shoes? *Pretty* shoes?" This was a *seminary*, he was told, not some lounger's café on the Via Veneto. . . . Take those shoes off instantly! Destroy them! *Burn* them! And as a penance. . . .

Father Salvatore, praying mightily, had forsworn pride on that day, and for ever afterwards; and as a mark of his submission, he still bought, every three years or so, a pair of this same model of black, stubby, ungainly boot. After more than a quarter of a century, such boots had even become hard to find.

Father Salvatore hated his boots most especially this morning, as he toiled up the steep street of steps from Lascaris Wharf to the crown of the city of Valletta, where his mother's house reigned supreme, alike in its situation and in his heart.

It was nearly six o'clock, and Valletta was already bustling. Across the harbour in the "Three Cities" (so christened by Napoleon of the tidy mind and tyrant will, in his efforts to impose civic order and logic upon the Maltese who were indifferent to both) the buses were disgorging streams of dockyard workers. Ferries and *dghajjes*, the slim gondolas of Malta, were intent on the same job: bringing Three Cities men from Cospicua and Senglea and Vittoriosa to their work in Valletta, taking return-loads of the citizens of Valletta across Grand Harbour to the dockyard.

It was a daily exchange, the one sure tide in a tideless sea. If one had asked such men why they did not live where they worked, or work where they lived, the question would have been answered with a shrug, and not too friendly a shrug either. Who could ask such foolish questions? If a man lived in Senglea, that was where he lived until he died. If he chose to work across the harbour in Valletta, that was where he would work until God gave him rest.

All round Father Salvatore, as he toiled upward on feet already cramped and painful, Valletta itself was well into its new day. Shopkeepers were slamming back their barred doors, and rolling down the bamboo curtains which softly replaced them. Silversmiths marshalled their array of tiny hammers; lace-makers picked up once more the intricate threads of life and labour. Goats were being milked from door to door, as obliging as village taps; dogs nosed against garbage-cans, rocking them adroitly until the contents spilled out and could be wolfed at leisure. All the world, in fact, woke to its due endeavour.

One third of his way up, still outside the main bastions of Valletta, Father Salvatore paused, as he always did, to rest, to look back, and to enjoy.

He could never have explained, in simple words, the astonishing awareness which could take hold of him whenever he stood on the good earth of Valletta and felt once more, in piety and pride, the city's ageless embrace.

It was something in the streets, the narrow linkage of their criss-cross pattern; the way the jutting balconies reached out towards each other, the way the wrought-iron grilles insisted on a private world for those within. It was something in the buildings themselves, simple and solid as the rock they stood on; and in the proud armorial bearings carved as deep as history into the fabric of great porticoes. It was something in the smell of sun-warmed stone which persisted over all other smells; and the sudden startling glimpse, at the end of so many streets, as if at the end of a cave, of blue water with the sunlight sparkling on it. . . .

But now it was time to move again, and as Father Salvatore came to himself, he remembered that today the people of this island were at war. There seemed to be perplexity on every face he saw. It was because of the rumours of the night. Many of the people had listened on the radio yesterday to Mussolini's actual declaration of war shouted from a balcony on the Palazzo Venezia in faraway Rome.

"Fighters of the land, the sea, and the air, Blackshirts of the revolution and of the legions, men and women of Italy, of the Empire and the other kingdom of Albania, listen! The hour marked out by destiny is sounding in the sky of our country! This is the hour of irrevocable decisions! The declaration of war has already been handed to the ambassadors of Britain and France!"

These bombastic words had been followed by an animal roar

from the vast crowd below the Roman balcony. It seemed to be baying for blood. For Maltese blood? Who could tell?

Then, after the bellow of the Duce, they had heard a very different voice, a British voice, measured, low-keyed, that of the island's Governor, General Sir William Dobbie, assuring them that all would be well. His message was brief, and none the worse for that. Hard times might lie ahead of them, but with divine aid they would maintain the security of their island fortress: "I therefore call on all humbly to seek God's help, and then in reliance on Him to do their duty unflinchingly."

The contrast in the two styles was almost laughable, but the laugh could only be on Mussolini. There was no doubt which was the man for the Maltese. . . .

After that, because it was so like the first day at school, they had all done exactly as they were told. While men from the Air Raid Precautions toured the island, and the fighting men stood to their guns, curtains were drawn, lights turned low, and windows screened with meticulous care. Some thousands flocked to the ready-made shelters: the ancient caves beneath the massive bastions, the old railway tunnel, and the scooped-out galleries of the Cottonera Lines—the splendid fortifications built in the seventeenth century by Grand Master Nicholas Cotoner. The rest closed their shutters, barred their doors, and waited for what must come. The enemy, as all the world knew, was no more than sixty miles away. Yet nothing had happened: nothing all night, nothing at dawn, nor at sunrise. There was nothing happening now, except a new day.

What could it mean?

A mountainous market-woman with the arms of a stonemason, standing on a street corner with a small crowd round her, put the people's uncertainty into words. When she caught sight of Father Salvatore, she called out to him: "Eh, Father! Can you tell us? When will the war start?"

All Father Salvatore could answer was: "I know nothing. We must pray. Work and pray."

The answer was repeated among the crowd. Though it was an answer to be expected, it was not what they wanted to hear.

He half-raised his hand, in the traditional gesture of blessing, and went on his way.

The way he now trod, towards the summit of the city, was steep, and tiring to the legs, and especially harsh to the thick boots. Father Salvatore sighed as he toiled upward. He was forty-five, not a young man with the lithe muscles of a Maltese hound! Besides, God had given him a short thick frame, big-boned, slow-moving and awkward. He could stack clover-ricks or swing a hoe tirelessly in the fields, but he could never walk into a drawing room, nor even assist at High Mass in the cathedral, with the easy grace which both deserved.

The streets were airless under the encroaching sun, and sweat trickled down his broad face and under the collarband of his cassock. It was his best cassock, with all the buttons intact and not a stain or mend to be seen, since this was the day for visiting his honoured mother and his beloved sister. He summed things up in his thoughts: I am a small, simple, lumbering priest, with faith, and only faith, to take the place of style. I will always be so. My family, the great family of Santo-Nobile, has sired its last cardinal, and it was not myself—it was more than a hundred years ago, in the blessed reign of Gregory XVI.

Father Salvatore lived among the fathers of the Capuchin Monastery, across the harbour beyond the Cottonera Lines. It would be his home until his little church nearby was built. He had spent last night there, and had found it in the same state of doubt as was all Valletta. The friars had questioned him eagerly. He was from the outside world; his mother was a great lady who knew all those in power; he *must* have heard more than they. All he knew was what they knew already, but at least he could tell them about Sir William Dobbie, whom he had met at his mother's house: how he was a God-fearing old man (well, sixty-one, old for a soldier) and one of the Plymouth Brethren of England, a strict sect of believers: how he had big ears and a grey moustache, a sad face and a steely spirit. But beyond that? Nothing but hopes and fears.

On this the first morning of the war, he had attended the earliest Mass of the day ("the fishermen's Mass", they used to call it as children, with the men on their knees at four-thirty and at their nets by five). He had broken his fast with coffee and dry bread. Then he had walked the short distance from the monastery to the building site below the Cottonera Lines, where the church of St. Barnabas—his church, his St. Barnabas—was rising to the glory of God.

He went there every morning; sometimes he worked with the men, carrying stones on his broad shoulders, pacing out the length of a wall to enclose, one day, the private chapel which was his mother's gift. But on this bright and ominous morning, the place was deserted; even Rafel Vella, his sacristan, was not to be seen.

He looked at the walls, strong and thick; he looked at the arches of the roof and the small dome, now nearly completed; he looked at the place where he would stand one day, perhaps this time next year, the very feast day of the Saint. He said his daily prayer to St. Barnabas, the lonely outcast saint on whom his special devotion had always been centred.

"Blessed Saint Barnabas, ask God to speed the building of our church. Ask God to take care of today. Ask God that we should win the war, or survive the war, or die in the war, yet in His service, whichever is the most acceptable in His sight. Amen, amen."

Life was so simple, so wonderful, with the help of God. . . . Now nearly two hours later, he stood on a street corner, halfway up the cluttered mountain which was Valletta, and renewed those joyous prayers, and then, head down, continued his climb. War or no war, he was on his way to see his mother and his sister, as he had done every week for as long as he could remember. . . . This, especially, was not a day to fail either God or man.

Presently he became aware that his way was barred: a huge shadow was blocking the sun. A gruff voice said, "*Bongu*, Dun Salv. Happy Feast Day!" It was his sacristan, Rafel Vella.

Though he had ceased to marvel at Rafel's height, Father Salvatore never failed to be aware of it, whenever they met. He himself, thick-soled boots and all, could not aspire beyond five feet six inches; Rafel Vella must top him by another eighteen inches— nearly seven feet of solid, slow-moving flesh.

He was aware also that this was a simple giant. Rafel was not stupid—no man should call another stupid—but he was slow in wits and small in imagination. Give him something precisely stated to do and he did it; leave him without direction, and the huge man often ground to a halt.

"Where have you been, Rafel?" he asked. "I waited for you."

The giant bent his mind to this, and the answers came slowly but steadily. "I had to go to Gozo last night. To see my mother. I got a boat back this morning. I knew that I would meet you somewhere here, on your way to see the Baroness."

Rafel never said "your mother". It might have been a peasant snobbery, or a decent respect for rank. It did not really matter: Father Salvatore had grown used to every variation on this theme. Great men found it impossible to see him as a parish priest, when his family was noble. Small men of no pretensions found it natural, even logical: nothing could be more noble than the calling itself. The only people he could not love were the sycophants who said: "With your family connections it should be easy," and waited for favours.

Now he said: "But why did you not tell me yesterday?"

Awkwardly, Rafel answered: "I did not know. It happened so quickly."

Very well, thought Father Salvatore: he is ashamed, and that is enough. Seeking for gentle disengagement, he asked. "How is your mother, Rafel?"

But even as he spoke, he knew the answer. Rafel's mother would not be well.

Rafel's mother was like a character in a play, who exerted tremendous pressure on the plot but was never seen on stage. Father Salvatore knew her solely from hearsay, and from Rafel's halting comments over many years of family disputes.

It had been established long ago that she did not like Rafel's wife; the idea that her son, a native of the island of Gozo, should have married a girl from Malta, was a notable stain on the family honour, and she had never accepted it. The rules were simple, and unbreakable. A man married a girl from the same village. If he chose to marry a foreign girl, even a girl from five miles away, there was something wrong with the girl: she must have been rejected by

22

the whole regiment of local suitors, and for some very good reason.

Worse still, Rafel had chosen to emigrate to Malta—one could hardly call it less—with all that this involved in sundered ties and divided loyalties. A son was expected to visit his mother, and bring his wife with him, two or three times a month at the very least; but Rafel's wife's mother had the same idea: her daughter would naturally prefer to stay in Malta, at the parental home, at weekends and on holidays, instead of travelling all that way to Gozo, just to see her mother-in-law. So, for the last thirty years, poor Rafel had dreaded every Saturday and Sunday, every *festa*. Whatever he did was wrong, on one side of the water or the other.

Rafel said: "My mother is not well, Dun Salv. Sometimes she can hardly fetch water from the tap. She wants me to come home."

Father Salvatore found himself making the conventional responses. Rafel's first duty was to his wife. He must explain this dutifully and kindly, without hurting anyone's feelings—he could not leave his wife and go home to his mother. He was about to add that on the first day of the war the problem must take second place to all the more important problems, when Rafel himself made the point, in a different way.

"She was worried about the war, also," he told the priest. "That is why she sent for me. She does not understand." His stolid face on top of the towering body was showing confusion. "I do not understand either, Dun Salv. What is going to happen?"

"We do not know," Father Salvatore answered. "War has been declared. Soon it will start. Soon it *must* start. That is all I can tell you." Then his heart softened at the troubled look in the other man's face. "Rafel! Trust God, and trust me! There will be work to do. When the time comes, I will tell you how to do it."

"Thank you, Dun Salv." Rafel's simple brow cleared. "I was told there was fighting in Valletta last night. All the Italians— I mean all the friends of the Italians—had their windows broken." He was smiling; this, perhaps, was his idea of war. "I wish I had been there. I would have broken a window or two!"

Father Salvatore shook his head. "No, Rafel, you must not say that. Breaking windows in Valletta will not win the war."

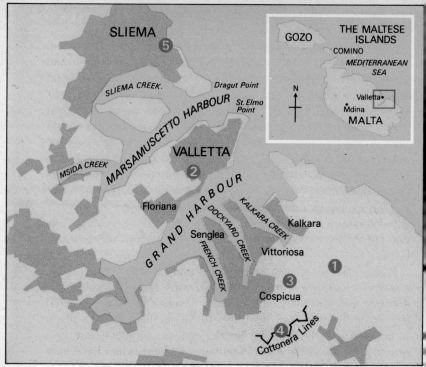

1. *Capuchin Monastery;* 2. *Palazzo Santo-Nobile;* 3. *Church of St. Barnabas;*
4. *Catacombs;* 5. *Debrincat house.*

"But it is *something*, Dun Salv."

"It is wrong."

With that abrupt dismissal, Father Salvatore became aware, once more, that it was time to take up the business of the day. "Go back to the church," he commanded, "and help the men. I will come later, this afternoon. And go carefully, Rafel."

They parted and Father Salvatore started to climb again. Because the slopes were now easier, he soon stood at the summit of Valletta, on the broad bastion in front of the Auberge de Castile. This was his favourite building in all the city. It had stood four-square against the world for nearly 370 years, starting life as the hostel of the Knights of Spain and Portugal. It was a marvel of yellow stone, its windows wonderfully ornamented, great coats of arms over the door and on the rooftop.

Today soldiers moved in and out of that massive front door—
for it was still the domain of fighting men, as it had been when
soldiers wore vizored helmets of burnished steel, instead of the
ugly snouted gas masks which themselves seemed to pollute the air.

Father Salvatore, before making the last short detour which
would take him to his mother's house, looked at it with pleasure.
He was still looking at it when the air-raid sirens began to wail
just above his head.

Father Salvatore was never to forget that moment, nor the sick
dismay which seized him as the first strident note split the air.
Though he was to hear thousands more such alarms, with a promise
of slaughter not then imaginable, it was always this baptismal one
he heard, Malta's first terrible summons to arms. For him, it
marked the division between heaven and hell; the heaven of
peaceful calm, the hell of wanton death.

A soldier, an officer with red tabs, had been passing when the
sirens started. At the sound he paused, his head on one side.
Then he said, crossly: "*Now* what?" and walked back into the
Auberge. Almost immediately the question was answered by a new
and frightful noise, a noise such as no one could be ready for, as the
air above them was rent by a tremendous barrage of bursting shells.

People started running, while Father Salvatore stood irresolute.
They had been told to take shelter at the first warning; he had
told many this himself from the pulpit. But surely he should
stay on watch, the shepherd faithful as the eyes and ears of his
flock? So he waited and stared upward, searching the innocent sky.
Then he saw them.

They were big planes, flying high up, covered by little planes
flying even higher. They were coming in from the northwest,
making a ruler-straight run over Valletta and Grand Harbour.
The bombers flew overhead in two neat groups, seven first and
then three more. There were only ten altogether, but ten was
enough. Just as no one could have been ready for the first shattering
sound of the barrage, so no one could have been steeled for what
happened next. Fantastically, bombs began to fall: to shake the
earth, astonish the city, and kill the people.

The very rock under his feet jumped at the first explosions.

Flocks of terrified pigeons soared up and away. There was screaming as people rushed out of their homes, and then darted inside again to cower under any shelter they could find.

A woman a few yards from him had fallen on her knees, her head pressed close against the glass front of a shop window, and was screeching *"Gesu! Marija! Gesu!"* in an extremity of fear.

Father Salvatore lifted and guided the screaming woman through the shop door and under cover. Then, once the first bombing had ceased, and the sky was empty and blameless as a pool of blue water, he began to walk back downhill, towards the lower town where bombs must have fallen.

Fighting his way through a crowd of frantic, frightened people, he came to a place where a corner house, wrenched sideways, had been sent sprawling into the street. A reek of cordite, acrid and horrible, lay over the whole desolate scene, and across the doorstep lay an old man, with a leg fearfully gashed by a stone splinter, bleeding to death.

Was it for this that Christ was crucified? . . . Father Salvatore dropped on his knees beside the terrible figure. *He must do something.* Just before he flexed his hands to staunch, somehow, the gross flow of blood, which was now seeping across the pavement into the gutter, he glanced up at the sky. Where a moment ago there had been nothing, there were now three tiny planes, with red-white-and-blue markings, streaking across the sky in the direction of Sicily, whence the enemy must have come. He heard a man say in astonishment: "They're ours."

THE OFFICIAL PRE-WAR "policy line" was that if the Italians came into any future war, Malta, one thousand miles from the nearest British bases of Gibraltar or Alexandria, could never be defended from the air. But when the crisis loomed, a certain air commodore at Malta had other thoughts.

He looked around him. For the island's defence, he needed planes. Presently he found some, neatly crated, in various numbered pieces. They did not belong to the Air Force; they were Fleet Air Arm *matériel*, and firmly branded "Property of the Royal Navy". But that, he decided, was something which could be left to come out in the wash. With the minimum of formality, the air commodore appropriated them. The pieces were unpacked, neatly laid out on the floor, and put together; when this jigsaw was completed they emerged as four Gloster Sea Gladiators, the last of the biplane fighters, with wooden propellers, armed with four rifle-sized machine guns, and a maximum speed of 250 m.p.h. when going downhill. When ready for action on the outbreak of war, with fuel supplied by a submarine, they stood (three at the alert, one kept in reserve for spare parts) on a half-finished airfield defended by Lewis guns.

Months later, when the trio had been christened Faith, Hope, and Charity, and had actually shot down enemy planes, and had emerged deliriously as Malta's darlings, the island's Commander-in-Chief was still the target of pained inquiries from the Director of Naval Supplies as to why he had allowed Fleet Air Arm spare parts to be turned over to the Royal Air Force.

Chasing the enemy on Raid One of Day One, the three Gladiators were too late on take-off and too slow to intercept. But it was a try, a good try, with more to come on that very morning.

FATHER SALVATORE, having fashioned a tourniquet out of a strip of curtain and the handle of a spoon, was applying pressure to the leg of the old man who was now mercifully unconscious. Round about him was a most miserable turmoil: men raising clouds of choking dust as they burrowed under the wreckage of the house; women crying, children staring avidly at what they should never have seen, dogs licking at spilled blood. When the air-raid sirens started to scream again, people screamed with them, and huddled in doorways. Then a doctor touched him on the shoulder and took over, with blessed skill, the care of the casualty.

Father Salvatore rose to his feet. His hands were filthy with blood and dust, and his best cassock no longer any better than the one he had lately thrown away. He had knelt in blood, he observed, though this did not seem at all disreputable. There could be no shame in kneeling, and no longer any astonishment in blood.

The sound of the sirens had died away, and now, giving him a moment of superb, unreasoning happiness, it was replaced by the sound of the Angelus. Eight o'clock. . . . He noticed, still with satisfaction, that many of the people on the street, reverting to a piety no longer universal, had fallen on their knees at the sound of the bells: that men had uncovered their heads, and children been hushed to silence.

A stretcher had at last arrived for the old man, and he was borne away amid lamentations; to life, or to death, was something for divine disposition. A woman with a tear-streaked face—the wife? the daughter?—brought Father Salvatore a bowl of water, and he washed his hands and tidied up as best he could.

But then a mutter of guns—or were they bombs?—to the north-west told him that all this might happen again, within a few moments. The woman, on the verge of hysteria once more, asked: "What does it mean? When will it end?"

He comforted her as best he could, speaking of God's will with more authority than he really felt even in his most subservient heart. Then he took his leave, and began to make his way towards his mother's house.

He was late, in disarray, and sickened by all this terror and pain. But at least, like the air commodore, at the first stroke of war, he had been able to do something for his side.

THE MOST NOBLE THE BARONESS Celeste Emilia Santo-Nobile sat in a chair as straight as her own back, and waited for her son, who was late.

She sat upright, because that was the way she had been taught, sixty years ago. Her hands were folded in her lap because that was how hands, if they had to be idle, must always be composed. Her face, exquisitely beautiful when young, markedly handsome in old age, betrayed nothing of her feelings. Faces, even in private, should behave like people: with absolute control.

Her black silk dress was composed in the same way, in straight folds which almost reached her footstool. The high silent room, with its louvred windows and tapestried walls, was only a setting for its occupant; when she was there it was, for all its magnificence, scarcely a room in its own right. Rooms also should know their

28

place, and observe it meticulously. At her feet a Maltese terrier dozed contentedly, its front paws crossed one over the other.

It was only her thoughts which Emilia Santo-Nobile could not quite control. Her son was more than an hour late; morning coffee was at seven-fifteen precisely, and had been so for fifty-two mornings of every year for at least twenty years, and it was very unlike Salvatore to keep her waiting without a message. Especially on a morning such as this, when the city, and even the massive walls of the Palazzo Santo-Nobile, had been so insulted.

It was possible that something might have happened to him (this form of words had served for her thoughts about her husband also, Commander Westgate-Saul of the Royal Navy, up till the very moment when death had crudely translated them in the old, forgotten war). She felt herself vulnerable, which was a hateful novelty. With an elder son, Benedict, who passed his life in a section of Parisian society so smart that it could only be seen as false; with a younger son who was a priest and no more—God forgive her—than a priest: a dear daughter, Giovanna, allied with a son-in-law whom she had long found odious—

Far away, a bell rang, and the dog at her feet gave a small, well-bred growl of warning. In an unusual movement—because to watch one's guests arriving was an unacceptable vulgarity—she rose, and crossed to a window which gave onto the courtyard below.

A liveried footman—it was Francis, a new well-mannered boy, but he slouched when he thought himself unobserved, and she must tell Gregory to correct him before it became a habit—a footman crossed the courtyard, moving from shadow to bright sunshine and then to shadow again. He opened the postern door. Then Salvatore, a black figure extraordinarily distinct against the sleepy, sun-warmed greens and yellows of the courtyard, came into view.

Framed by a huge bougainvillaea in full scarlet flower and a massive lemon tree, he looked the same as he always did: small, and self-contained, and solid as the Church he served. He was alive after all. . . . Baroness Santo-Nobile drew back from the window, and when Father Salvatore presently came into the salon, his mother was back in her chair, with the dog at her feet to complete a picture he remembered, and loved.

"Good morning, mother." He advanced and kissed her cheek. "I am so sorry to be late. I couldn't even send a message."

"What delayed you, Salvatore?"

He could not be surprised, only pleased. "Mother, you're magnificent! You must have heard the bombing. I was terribly worried—I was afraid it would be near here."

"The bombing," she repeated, as she might have said "the heat". "You mean, it was made difficult to come here? Surely you could have taken a *karrozzin*." She looked at the great clock standing against the wall. "Nearly half-past eight. Coffee will be ruined!"

Father Salvatore forgave her for seeking to maintain that this was a day like any other day. He smiled, and met her lively eyes, which were examining him with their customary thoroughness.

"You have a new cassock," she announced. "I suppose you did not think of a pair of new boots as well."

"A cassock was all I needed. I bought it on the way here."

"*Ready-made?*"

He smiled again. "I am size one. There are small priests, and medium priests, and large priests. It is really quite simple."

"*What* your father would have said!"

They were interrupted by the ceremony of coffee. It arrived in a delicately curved silver pot, with blue-and-gold fluted cups carried high on a silver salver by a footman. It was preceded by Gregory, the major-domo of the household, who had himself been a senior footman when Baroness Santo-Nobile awoke to her wedding day: a little walnut of a man, stooped but majestically dignified in every movement and every stillness, his silver buckled shoes moving soundlessly, even on polished marble.

Now he supervised the setting down of the tray, the pouring, the serving, with small waves of a gloved hand. Then he nodded to the footman, who withdrew. Then he bowed, murmured "Madame," and left the room in his turn. The doors, twelve feet high, closed behind him with a gentle click.

One lived by contrast, Father Salvatore thought, as he sipped his coffee, which was not "ruined" at all but made, as usual, from Colombian beans hand-ground at the moment the doorbell was heard. If he had not lately walked in fear on the lower streets of

Valletta, he would not now so enjoy the deep peace of this well-ordered house; if he had not the measuring-stick of the Palazzo Santo-Nobile, he might not realize so vividly the violence of the world outside, nor be so determined to return to it. . . .

But it was those lofty ceilings which now gave him uneasiness.

"You should really be on the ground floor, mother," he advised. "Particularly when the warnings sound. It would be safer there."

"It would be very *peculiar*," she answered tartly. "In the kitchens? In the coach house? In the ballroom? In the chapel? Am I a *soldier*, that I should camp out?"

"Mother, you must treat this seriously!" he admonished her, quite sharply. There were moments when he could presume on the authority of a priest, in place of the duty of a son. "There *is* danger. There have been raids already, and this is only the first day. This house can be hit, just as easily as anywhere else."

"Has there been much damage, Salvatore?"

"I'm afraid so."

She sighed. "Very well. . . . I will think about it. . . . I hope my son-in-law is satisfied."

Though the subject had been a matter of family controversy for more than a year, it was still a shock to hear his mother make such a remark, on this morning, in such bitter terms. The fact that it *was* a family concern, yet might now invite the attention of a much wider world, made it even more disturbing.

Father Salvatore had always accepted his brother-in-law's pro-Italian inclination as perfectly understandable—a matter of aesthetic preference. For Lewis Debrincat, Italy, whatever she did, was still the nation of Michelangelo and Verdi. . . . But on the morning when the bombs were falling, Italy could only be seen as the nation of the hated Mussolini. That was what Lewis would now have to face, or else suffer the fate of all traitors.

The Baroness, seeing her son silent, was continuing to speak in a way which had become familiar, and ominous.

"I know you make allowances for him, Salvatore, but such opinions are really insufferable! I have heard Lewis say, in this very room"—and she mimicked him, a very rare departure from good manners: "'Italy is closer to us than Britain can ever be'."

"But mother, you know that he meant—well, the whole range of cultural ties. He did not really mean it politically."

"He meant that he had made a choice." The Baroness, sitting straighter than ever, spoke with a steely determination. "His choice is the people who are bombing Malta this morning. . . ."

"Oh mother!" he began, sick at heart to see her so angry, so uncharitable, so less than Christian. If her son-in-law erred, then he was to be pitied. Hate the sin, love the sinner. . . . He was about to admonish her when the subject was brought to an abrupt halt, in the most appropriate way imaginable.

The sirens set up their wailing, the guns opened their iron throats, and almost immediately the bombs began to fall.

Isolated in the huge house, they could not tell the direction from which the explosions came; they were all about them—in the trembling air, the fretful movement of a chandelier, the fall of plaster from the ceiling. While it endured, they endured: the Baroness in absolute stillness, the priest with hands and fingertips composed in prayer.

In some strange way, the terror of the raid brought a cleansing of the spirit, a surcease to pettiness and recrimination. When the noise ceased, as suddenly as it had begun, they spoke no more of Lewis Debrincat, but rather of the little church of St. Barnabas, and the people it would serve, and the Santo-Nobile chapel, dedicated to God and to the memory of her husband, and Salvatore's father. Had ever a British naval officer been so commemorated? Well, there was Nelson . . . and Francis Drake.

"You should have been a great historian, Salvatore," she chided him gently. By this she meant, a historian instead of the priest he had become: a priest without preferment, nor the wish for it. But he did not mind. Such questions had been settled long ago.

He spoke once more of her safety. "Should you not leave for the country? Valletta *must* be the place they will drop their bombs, because of the harbour. You could move across to Gozo."

"I will stay here, whatever happens," she answered. It was a matter that was firmly settled. "But what will you do, Salvatore?"

"Take care of the church, and work in Cospicua."

The great door to the salon opened softly, and it was Francis.

"It is Monsignor Scholti, Baroness. He apologizes for being a little early. Mr. Gregory has shown him into the chapel."

"Ask him to come up."

Father Salvatore rose. "Well, I must say good-bye. I have some things to do before lunch."

"Oh, stay a little longer. Scholti is sure to be full of news. Why do you always avoid him?"

"I do not avoid him. But he is always so busy, and I am— always so busy." He smiled as he bent to say farewell, and he blessed her. "*Tkun imbierka.* . . . And please go downstairs, when the raids are on."

"I promise." Since he had accorded her God's protection, she could hardly answer otherwise. "Give my love to Giovanna and the children."

"And Lewis?"

She was consistent to the last. "Give him *your* love!"

Father Salvatore made his way downstairs slowly, for the sheer pleasure of savouring the tranquil glory of the house where he was born. He paused at the foot of the stairs and listened to the silence: silence, and the feeling of history encased in golden stone.

This was a house that rivalled in age and splendour even the Auberge de Castile itself. There could be no question why it should not be so; for to the proud and ancient Barony of Santo-Nobile the Knights who had built the Auberge in the sixteenth century had been interlopers. Now the Barony, which could pass from male to female, had passed to his mother. It was she who ruled here, and preserved, and endured. One day it would be his elder brother's, the "man of the world" whose Parisian follies were as foolish as anything in a foolish universe. It would never be his own; and though he loved it, and honoured it, he did not want it. He only bore its name; which by custom persisted even though by English law he would have his father's name of Westgate-Saul.

Now at the courtyard door, a man moved to greet him. It was old Gregory, the major-domo.

In *Hamlet*, Father Salvatore's favourite play, there was a line: "He hath borne me on his back a thousand times." This was his childhood memory of Gregory: as a mettlesome steed which could be whipped—well, pretend-whipped—into a galloping, plunging ride all round the courtyard—this very place where they now met.

Gregory bowed, with a grace which Father Salvatore could never have matched. His shrunken body—he must be over eighty now—was still as sinewy and controlled as that of a man half his age. Only his face was troubled. "Dun Salv," he said, and gestured, to show that he wished, this morning, to conduct Father Salvatore round the courtyard. It was immediately apparent why. "Dun Salv," Gregory said again, as he began to walk beside the priest. "I heard the bombs. I *felt* the bombs. Is it safe here?"

"As safe as anywhere else. But I have asked the Baroness to come downstairs—to the old armoury—when the warning sounds."

"The armoury! But there are no chairs! It is so small!"

"That is why it is safer. Bring down some chairs. Even a bed. Make it a place to live in." He touched the old man on the shoulder. "There will be many changes like that. You must look after her, Gregory."

"With my life!" Gregory answered, and the formal phrase took on sudden reality. "But should we not go to the country?"

"The Baroness does not wish to leave here."

Silence fell: the answer was enough for Gregory. They walked together in the shadows. Then another shadow moved towards him, a bulky shadow emerging from the small chapel as if the chapel had released one of its buttresses for service outside. With a feeling of un-Christian regret which he tried hard to suppress, Father Salvatore saw that it was Bruno Scholti.

Monsignor Scholti was all that he would never be. Father Salvatore admitted the fact calmly. Just as he had forsworn pride, so he had forsworn envy. It was obvious that Scholti was destined to take the high road, he the low. His only regret was that he had to disappoint so many people on the way.

Whereas Father Salvatore was small, awkward in his movement, simple in his thoughts, Monsignor Scholti was large and bland, utterly assured, never without a point of view calculated to set everyone present nodding their agreement. At thirty-five he was committed already to a certain fleshiness which would advance with age and with advancement itself.

Monsignor Scholti was a man busy at all times—busy with people, busy with Church affairs, busy with opening things, and blessing things (new houses, new fishing-boats, new wells and donkeys and tractors), and making speeches on any doctrinal matters that had special significance. He was "very close" to the bishop—or at least, this was what everyone said of him, which was just as effective. And with his fine sonorous voice, his celebration of the Mass could be truly beautiful—which was all to the glory of God, and should never be forgotten in the accounting.

A future cardinal? It was not impossible. Father Salvatore grudged Scholti nothing, and would not grudge him this: it was part of the awesome pattern, proof of the divine love of Christ which they both shared.

"Salvu!" Monsignor Scholti advanced towards him like a one-man tide of benevolence, beaming a princely welcome, as if he were the host, and Father Salvatore, a son of this house, were only a wandering traveller who had made his way to sanctuary. "How very nice to catch you, on the wing as it were! Tell me straight away, how is the Baroness? Is she well? I was so *worried* about her!"

Old Gregory had melted away. The two men were alone.

"My mother is well," Father Salvatore answered. "But thank you for coming to see her on such a terrible day."

Monsignor Scholti raised eyes and hands heavenward. "The worst day of our lives! Have you heard any news?"

"No. Only the raids."

"Three raids so far." Scholti had naturally heard all the news, and more. "They say the bombing in Senglea and Cospicua has been terrible. They are going to evacuate the whole of Valletta, if this goes on. As many as a quarter of a million people. The bishop is to make a statement. . . . Are you going to the Debrincats for lunch?"

"Yes."

"I hope Lewis will be all right."

Something in the other man's tone caught Father Salvatore's attention. "How do you mean, 'all right'?"

Monsignor Scholti assumed a look of diplomatic intensity. "I think we both know that Lewis has made himself something of a

36

reputation. His sympathies have seemed to lie with the Italians. You know that there have been arrests already?"

"No."

Monsignor Scholti flashed his most understanding smile. "Salvu, you *must* take an interest in these things! Yes, a number of people were detained, last night. In some cases it is certainly unfair. But in war sometimes the innocent have to suffer. One cannot be too careful. One must guard against the enemy within."

So that, Father Salvatore thought, was going to be Bruno Scholti's line of argument, for public consumption anyway. . . . He was about to agree, and thus dispose of the matter when he found himself set in the most curious rebellion. . . . He heard himself saying, with a directness which astounded him: "Will *you* be all right?"

Scholti looked back at him, with a most genuine expression of astonishment. Then the brown eyes grew reproachful as a cuffed spaniel's. "My dear Salvu! What *can* you mean?"

"You seemed to be hinting that Lewis Debrincat ought to be interned, for being pro-Italian. But I have heard you agreeing with him many times. You once said—" he searched his memory for the florid phrases: "'I would forgive Italy anything for one line of her poetry! A people of such genius cannot be bad! In fact they cannot be wrong!'" He saw a sulky look come over Scholti's face and he thought: On a morning such as this when one needs friends almost as much as one needs the help of God, I have made an enemy. . . . But, though he would suffer torments of conscience for his outburst, he persisted to the end. "Are the Italians right this morning? Do you still admire their genius?"

"But Salvu—" Monsignor Scholti recovered his utterly reasonable good humour, as easily as a man picking up a dropped handkerchief, "you cannot be so unfair! It is unlike you to take a few chance words out of context. . . . Of course I was only speaking of poetry." He looked at his watch. "Well, I am expected, as you know. Good-bye, Salvu. Try not to worry too much. And please give my greetings to Giovanna and Lewis and the children."

He turned without waiting for an answer, was joined by Gregory, and a stately progress began across the courtyard.

Father Salvatore opened the postern door, stepped outside into a narrow crowded street, and, with relief, became once more a citizen of Valletta.

FROM THE GREAT MAIN GATE of Valletta to Sliema along the coast was a distance of four miles, and downhill all the way. For Father Salvatore, already ashamed of himself, there was something entirely appropriate in walking downhill; it was what he deserved, a descent into humility after the pride of his confrontation with Monsignor Scholti. From any point of view, his collision with his superior was disgraceful. This was something he *must* conquer, if he was to have any peace within himself. Today's lesson was the lesson of life, the same for a priest as for everyone else. God's will was made up of small things and great; the great were often inexplicable, but the small were still too big for private resentment.

Immediately he found that in walking downhill he was not alone. In fact he had never been less alone, on any walk in Malta. An exodus from the high ground of the prudent, the fearful, and the desperate, was in full spate—a great sea of people from whom rose a wailing such as he had hoped never to hear even in purgatory.

Under a blazing sun, choked by their own dust and escorted by flies, men, women, and children were stumbling downhill in a forlorn torrent, laden with their goods. Some were carrying the first things they had seized on in their panic: sensible things like bedding and cooking pots, foolish things like clocks and lampshades. Some were pushing bicycles weighed down with mattresses and baskets of food and crates of live chickens. There was weeping, there was public cursing such as he had never heard before; there was entreaty to God, made in resentment and animal terror, as if God were going to be blamed for all this, unless He could give them a convincing answer.

There were even, he thought, some side-glances at himself, glances of suspicion and mistrust, as if his very cassock made him a uniformed agent of this awful visitation. Even if this were his own imagination, it was only part of the same evil dream which gripped them all, the private sector of public chaos.

As he neared Msida Creek, the second of the coastal inlets, the air-raid sirens began to scream, and the fourth raid of the first morning began.

Father Salvatore considered what he should do. The road on which they were moving was bounded by cheap shops on one side, and was open to the harbour on the other. It was not the best choice in the world. But within a few moments the bark of guns and the snarl of aircraft overhead had driven everyone for sanctuary through the nearest doorway.

The nearest doorway to Father Salvatore was the entrance to a wine shop, a mere slit in the wall which widened to a broad passageway flanked by wooden trestle tables. It was half-full already, the place sordid and sodden, people lolling half-drunk against the walls. Father Salvatore felt deeply ashamed for them—and then he remembered that nearby Pieta had been bombed that morning. These must be people who were regaining their courage in the only way they knew, after enduring sights which he could easily imagine.

He greeted anyone who would meet his eye, and sat down near the doorway. A man in a dirty apron brought him the coffee he ordered, without a word or a smile. He did not want a priest in his shop. . . . Father Salvatore sat and waited and listened and watched; and what he saw made him sadder still.

There was little talk; most of the people there just drank and stared in front of them. But there was one man near the bar repeating the same sort of phrases over and over again: "What do we do?—just sit here and be killed, I suppose! Who asked for this war? Only the rich men and the politicians. . . . What has it to do with Malta, I'd like to know!"

A gross man, fat with dropsy, called out: "Why don't you shut up! There's nothing we can do about it anyway."

Never argue with a drunken man, Father Salvatore thought. . . . It was all so silly, so sad and foolish. But the fat man's words— "There's nothing we can do about it"—were authentic Maltese.

Father Salvatore knew his people well. Though they could work very well, they preferred to be lazy; after sweating hard for three days, they would go fishing or loafing or bird-shooting for the next three. They had earned enough for that week's needs. What man with his wits about him wanted more?

They could also be brave, but usually they preferred not to be. Bravery was for other people; for fools, for braggarts, and for dead men. Only once or twice in the past had they been stung to violence themselves, in self-defence, in pride, in anger or in despair. Then they had been superb.

What was to be their story this time? Would they lie down and wait, or stand up, and if necessary be killed?

His sombre thoughts were interrupted by an excited man who rushed in, a street-cleaner, a breed not given to enthusiasm. But this one was inspired. "Hey!" he shouted. "Come and see the fun! There's a dog-fight going on up there!"

A dog-fight. . . . Father Salvatore stepped outside onto the pavement. He knew that this was a stupid thing to do, against all the regulations. But an actual dog-fight! In Malta!

For a few moments the harsh sunlight, after the gloom of the wine shop, made it difficult to see anything. Then his vision cleared, and the sky above him seemed full of planes, weaving like pretty dragonflies, flies gleaming silver and white against the smoke-puffs of exploding shells which punctured the blue sky. He could not understand much of it, but he understood what happened next. One of the larger planes, with black smoke pouring from its tail, began to spiral down, like a leaf, like a beautiful silver leaf.

Father Salvatore prayed for dying souls unknown, while the knot of people round him shouted and laughed and cheered the kill. The plane disappeared from their sight over the hill: a funeral pyre of black smoke rose skyward, mingling with the smoke of its downward ruin.

Then, quite near them in the Msida inlet, there was a shattering explosion as a bomb hit the water. It threw up a gigantic column of muddy grey liquid, which a moment before had been a soft azure blue. The blast of shock, reaching the men on the pavement, sent them scurrying back into the wine shop.

The drunk man took up his whining commentary: the futility of such a war, the futility of everything. He said: "What is one plane to them? They must be sending hundreds."

Father Salvatore sat silent, his hands folded. He knew that he should have been praying—and *seen* to be praying, as an example

40

to all—but something quite different was forming in his mind. He did not know what it was: a spark of impatience, a flicker of rebellious thought—no more than that.

When the all-clear sounded he left the wine shop gladly, and started to walk once more towards his sister's house.

LEWIS AND GIOVANNA DEBRINCAT, together with their two children, one dog, and four maids, lived in some style in one of the elegant old houses bordering the sea-front at Sliema. It was not in the ancient style of the Palazzo Santo-Nobile; but the tall three-storeyed mansion, with a columned portico to set off its impressive yellow-stone façade, carried its own stamp of consequence. It was exactly the sort of house which Lewis Debrincat, the young lawyer of twenty years ago, had always dreamed of; and with the massive injection of Santo-Nobile money which came to him as Giovanna's marriage portion, he had achieved it earlier than he had ever hoped.

It always afflicted Father Salvatore with the most mortal doubt of all, as far as a marriage or a family was concerned. Though the house was handsome, and supremely well-run, a positive power-base of chic entertainment, it was still cold to his senses. Here people lived in luxury. But did they love in the same degree?

The youngest of the maids, Carmelina, who opened the front door to him, was red-eyed from weeping. He felt able to ask her why. A priest could ask questions which a visitor should not.

"Oh, Dun Salv!" she exclaimed, and began to cry again. "It is the war," she said, between sobs. "They say there has been terrible bombing all over Senglea. My father works in the dockyard!"

"I know." He touched her shoulder. "But they have built some deep shelters there, enough for the biggest bombs. I shall be crossing over later. I'll make sure he is all right, and then I'll send a message."

"Thank you, Dun Salv. You are so good." Since she was young, she was also quick to change her mood; a smile, which would soon be enough to make any young man's heart miss a beat, now took the place of tears. "Is it true there was a big battle in Gozo, and the Italian boats were driven away?"

"No." He shook his head. "They were firing at the aeroplanes, that's all. You mustn't listen to too many stories, Carmelina."

There was a patter, and then a positive thunder of footsteps coming down the stairs. As Carmelina withdrew, the son and heir of this house, Pietru Pawl Santo-Nobile Debrincat, cascaded into sight. He was tall for his thirteen years, and fair-haired from his English strain, and at this moment panting with excitement.

"Uncle! Uncle Salvu! Did you see the aeroplane shot down? Oh, I *wish* I could have been up there, firing all those bullets!"

Father Salvatore found this boy a delight. Since there could be no sons for priests, nephews must fill the void. However, as the only uncle within a thousand miles, he felt it his duty to bring the temperature down a little. "Good morning, Peter Paul. That was a very dangerous way to come downstairs."

Pietru, subdued for at least five seconds, advanced more formally to be kissed on the forehead and blessed by his uncle. Then he burst out again: "I was on the roof, and I saw the whole thing, Uncle Salvu! The bombers came over in *swarms*, and then one of those little British planes went up—"

"But, Peter Paul, you know you're meant to take shelter—"

His sister Giovanna appeared at the head of the stairs, and called out: "Salvu! Thank heaven you are here!"

The relief was mutual. This much-loved sister was, next to God and his mother, the staple blessing of Father Salvatore's life. It had started in the nursery, with the arrival when he was five years old, of a little sister whom he must love and protect. It had continued throughout their adolescence. It had survived the blow of her marriage to Lewis Debrincat.

Did Giovanna regret her ferocious determination, which had had to overcome so much parental opposition, in order to bring the two of them to the altar? Was she happy with such a man? Certainly, if love had eluded her, she did not show it; it was a mistake utterly private, eating into no heart but her own. She was still slim, and elegant, and serene; still beautiful, with touches of grey in her dark hair which she disdained to conceal.

She was smiling as she came down the last flight of stairs to kiss her brother. "When I said, thank heaven you are here, Salvu, I hope it didn't sound too dramatic. What I meant was, the sight of you turned it into an ordinary day after all, in spite of the awful things that are happening. Have you come from mother?"

"Yes. She is perfectly well, as always."

"Thank heaven again." She turned to her son. "Pietru, I want to talk to Uncle Salvu for a moment. Go and pour out our drinks on the patio. Sherry for me, and Dubonnet with ice for Uncle Salvu. We'll be out in a minute or two."

He disappeared swiftly. "I just wanted to tell you about Gigi," she began. Father Salvatore could never think of Lewis Debrincat as Gigi; the diminutive—Gigi standing for Luigi, and Luigi for Lewis—was not for him, only for her. "He has taken everything very hard. He always said it couldn't possibly happen. . . . He won't talk to anyone. He doesn't want to come down to lunch."

Salvatore nodded. "All right. But he *needn't* hide, especially from us. Shall I go up and see him?"

"It would be better after lunch." She sighed. "That's all I wanted to say, really. I knew you would understand. Now let's have our drinks."

The screened patio, which gave onto a narrow walled garden, was the favourite family meeting-ground, and the welcome drinks were waiting. Waiting also, in dreamy expectation of all the joys of love and life, which must surely be just round the corner, was the pride and decoration of the household, Marija Debrincat.

At seventeen, she gave promise of great beauty: she was dark, like her mother, and long-legged (a happy accident for a Maltese); with large grey eyes, and a mouth as happily formed for smiling and kissing as a ring to a finger. Her budding figure was something no longer for concealment under folded arms, but for shy display and shy pride.

What did young girls *really* think about, Father Salvatore sometimes wondered when he watched Marija. The trouble was celibate priests were far too preoccupied with sex: let this not be so today. . . . He smiled as he greeted Marija, and blessed her, and said: "Your grandmother sent her best love to you. And"—with a side glance at Pietru, "she said to be sure to take shelter, *downstairs*, as soon as you hear the sirens."

"Uncle Salvu," said Pietru, "you made that up."

43

"I made it up with the best possible motives." Father Salvatore sipped his iced *apéritif*, hugely welcome after his long walk and all that had gone with it. "It really is dangerous, you know. Not just the bombs." He could never tell them about the old man bleeding his life away on the dusty pavement; that was something locked away already. "When the guns start firing, anything can happen."

Giovanna said: "Do you think we should build a shelter here?"

"I don't think so. The cellars must be very strong."

Marija asked: "Uncle Salvu, how long do you think it will go on?"

It was a serious question, for young and old alike. "I don't know, Marija. No one knows. The last war went on for more than four years."

"That was when grandfather was killed," said Pietru.

But Marija, just at that moment, did not care about grandfather. "*Four years*! I shall be twenty-one!"

"I shall be seventeen," said Pietru. "I hope it lasts a year longer. Then I can be conscripted."

"I shall be forty-nine," said Father Salvatore.

"And I shall be sixty-seven," said Giovanna.

"Mother, you *won't*!"

Giovanna laughed. Lunch was announced and she stood up. "Your father won't be coming down today. The bombing has given him a headache. Let's go in." It was as easy as that.

Lunch was excellent, as usual: the brightest occasion of his week, compounded of the joy of family life, and the pleasure of good eating. A *gazpacho* soup of coolest texture gave place to the children's favourite, chicken-pot-pie, surviving from the nursery to grace the adult dining table; then a concoction of peaches, ice-cream, and meringue. Would that the good brothers of the monastery could be inspired to glorify God in such a fashion!

Yet it was not an easy meal. Though there were cheerful moments, the anxiety which lay over the city lay over this room also. But it was the missing head of the family who most disturbed Father Salvatore. The idea of any human being hiding himself away like a cornered animal, was not something which could be forgotten.

44

As soon as he could after lunch, he went upstairs. His knock on Lewis's door was answered by a growling sound which might have meant anything. Acting on certain privileges, he opened the door and entered.

The room, heavily louvred, was almost in darkness. He made out a figure huddled deep into an armchair as if it would have preferred to be part of the furniture. A voice said: "So you have come to see the condemned man."

It was not the quality of voice he had been expecting. Lewis Debrincat sounded jeering, impenitent; he was right, the rest of the world was wrong. He was also rather drunk.

Father Salvatore said gently: "No one has condemned you, Lewis. But naturally I am worried. So is Giovanna. You must not hide like this."

"*I am not hiding!*" The voice changed to a snarl. "On the first day of their stupid war, I don't choose to see anybody. That is all."

Father Salvatore advanced to the armchair. "May I sit down, Lewis?"

"I suppose so. But spare me the absolution for my sins. I don't feel like it."

In a moment of anger and dislike, Father Salvatore could still smile. "I will leave that to God, if you prefer."

Close to, Lewis Debrincat was a sad sight. He had been running to fat during the last few years, and the pudgy body and over-fleshed face were now no more than a caricature of the good-looking young lawyer of twenty years ago. The neat black beard, which had been the Italian cult in Malta up to that very morning seemed the only steadfast thing about him; it stood out like a badge, imprinted on the sweaty pallor of his face. His shirt was unbuttoned, his eyes blinked nervously, and the hand which held his glass was trembling. Was this the man with whom Giovanna had to lie, every night of her life?. . . . Father Salvatore leaned forward in his chair, penetrating the reek of whisky.

"You have done nothing wrong, Lewis, have you?"

Debrincat glared at him. "*No—I—have not!* But that's not going to help, is it? There have been arrests already. And all because of this stupid war! We're only in it because we're a damned British colony. What quarrel has Malta got with Italy?"

"Lewis, you're confused. You don't want Malta to be ruled by Mussolini, do you?"

"I'd rather have Mussolini than that old idiot Chamberlain." Debrincat took another swig of whisky. "I'd rather have the Italians than the British. There, I've said it! Is that a crime?"

"I don't think you really believe it. Not if you think about it properly."

"I have thought about it *properly*," Lewis answered savagely, "for more than twenty years." He passed his hand over his eyes. Then suddenly the working face seemed to collapse into ruin and he was crying. "You know what will happen?" he said, between sobs. "They'll put me in prison. I won't be allowed to practise. *I'll probably be expelled from the club!*"

Father Salvatore was not sure that he could, even with the greatest compassion, help the other man at this moment. The test—perhaps the first real test of Debrincat's life—had found him out. From being a secure man, he had become a sick animal. When the lordly prince became the craven serf, it could be seen as God's rebuke to pride. But it was not the less disgusting, for all that. . . .

There was a knock on the door, and Giovanna's voice called out: "Gigi? Salvu?"

Debrincat's reaction was immediate. He whipped his tear-stained face away from the light, and whispered: "She is not to come in!"

Father Salvatore made for the door, ready to interpose himself, if need be, between the head of the household and his wife. At the door he turned, "Good-bye, Lewis. God bless you. Think about what I've said. People need you, and you need people."

There was not a sound from the huddled figure as he closed the door behind him.

"I'm terribly sorry," Giovanna said. "I didn't want to interrupt. But it's Rafel."

"Rafel? Here?"

"Yes." She laid her hand on his arm. "Salvu, I think something awful has happened. He's crying."

Everyone was crying today.

Giovanna left the two of them alone, as soon as they reached the hall. Rafel had indeed been crying, and he started afresh as soon as he was alone with Father Salvatore.

"Calm yourself, Rafel. Stop crying. Tell me what's happened."

Rafel uncovered his face, now swollen and ugly beyond belief, and said: "I ran all the way, Dun Salv."

"But why? Tell me, why?"

Rafel looked at him, wild-eyed. "The little church is destroyed. It was hit by a bomb. Oh God, that I should have to tell you such a thing!"

It was indeed the most fearful shock of Father Salvatore's life. The great ambitions, the humble hopes, had all been centred on the building of the church; and since it was likely to be all that he would ever achieve, he had grown to love it on a scale to match its meaning. Could it really be true that there was now no church, and might never be one?

"Tell me all that you saw," said Father Salvatore.

"I was down at the harbour when the raid started. We ran about like mice, and then we kept very still. Even the guns were terrible, and the bombs—I thought my ears would crack. . . . When it was over I walked through the burning dockyard, and out to Cospicua." Rafel was near to tears again. "I noticed the cloud of dust a long way away, and I thought, that must be the church, though I could not really believe it. But when I came there, it was lying on the ground. All the arches, the beautiful dome. Eight years of work. Now you could not tell which was the roof and which was the floor. . . . I talked to the people, but they had nothing to say. They are very afraid, Dun Salv. They need you. I told them you would come. . . . And I ran all the way."

Father Salvatore, sick at heart, felt as if he himself had run all the way. Enough was enough, he must think, the soul must have time to breathe again. . . . He found himself in an immense hurry to get rid of the sacristan, and to be alone. It was unworthy, but he could not help it. "You must go back, Rafel. Do the best you can. Tell the people I will come, as soon as I can."

"But when, Dun Salv?"

"Soon. Later this afternoon. Go now."

If he was puzzled by the abrupt dismissal, Rafel did not show it; he took orders from so many people, and on such a day he might have been glad that this, at least, had not changed. As they walked towards the front door the maid, Carmelina, was crossing from the kitchen to the patio. Rafel stopped as if paralysed. "I must speak to you again, Dun Salv."

"What is it now?" Father Salvatore asked impatiently.

Rafel put a hand to his brow. "I forgot! I forgot! The police at Senglea told me, just before I got onto the ferry, and I promised to tell you."

"Tell me what?"

"Carmelina's father. He was killed in a raid. When the sirens went he said 'I have work to do', and he did not take shelter. He was blown high into the water, and then he floated like a dead fish. They say he was the first man to be killed, in the whole of Malta."

FATHER SALVATORE never really knew how he got through the rest of that day. He wanted, every moment of his time, simply to cross Grand Harbour and go back to his church, or what was left of it, and to his people, or what was left of them. But inevitably he was delayed, and the hours slipped away, forfeited to other people who needed him.

He spent a heart-rending hour with Carmelina, who was distraught with grief. All the time that he was talking to her, an air raid was in progress, with explosions, and a constant onslaught of shell fire overhead. To tell her: "Your father is with God, my child," was arid consolation for a daughter's loss of an adored parent.

As soon as it was safe to move, he shared a taxi with her as far as her house—a house already with a black mourning-band draped over the handle of the door. He had said all he could to Carmelina; now he had to repeat it to her mother, who had woken as a wife and would sleep as a widow.

He went on his way as soon as he could, and then, trudging through the streets of Floriana he was caught in another raid. He'd lost count of how many there had been, on this appalling day. At long last the sirens screamed the all-clear, and eased the terror which gripped him. But after heat and dust came blood and tears.

Just up the street was the same scene as he had witnessed earlier that day: a building collapsed into the roadway, wounded men and women lying about like discarded, bloodied dolls. He did his best, as he had done before. He bound up wounds, he staunched blood, he wiped away tears. He set a broken leg, though it was done so roughly and clumsily that he feared the man would walk crooked for the rest of his life.

Three times he drew from his pocket the small golden phial of holy oil, and dipped his fingers in it, and gently smoothed across the eyes, the ears, the nostrils, the mouth, the hands, and the feet of a shattered human being the balm of extreme unction.

As the shadows lengthened, and the first evening of the war was already upon him, his hunger to return across the harbour grew unbearable. It was clear that he would be needed wherever he went; where better, then, than among his own people, who all day must have been suffering dire punishment? And he had not even seen his crucified church. . . . *He must reach it.*

The ancient *barklor* who rowed Father Salvatore, and the other chance passengers, across Grand Harbour had already had enough of the war. Though it was only seven o'clock on the calm evening of Day One, he was ready to call a halt to all this nonsense, and go back to peace and plenty. As he rowed, standing high in the bows of the tall-stemmed *dghajsa*, he grumbled churlishly.

"May heaven help us," he said, though he did not sound as if he believed that this would happen or that he would welcome it if it did. "Another day like this will kill me. It will kill us all! If I could tell you what I have seen. . . . Four bodies I've fished out of the harbour today. Four bodies in this very boat! They used to pay me five shillings for every one I brought in, and that's little enough, the way some of them stink. But now the police say, they won't pay me *anything* any more, it's the war and it's my duty as a citizen!" He rested on his oars, and looked round at his passengers, with a whole world of contempt in his rheumy eyes.

Father Salvatore, sitting on a wooden bench amidships, had been reading his breviary. Today he had fallen woefully behind in this duty, forgotten in the turmoil of other events. He would have preferred to ignore old Angelo, but he found that he could not. On this day of all days, the children of God must surely be more important than the set forms of His worship.

"We must all help each other, Angelo," he said, lowering the breviary to his knees. "You should do your duty, and not think about money. Money will not bring back the dead."

An old woman crouching under an umbrella interrupted him. "What is four bodies?" she croaked. "I have seen *forty* bodies. . . ."

Suddenly everyone was talking at once, and no one was listening. They all had their own stories of this terrible day of war, and they would not be denied. Angelo took up his rowing again, sulky at the loss of his audience.

"The bomb made a great hole in the road, and the bus ran right into it. I heard them screaming."

"They say we must take people in if they lose their homes, but who wants strangers?"

"They bombed the cemetery. Why should they do that? The dead are dead already."

"A new sewing machine. I saved for two years to buy it. Now it's nothing but a lump of metal."

"Hit in the face. They say it wasn't a bomb at all, but a bit of shell from one of our own guns. What can you do if your own side goes shooting at you?"

Father Salvatore had returned to his breviary, but the voices, with their burden of fear and despair—a burden which, it must be said, often seemed wholly selfish, with an additional pleasurable interest in the blood of others—came between him and the holy words. What could be done with such a crew as this? They were like the people in the bar, so spiritless, so unworthy of the moment.

Then his ear, which had heard nothing but tales of private woe, heard a new voice: "Who cares about all this? They want to kill us? They want to take our land? We must fight back, that's all!"

Father Salvatore turned round to find a young dwarf, not more than eighteen, sitting just under the stern-post, his stunted legs dangling above the floorboards. He was a good-humoured young man, with a fierce hooked nose, and burning eyes, and he was smiling now, all round him—at his startled neighbours, at Father

Salvatore whose eye he had caught, at Angelo bending to his oars.

Look about you, the smiling young dwarf seemed to be saying. Look at yourselves. Look at me, if you like. This is war! It is something to be *won*, not cried over, not run away from.

Father Salvatore found himself drawn irresistibly to the young man. From this small misshapen frame, from such a tiny grain of mustard seed, all faith and strength could spring. Here was a man at last. But were there many like him in Malta this evening?

They landed at last and Father Salvatore began to walk the last mile of his day, among the missing buildings, toppled cranes, dust clouds still settling, towards the church which was no more. Presently, he found that he had company. The little dwarf, the young man with the ancient spirit, had fallen into step beside him.

"Fallen into step" was a relative term. Since he had to take two strides to the priest's one, the dwarf's progress was erratic, like a puppy striving to keep up with a full-grown pack. Yet all the time he smiled, and chattered. His bounding spirits were the best tonic that Father Salvatore had had for many hours.

"I liked what you said in the boat," he told the dwarf.

"Thank you, Dun Salv."

"You know my name?"

"I heard that old misery Angelo use it. My name is Nero, Father. Nero Cassar. A little name for a little man."

Father Salvatore smiled. "Where do you live, Nero?"

"Near the Salvatore Gate. I'm a carpenter. Not the best in the world, but the best in the village, anyway. I made myself strong with exercises."

It was indeed true, Father Salvatore noticed: the small body was sinewy and compact, the shoulders and forearms rippling with muscle.

"One must do something, if one is little," Nero went on. "One cannot sit down and cry." Had there been a time when he had done this? "Any fool who is six feet high can get a job. But three feet and nine inches—now *there's* a problem worth having! So I made myself a carpenter. What does a dwarf need to be a good carpenter? Only a longer ladder!" He laughed aloud; it was clear that he had made the joke many times before. "I'd like a girl, too, but that's a bit more difficult." Briefly the little face was clouded. "Can you find me a girl, Dun Salv? I do not want a—I want an ordinary girl. You understand, Father?"

Father Salvatore smiled again. "Then you'll find an ordinary girl, Nero. Just as you've found a job for yourself, and made a success of it." Something made him add: "Malta is small too, Nero."

"*Exactly!*" The face lit up again, with all its jaunty, irrepressible good humour. "Why should we sit down and cry?"

They had come to a crossroads, and to a familiar scene: buildings in ruins, people in despair, all the aftermath of a savage attack. But there were police everywhere, and two ambulances at work, and an air of official control.

"I go to the left, Dun Salv."

"Then good-bye, Nero. I'm glad we met. Take care of yourself."

"I'll take care of others too!" The words were said with perky assurance. He really meant it.

Nero wheeled, and ran off up the street, as if he could not wait to confront his next problem. Father Salvatore inclined to the right, and began to walk with something of the same confidence. What a lesson. . . . Surely there was nothing which, with the help of God and the driving spirit of man, could not be solved.

Almost immediately the sirens sounded. He scarcely had time to master the sick feeling of fear when a bomb, screaming down with that eerie whistling sound which seemed already to have become part of life in Malta, fell at a street corner about a hundred yards away. The tremendous blast knocked him off his feet, and his head caught the sharp edge of a doorway. Then a scarlet film of blood ran into his eyes, and turned black as his senses left him.

He awoke to a blinding headache, and when at last he opened his eyes, it was to find an old woman sponging his forehead.

"A priest dying on my doorstep?" she murmured. "What next?"

Father Salvatore sat upright, and summoned a wan smile. "This priest is not dying. . . . Thank you, *nanna.*" He was sure she was a grandmother: she had the worn hands and the compassion of all this honoured tribe. The old woman, whose black widow's dress was as neat and clean as her touch had been gentle, tied a rough bandage round his head, and Father Salvatore pressed her hand as he rose unsteadily. "Thank you for looking after me."

She clicked her tongue. "*Sur Kappillan*, if we can't help each other, what is the world coming to?"

Suddenly, as he was bidding her good-bye, a noise came up the street, a kind of lowing, moaning sound which put him in mind of terrified cattle. But these cattle were people: a solid river of people, moving in blind obedience to their fear, craven fugitives from war. It was worse than the morning; he was launched into the mob, and swept along helplessly. It was the way he wanted to go, towards the Cottonera Lines; but not like this, not like this. . . .

Some of them were his own people, and they recognized him; they even exclaimed at the sight of his bandaged head. But it changed nothing in their distraught purpose. Their flight would not be stopped by man or wounded priest. And by now it was nearly dark; the gloomy twilight and the tossing shadows adding a special element of dread.

It would not do. This abject surrender was not to be borne. . . . Father Salvatore wrestled himself free of his companions, dived into an open doorway, and let the crowds swirl past.

Then he peered out, in the direction whence the people were coming, and saw a most welcome sight. Under a street lamp only a few yards away, Rafel Vella was moving towards him.

Father Salvatore called out. Rafel turned, and stared, and a beam of pure joy came over his harassed face. Then he lurched sideways, and somehow fought his way to the doorway. There, the small priest and his huge servant embraced like long-lost brothers.

"Oh, Dun Salv, I thought I would never find you! I thought you must be dead. Your head—my God, what has happened?"

"It is nothing. I fell against a doorway, and cut it."

"But you should go to hospital."

"The hospital has better things to do than treat a little cut on the forehead." Father Salvatore looked up at Rafel. "Where are all these people going?"

"Anywhere. Some to the country, some to the new catacombs. They are running from the last raid. It was the worst of all."

"Catacombs? What catacombs are these, Rafel?"

53

Rafel's eyes opened wide. "They are a new place, Dun Salv. This morning a huge bomb knocked off a piece of the Cottonera bastions. When all the dust had cleared the people went to look. It was an old burial ground, with long passages and caves, deep down beneath the Lines. It's a great shelter, nothing could hit us there. But I would not like to be there alone, I can tell you!"

"Why not?"

"It was full of little dead brothers—friars. Each one is in a little bed in the rock and the date carved above his head. I saw one date that said 1725! There must be hundreds of them. Of course they are all dried up. There is just a few bones, and the dust of the habit." Rafel was looking anxious. "I know it is holy ground, Dun Salv," he said. "But there is room for people as well. There is one great cave in the middle, where we could all shelter. It is like a church, hollowed out of the rock."

Father Salvatore smiled. Rafel was right. What harm could there be, under the hand of God, in taking shelter among the dead? The little brothers of long ago might be glad of the company. . . . He reached up and patted the sacristan on the shoulder.

"All right, Rafel. We'll go to the church, and then to your catacombs. Perhaps I could say a prayer. And then speak to the people. They have suffered so much. . . ." Conscious of his own weary limbs and throbbing head, he braced himself, and took Rafel's arm. "Now then! We have work to do."

Together they launched themselves upon the jostling throng.

AFTER ALL THE TURMOIL of the journey, there was nothing to see on the site of the church of poor St. Barnabas, only a desolation, the rubble of faith betrayed. The moonlight fell on jagged corners of wall, on the up-ended saucer which was the shattered dome. But that was all. It was not even as heart-rending as he had feared. This was no longer a church. All that was left was a heap of stones, and a heart too empty to feel its own sickness.

Father Salvatore pulled himself together. He must not fall into the sin of Malta today: the sin of apathy, the sin of surrender. "We can do nothing more tonight, Rafel. But tomorrow we must think about clearing things up here."

54

"Shall we start building again, Dun Salv?"

"Certainly! As soon as men can be spared." His mind went off at a tangent. "Tell me, do you know a boy called Nero Cassar?"

"The little carpenter? Yes." A note of derision came into Rafel's voice. "They say his mother was frightened by a mouse."

"Rafel! That's a cruel thing to say." But he could never quarrel with Rafel; so he continued, on a gentler note: "I met Nero on the *dghajsa* coming over. I liked what he said about the war. He had plenty of spirit! I was thinking, he would be a good one to help us."

After a pause, Rafel said humbly: "I have plenty of spirit too, Dun Salv. When I saw all this, I said: But Dun Salv has no church any more. How can he bless the people? So I went home, and fetched the little altar for you. It is here, Dun Salv!"

"Why, Rafel—" Father Salvatore began, moved near to tears.

"I hid it in a sack, under a pile of stone," Rafel said, and walked a few paces away. Then he returned, a bundle in his hands, and Father Salvatore recognized its outlines. Always entrusted to Rafel for safekeeping, it was the small oblong of marble, his "travelling altar", in which he had enshrined one of his precious relics, a minuscule fragment of bone from the forearm of the blessed saint and martyr Lawrence.

"Why, Rafel," he said again, "that was *very* good of you. Very thoughtful." He took the altar-piece, and cradled it. "Now wherever we go, we still have a church."

"Even in the catacombs?"

"Especially in the catacombs."

It was a weary journey back, under a cruel moonlight which revealed only desolation. From the top of his aching head to his bone-tired legs and blistered feet, Father Salvatore hated his whole exhausted body. He had seen too many fearful things that day. But he was on his way to comfort people who might have seen worse, who must have suffered more.

As they neared the great wall of rock that formed the bastions of the Cottonera Lines, they found it lit here and there, at its base, by flickering lights. Slowly, they picked their way round a mountain of ruined masonry, and cooking smells met them: grosser human smells: ancient smells of burial and dry bones: comforting smells of wood fires. A child cried, and it was as if the great grey bastion of the Cottonera Lines, long the abode of death, had miraculously given birth to infant life and hope. Then a woman's voice, astonished, called out, "Dun Salv!" and his name was repeated like a ghostly murmur from all over the wall of rock.

Bearing his church with him, Father Salvatore had entered into a new kingdom.

HEXAMERON I
1500 B.C. The Fore-Runners

"Let us now praise famous men," Father Salvatore began as soon as he had finished his brief prayers. He sought to catch his listeners unawares, between silence and tears, tears and sleep. So much was thundering in his brain that scarcely had he begun to hear his own voice echo round the great shadowy vault of the catacombs, flowing over the men and women and children in every stage of tumult and misery, flowing past the bones of the little brothers, than he was possessed with ´tongues, and other powers took command. With a pious madness, he began to stab with words and phrases, words never to be recalled by himself. It was other people who remembered and marvelled and told him what he had said.

"We have lived through a terrible day and we end it hiding in the rocks, as if we were nobody.

We must not hide tomorrow.

We have a thousand ancestors to be proud of. Bravery and adventure is in our blood.

We have been conquered before, but we have always overcome.

We have a glittering history. We must know, and remember, what the history is. We are Maltese. . . ."

LONG AGO, this island was not an island, but only an up-thrust of high ground, in the vast land-bridge joining Italy with Africa.

The Mediterranean Sea was no sea at all, at that time, and wild animals roamed its forests. Then,. under the hand of God, the good earth sank and the Atlantic Ocean began to roar in through the western sluice gate, the Pillars of Hercules, now named Gibraltar and Ceuta. Malta was left an island.

In a few years, as time must be reckoned on this unimaginable scale, Malta turned from green to pale grey, to burnt-out yellow. Very soon, it could no longer support the animals which had taken refuge on its high ground, and after they had ravaged every blade of grass, they fought each other with murderous savagery for what remained. They turned carnivore, and cannibal. They grew fewer, and smaller, and then they began to die.

They left their bones behind them. In forests stripped down to tattered bark, wild boars shed their tusks for the last time. Mammoths left monstrous skeletons. Wolves, with no softer prey to tear to pieces, turned upon their own pack, and then on their young. Among the last to die were dwarf elephants, starved and stunted—and *their* bones were gnawed by ravening bears.

Then, when it was safe, men came to Malta: untraceable men, who lived, and built, and died, and were swallowed up. There was a pause, a missed heartbeat, a thousand-year catching of the breath. Then *we* came, and our name was Phoenician.

It was the proudest name in all the known world. They were Semites, and their cradle was Lebanon. From this tiny base of power, they swiftly made themselves supreme as merchants.

Their reputation as the world's bravest sailors was never questioned. From their thriving seaports of Tyre and Sidon they set out in search of all the ocean deeps, and even here their cradle was still Lebanon. The fabled cedars of Lebanon furnished the great curved planks, made secure with resin and pitch, from which their hulls were fashioned. These ships had a high stem with a ram's head emblem, and a matching high stern-post for the pilot to stand on. (A *luzzu* from Gozo, four thousand years later, was an exact copy, with the Eye of Osiris replacing the horse's head.) The big square sail was sometimes dyed a proud purple, so that any watcher, spying a purple sail on the horizon, could say, in admiration or envy. "That one is Phoenician."

They took these ships to India and Ceylon, to Cornwall, where they mined the tin, to townships not yet named Oslo or Copenhagen. In a three-year voyage round Africa, their crews would go ashore each autumn, build a camp, sow a crop of corn, wait to reap it, and then sail on.

Sometimes they stayed, and set the commercial pattern for a quarter of the world. Thus they became masters of three hundred towns. They employed forty thousand men in the silver mines of Spain. They had their own insurance business, for ships and cargoes. Their word was their bond.

These our famous forefathers first came to Malta some fifteen hundred years before Our Saviour's birth. They called it Malet, meaning shelter; it was the same shelter as Ulysses, another matchless sailor, had found when he was wrecked on Gozo, and there spent seven years in seclusion with the nymph Calypso.

They were small men, as tough as their ships, with dark eyes, black hair gleaming like metal, and the hooked noses of the eastern Mediterranean. They wore woollen clothes to absorb their sweat, and long baggy trousers to outwit mosquitoes. As they poked about the island, they found that someone, some people with a lot of sense and skill, had been here long before themselves—perhaps as long as a thousand years before. These people had been farmers and hunters. They had lived in caves, used copper daggers, and arrows tipped with obsidian, the dark lava which could be cut and polished till it shone like bottle-glass. Already they had learned to make bronze, by fusing copper and tin.

They had built temples, and catacombs hollowed from living rock like this one, and they buried their dead in rock-tombs, or stored their dust in cremation urns lovingly ornamented. They could handle enormous blocks of stone without benefit of modern tackle; one upright stone at the place known as Ggantija measured twelve feet broad by seventeen feet high.

They honoured their dead, as the Phoenicians did: besides bones, the rock-tombs contained objects of alabaster, glass, terracotta, and marble: figures of clay for the amusement of the dead: cooking utensils: meat and drink for the long journey. Since women would wish to please, even in death, they were buried with their necklaces, rings, bracelets, ear-rings, metal mirrors, and little "vanity boxes" of cosmetics and perfumes.

There were seven thousand of these long-ago people buried in one place, the inquisitive Phoenicians found, in a vast, three-tiered, underground vault. How death had struck on such a scale, one could only guess. But whether it was a war, or a plague, or a single tribal burial-place, the dead had been duly honoured, and the living had gone back to living, and to work.

The Phoenicians came to like Malet very much: the island became a trade link and many Phoenicians settled there. When their homeland to the east came under attack from the Israelites, and waned in power, Carthage was founded, a thriving town only two hundred miles away on the African mainland, and Malet became even more handy, a secure haven for ships, not to be matched in the whole of the Mediterranean.

Then Carthage fell. One of the last boats out, before the Roman legions moved in for the kill, was bound for Malet. It carried a man called Joseph Saadi, his wife, his three children, and maternal grandfather, their furniture, some money saved from his military pension, and a few goats which did not survive a very rough voyage.

But the family survived, and under the lead of Joseph Saadi, a strong and self-reliant man who, as a soldier, had seen far worse things than this, they quickly regained their spirits, as soon as they put foot on the good firm earth of Malet. Anything was better than that terrible boat in a storm, and anything was better than Carthage, in its present peril and chaos.

It was the old story: the story of anyone who opposed the Romans.

Carthage had grown strong and proud; Rome had grown strong and proud; the adversaries glared at each other across the Middle Sea, making faces, bawling threats. Carthage had shouted: "No Roman shall dip his finger in the Mediterranean without our permission!" Rome had shouted back: "Carthage must be destroyed!"

This challenge had slowly advanced from a windy threat to a poised sword.

Now Carthage *was* about to be destroyed, though it had taken a hundred and twenty years to do it, and they had had a good run for

their money and their blood. Indeed, under General Hannibal, they
had nearly won. But now the balance had tipped: over the years
the city-state was ringed, and inexorably throttled.

For Joseph Saadi, it was a sad retreat, from a city which was
part of his man's pride and his heart's blood. He had served his
country honourably. He had earned his pension and his peace.
Now it had all gone for nothing.

Perhaps in Malet. . . . He brooded on these matters during the
voyage, when all his family were sick as dogs, and he could brood
alone. It was enough to make a man give up, and turn pimp or
thief instead of soldier. It was so unfair. . . . But by the time they
had sighted the island, and had shortened sail to make for the
anchorage, he felt that he had come to terms with the future.

It was not true that the past had all gone for nothing. A man
was a man. In victory, he held his back proud and straight. In
defeat he did exactly the same. He did not wait for the Carthage

City Council to come to his rescue. He came to his own rescue.

Himself, he had his health and his strength and his wife and his children and a little money saved. All that was needed was a new start in a new land. A new start at forty? Why not? He had heard a lot of good things about Malet. It could be done.

The newcomers set up house on the slopes of a hill overlooking the deep-water harbour. It was the principal settlement on the island, full of people with tales of bad luck in the old country, but determined also, like Joseph Saadi, to start up again somehow.

They had to contend with a frosty welcome from some of the "first families", who traced their pedigrees five and six generations back, and made it very clear that Malet was theirs, and that any new settlers had better keep their distance and their place.

To Joseph Saadi, this sort of thing did not matter at all. He was eager for the future. He wanted to buy a farm, somewhere inland, but with all the new people flocking in the price of land was terrible.

Meanwhile, he turned his hand to anything: first making their stone shanty fit to live in, then helping out with odd jobs down in the harbour—there was always a ship to be loaded, a fisherman who needed a hand, a night-watchman's job, a painting job.

The wife, who was a fiercely proud housekeeper, worked hard and kept her silence. The children loved every moment of life; the eldest boy, sixteen-year-old Hannibal (what else would a soldier's first-born son be called?), helped his father, and copied his straight back and determined pace.

Only the *nannu*, the grandfather, could not come to terms with any of this. He was nearly seventy; he had rheumatism; he had been uprooted, at the very time of life when a man wanted to sit back, and doze in the sun, and gossip with neighbours who respected his opinions. He grumbled. He grumbled all the time.

"What sort of life is this? What sort of an *end* to life? Haven't I deserved better? A man like me, who has sailed all round Africa, to finish up in this *shed*, in a country no one's ever heard of, without so much as a cup of wine to warm his bones."

"We can't afford wine. You know that."

"Why not? What has happened? We were smarter in the old

days. And as for the old forefathers. . . . Did I ever tell you how they founded Carthage? They went ashore, and bargained for a piece of land. 'For a thousand shekels,' said the other folk, 'you can have as much land as can be covered by an ox-hide.' An ox-hide? Such robbery! But we were smarter still. We cut the ox-hide into strips, and marked out a piece of land big enough for the whole city of Carthage.'' He crowed with laughter. "Big enough for the whole of Carthage. How's that for brains?" (They knew this story. Every last man, woman, and child in Carthage knew the story.) "Now why didn't *you* think of something like that, Joseph?"

"Stop complaining," Joseph Saadi commanded suddenly. "We're all in this trouble together. *These are hard times!* We're lucky to have a roof over our heads. You must just put up with it."

"You only speak like that because I'm old! When I was young, I'd have taken an ox whip to you, for saying such things!"

"Well, you're not young!" Joseph had been driven beyond his patience. "Come to that, I'm not young either. But I'm doing my best. Think yourself lucky."

Like many an old man, the *nannu* could shed tears at will. He shed them now. "That I should come to this," he sobbed brokenly. "But I'll be a burden no more. . . . You'll be sorry when they fish me out of the harbour. . . ." He tottered out of the stone shed, limping and gasping, a very moving sight.

After ten minutes he returned, glaring at them all. "I forgot my cap," he said. "But I'm prepared to accept an apology."

In the deep dark of the night, behind the ragged curtain separating them from the children, and from the old grandfather who coughed and hawked continuously, the wife rebuked her husband. "How can you speak to an old man like that?"

Joseph Saadi was already ashamed. But he was not quite ready to be repentant. "Well, why does he grumble so much?"

"*Your* father used to grumble enough."

"Not like this one." Joseph liked the old man well enough. It was just that this was a bad time to have to listen to other people complaining. "Anyway, we all have our troubles. I want to sleep. I've got to get up at sunrise to help with the grain bags."

"We should have our own grain," his wife said. "And a flock of goats. A cow, maybe. Joseph, we *must* get out of here. When are you going to look for a farm? Or a field, even?"

"I have work to do! I have to earn something every day, just to keep going. Our savings are for the house and the farm."

"What farm?"

". . . All right, all right. I'll take the time off somehow, and have another look. Now let's have some peace, for God's sake!"

As he drifted into sleep, Joseph heard his wife say: "You never liked my family, did you?"

On the morrow Joseph Saadi was as good as his word. He knew, only too well, that his wife was the rock on which all this family was founded. If she was defeated, then they were all defeated.

Before the sun was high he left young Hannibal to finish the job of stacking the grain bags, and spent the day wandering about inland, near the old walled capital which the Greeks called Melita. In fact, they called the whole island Melita, because Melita meant honey, and sweet honey abounded here. Joseph Saadi liked the sound of it. A land of honey. Would that it would prove so!

When he came back Joseph was greatly excited. "I've found the place we want. Another ten days, and we'll be moving in."

But before they moved terrible news came from Carthage. The remnants of its army had been routed by Roman legionaries.

"But what happens if the Romans come here?" the wife said. "There's nowhere else to go. Suppose they come here, just when we've got the farm going and the crops planted."

"I'll take care of that." For a homeless man, Joseph Saadi was very confident. "I can get on with them, as long as they don't want to make a slave of me. If they try *that*, there'll be trouble. Anyway, this isn't the sort of island you can just march in and take over. It could be made into a fortress! I'd like the chance of defending it myself!" He coaxed her. "Come on, mother. You'll like the little farm. At least there are no taxes to pay. And I think young Hannibal has his eye on a girl out there."

The wife was startled. "A girl? It's the first I've heard of it. What sort of girl?"

"Oh, a pretty girl with fair hair. Greek, I suppose. Well, she *was* Greek. Now she belongs to Malet, like the rest of us."

"A *foreign* girl? How will they ever talk to each other?"

Joseph grinned. "They'll find a way. . . . Come on, mother," he said again. "In a few years we'll be laughing at all this. It's a good place. A hard place, but none the worse for that. All we have to do is work till we drop, and we'll make something out of it."

The Fearful Day of Father Salvatore
16 January 1941

"Don't you bother any more, Dun Salv," Nero Cassar said. He was pushing a mountain of filthy rubbish, almost as high as himself, towards the nearest outlet into the fresh air. "We'll soon finish cleaning up here. Won't we, Rafel?"

Rafel Vella, grumpy as usual in the early morning, straightened his enormous back. His task was also menial—to carry buckets of water, slung on a wooden yoke, from the watercart outside to the underground cistern within the catacombs. "I suppose so," he agreed, without much spirit. "But I wish more people would help. After all, it's *their* home! Why can't they treat it decently?"

Nero grinned up at him. "Because they have a few other things to think about. Like the bombs and the food. Because they're a lot of jellyfish, and we are not. That's why!"

Bombs and food, Father Salvatore thought, as he dusted off his cassock: these were the twin elements to which life had been reduced, in the short seven months of the war. The first was terrifying, the second a nagging problem which could only grow worse.

Ever since that first night, he had toiled endlessly to make something of this sordid, smelly prison that ensured their safety: organizing food and water, settling quarrels, calming fears, rebuking flagrant sin, and always proclaiming, against all the evidence, that God's loving mercy still held them secure. Even when another such shelter received a direct hit, and everyone

65

in it was killed outright, except for a luckless handful who could be heard whimpering and moaning three days later, his message was still: "We are safe here, under the canopy of God." There was no other way to make their nightly vigil tolerable.

The citizenship of the catacombs had grown swiftly; now they could count on as many as six hundred souls using this refuge every night. It had won a reputation for solid safety, and a fair and firm hand in control; that of the beloved Dun Salv, whose astonishing contribution to the first night was still talked about.

The people he cared for were those he had hoped would come, the people most in need: the ravaged poor of Cospicua, the homeless, the frightened, the hungry. As he ministered to them, and prayed with them, Father Salvatore thought always of the terrorized early Christians, huddling together in the catacombs of Rome. These Christians of 1941 even behaved in the same way, somehow making homes for themselves, building together a brotherhood, which made the weak and lonely feel that together they might be strong.

Little Nero Cassar, who had found his own way to the catacombs within a week of their first meeting, had proved a tower of strength. While Rafel was the plodder, Nero was the spark. It was he who had somehow fixed up a system of radio reception, so that all within could listen to the news bulletins and government directives. The frequent broadcasts of the Governor of Malta, always stressing that religious note which came as naturally to him as to the Maltese themselves, thus rang loud and clear and comforting, all over the catacombs. Nero had extended this system to a microphone and loud-speakers, by which Father Salvatore too could be heard anywhere within this vast and gloomy warren.

When permission came for the removal of the remains of the little dead brothers who surrounded them, it was Rafel who was the sexton. But Nero somehow managed to turn this grisly task into a labour of love. He could be heard talking cheerfully to them, even as he disturbed their eternal rest. "Come along, my little friar," he would say, as he scooped the bones and the dust and the sentinel skull into a basket. "You have slept here long enough. We have a much better room for you, just round the corner."

It seemed hardly necessary for Father Salvatore to say a prayer. The blessing, from a devout heart, had been given already.

Sometimes Nero would ask: "When are you going to speak to us again, Dun Salv? I mean really *speak*, like the first time. I wasn't there, but they say it was really something! Don't you think the people need another dose? Some of them are just like jellyfish!" It had become his favourite word.

Father Salvatore himself could not fully comprehend what had possessed him, on that first night in the catacombs. He had spoken of matters which he scarcely *knew*. He had been compelled by so many things: by the terrible day, by the weight of human misery which bore down on them all, even by the stunning blow to his head during the last air raid. Then there had been the thin, lonely cry of the child which had greeted him as he neared the shelter of the Cottonera Lines. Had it been this which had set the strange pattern of the night? Father Salvatore could not tell. But he had never "spoken" again; there had been too much humdrum detail to take care of in the running of the great shelter. And after seven months all who were drawn to it had grown old in war, a little better able to cope with things.

Some drew comfort from belonging to the family of the catacombs; some saw it as a quick-profit market, others as their first and only chance to share and serve. There had also been misbehaviour, as Monsignor Scholti had not failed to point out. He had heard rumours, he said, of "goings-on" in the catacombs. The bishop had expressed concern. *Was* there drunkenness, dancing, gluttony? Were there worse things, perhaps? He only wanted to know. . . .

What were these "worse things"? Well, let us say manifest love-making between married couples, even fornication. . . . Father Salvatore sometimes wondered how to assess the scale of these sins. Drunkenness or fornication? Which was the winner? Both must be measured against the immeasurable cruelty of man to man, which now thundered all round them, every night of their lives.

He could only answer Scholti with the very words he used to Nero, on this later morning when the cheerful little dwarf seemed to be deriding all lesser men. "We must try to understand what the war is doing to these people."

He straightened up from his own task, which was to collect and stack the empty bottles of the night—not all wine, and not all milk either—out of harm's way, and went on, "Certainly there are jellyfish. But there are plenty of brave people. Those are the ones we should remember."

Nero put his broom aside. "I'll try," he said, "but won't you be on your way, Dun Salv? I know this is your visiting day. I'll see to those bottles. Some of them are worth a penny each—we'll put it in the fund. One day we'll be rich!"

"One day we'll all have our toes cut off, unless people are more careful about broken glass." But Father Salvatore knew that Nero would deal faithfully with the task. "Very well, Nero. I'll leave the rest to you. Remember about the kerosene coupons, when the man comes. And Gianni Calleja promised us a load of firewood from the dump. Better remind him. These nights are getting cold."

Rafel, who had been listening, unhitched the wooden yoke from his shoulders. "May I walk a little way with you, Dun Salv?" he asked. His tone was foreboding. "I have something to ask you."

On the cold and windy walk towards Senglea, the "something" turned out to be Rafel's eternal problem. Father Salvatore had difficulty in controlling his impatience, which made a very bad start for the day. Here was the whole world threatening to fall about their ears, and Rafel still had domestic troubles. His poor old mother in Gozo needed him. His wife in Valletta did not.

Father Salvatore found himself answering sharply, which was another bad beginning. "Rafel, I've told you a hundred times, your first duty is to your wife, *not* your mother. What has made you think of all this again?"

"She sends me letters when I don't come to see her. She sent me a *post card* last week! It was such a disgrace. You know how people read post cards. She is old and ill. She has a new pain in her hip." Rafel spread his enormous hands, in a gesture of despair. "You know how she is, Dun Salv. You have met her."

He had indeed. He had made a special journey to Gozo a few months earlier, when this same crisis seemed once again to be coming to a head. In a squat stone farmhouse, huddled against the ground as if determined to give nothing to the elements or to the

68

world around it, he had found a watchful, malevolent old woman.

He had not stayed long. He could not. Old Mrs. Vella had made it clear that she regarded Father Salvatore as the enemy, one of the people conspiring to keep a lonely old widow in fear and want. She made him feel very uncharitable, very irreligious. The trouble was that old Mrs. Vella was extremely religious herself. Her devotion made her proud, censorious, mean, and (she clearly thought) a match for any priest who withstood her holy intention.

Rafel's place was with her, not with *that woman*. It was his mother who needed him. It was he who needed his mother, the only one to understand him. And apart from all else, Rafel would surely be safer in Gozo, where scarcely a bomb had fallen.

It was true that sleepy Gozo had no "targets" in the military sense. It was thought of as a market garden and a "rest centre" for the weary. Was this what Rafel was really seeking? He was repeating one of these very phrases now.

"She says I would be safer in Gozo, Dun Salv. I can believe it. And she calls my wife nasty names. Well, *I* call my wife nasty names sometimes, but this is terrible! And she says, what am I doing in Malta anyway? There is no proper church for us—so what is the use of a sacristan?"

She would! Father Salvatore thought. He reacted vigorously once again. "We *have* a church! It is blessed by God, and its little altar is sacred, and you are its sacristan. You know that, Rafel."

For the first time Rafel betrayed his rebellious thoughts. "Little Nero can do my work, Dun Salv. Sometimes I think he is the sacristan, and I am just another pair of hands."

"But Rafel, this is ridiculous! Nero is just a helper. He's very good, very useful. But it is you I depend on."

"Then why put him in charge of collecting the bottles?" There was extraordinary bitterness in Rafel's voice: it was as startling as when a child, thought to be loving and contented, betrayed a spiteful hatred. "Am I too stupid, or am I not trusted?"

Father Salvatore stopped, and turned to face him. They stood at a windswept edge of the dockyard, the dockyard which was never free of fires and wrecks and the smell of death. But there were small things as well as great to trouble the spirits of men.

He spoke with great care. "Rafel, I told Nero to see to the bottles because he spoke about them first. It does *not* mean that anything is changed. You are my sacristan. I cannot spare you. And your wife cannot spare you either. Now I don't want to hear any more of this, Rafel. I have work to do, and so have you. Go back to the catacombs. They say that Carmel Caruana is keeping a pig there. Find out if it's true, and let me know. Chickens we can have, and rabbits, and goats for milk. But pigs, no!"

"Are you angry with me, Dun Salv?"

"Yes, I'm a little angry. But it will pass. I love you, Rafel, and God loves you. Never forget that. *Tkun imbierek.*"

Rafel, subdued, bent his head. "Thank you, Dun Salv. I will try to remember. Please give my respects to the Baroness."

"I will do that."

"And give my respects to the big ship, too, when you go past. May God keep her safe!"

THE BIG SHIP lay alongside Parlatorio Wharf in French Creek; a ship reduced to a wreck, after an ordeal such as no other vessel had ever lived through. Father Salvatore, passing close by in old Angelo's *dghajsa,* was amazed to see that she still floated.

She was, or had been, a giant aircraft carrier. Now her flight-deck, as big as a football field, was deformed by great jagged hummocks of smashed steel. She was tilted over, and in one side there was a gaping hole where, it was said, a bomb had passed right through. The steel was blistered and blackened by fires, but on the tall "island" in the middle, on a burnished plate, was still inscribed her famous name: H.M.S. *Illustrious.*

An army of men toiled all over her. She was festooned with repair-stages, fire-hoses, scaffolding. Filthy water cascaded from her side as she was pumped out. Much of her upper works had been roughly daubed with cream and yellow paint, to match the surrounding houses, and to ward off further attacks from the air—attacks which must inevitably come. But this was the strange thing about *Illustrious.* Ever since her desperate arrival at dusk five days before, pursued and harried, bombed and battered until the very last moment, she had lain at her berth, unmolested.

The old *barklor*, bending to his oars again, summed it up: "I don't understand it. One more little bomb would tip her over and send her straight to the bottom, as if she was this *dghajsa!*"

Father Salvatore knew, better than most, how true this was. Old Angelo was only going by what he could see of the ship, from outside. Father Salvatore had seen her full desolation at first hand. He had been on board *Illustrious*, within a few minutes of her arrival. Yet, of what must have been an epic sea battle, he knew only what he had seen with his own eyes.

First, soon after dawn five days ago, there had arrived certain deep-laden merchant ships, unscathed, steaming up the channel towards Grand Harbour. The noise of distant explosions, borne on the wind, told what they must have survived, to bring home their precious cargoes. Next a destroyer, the *Gallant*, with her bows blown off, had been nursed into safety by harbour tugs. Then, after a long lull, the battle noises were renewed, louder and much closer to the island: huge explosions and the scream of diving planes, murderous in their ferocity.

The people of Valletta saw swarms of planes, swooping westward towards some target of which they still knew nothing. But gradually the thunder drew nearer; the fall of bombs could be seen, and then this final straggler came out of the dusk, creeping towards safety, with smoke and flames marking the last few miles of her tormented passage. A vast sigh rose from the onlookers, and then a burst of cheering when this terrible wreck came at last under the guns of Malta, to join the convoy for which she might have given her life.

Drawn by the noise and the wild reports, Father Salvatore had his first sight of her, as with agonizing slowness, in the ten o'clock winter darkness, she slid into French Creek as if into her grave. He had never seen such a colossal ship, nor such a hideous piece of wreckage afloat. She was still on fire: great gulps of smoke, smelling of oil and boiling paint, wafted towards the quayside. Gangways came down from cavernous holes amidships, and a stream of jerking stretchers, each with its blanketed burden, began a slow progress ashore.

He waited for a lull in this dismal traffic, and then worked his way on board. Who would stop a priest? Certainly not any of the

sailors, on whose faces, in whose bloodshot eyes, could be read a desperate weariness. He began to walk at random, his thick boots echoing in this iron desolation. Soon he lost track of where he was. "I wouldn't go that way, mate," a tall sailor told him. "That bulkhead's red-hot." Father Salvatore turned, and walked down another twisted alleyway, and then another, amid chasms of torn and blackened steel, shattered hangars, aircraft smashed like the toys of a very rich and evil child.

He was afraid. If bombs could do this to such a steel mountain, what could they do to men? Presently he found out; for he emerged into a shadowy open space, and found he was alone among the dead. There were long lines of them, oily men, burnt men, ripped-up men, men unmarked and at peace. He counted, and then lost count. There must have been fifty, there could have been a hundred. He dropped on his knees.

They all seemed so touchingly young. He prayed: Oh God, take them, be merciful, give them peace! But he had the desolate feeling that he was no longer needed here. A man alive, even a priest, was a boastful intruder who should have stayed away.

As he knelt, two sailors, as matter-of-fact as barmen stacking empties, carried in a third. When they had laid him down with the rest, one of them said: "Sir, could you come to the sick-bay? There's one of our lads asking for a priest."

The sick-bay was not worse than he had imagined, but it was dreadful enough. The sailors were mostly burn cases; though tenderly treated, their agony was in the very air.

The "one of our lads asking for a priest" turned out to be a man of about forty, a veteran of much booze and brawling—if his face was anything to go by. But now, his face was nothing much to go by; the scars of self-indulgence, perilous to the soul, had been overlaid by others likely to prove mortal to the body.

"Thank God, Father!" he croaked, through blistered, bright-red lips, which made a horrid contrast with the greenish pallor of his face. "Help me. Give me the rites. I'm sorry for what I done."

"What *have* you done, my son?"

Muttering and gasping, the sailor launched into a confession of murder. Perhaps it was fantasy: something he had wanted to do, or had read about, or heard from a friend. Hong Kong, ten years ago. "She bit me, Father. You know, where it hurts most. So I picked up the candlestick, and smashed her head in. There was blood all over." Blood and silence, in some unspeakable house. "I washed it off, got dressed and ran. We sailed next morning. I never heard nothing more about it. I'm sorry, Father."

The hoarse words ceased. Father Salvatore, still holding the man's cold hand asked; "What else are you sorry for?"

"Christ, isn't that enough? . . . You mean, like a general confession?"

"Yes. And contrition. True contrition."

"Help me, Father. I forget the words."

When it was done, Father Salvatore anointed, as tenderly as he could, the ruined face, the hands which must have been wicked, the feet which had strayed. The sailor was now gasping, but he seemed comforted, and at peace.

"Am I all right, then, Father?"

"Yes, my son." God would correct all mistakes, his and this other sinner's, with the mercy and knowledge denied to mortal man.

Father Salvatore lingered in prayer. But then someone stumbled against his feet, and he awoke to urgency and need. There was so much to do besides pray. . . . He rose from his knees and, after looking round him, quietly joined in the work of mercy.

By the end of that night, Father Salvatore felt that he knew at last what sailors might have to go through, to bring food and weapons to an island under siege. What he did not know was what the ship herself had actually endured, to reach her state of ruin. Even a man who had seen her, and smelled her, and slipped on her blood-stained deck, and mourned the dead and seen the living, could not guess the half of her story.

H.M.S. *Illustrious* had long been a hunted and hated ship. She was something special: the first aircraft carrier in the world with an armour-plated flight deck, able to withstand anything up to 500-pound bombs. In particular, she had revolutionized convoy protection, and Admiral Cunningham, Commander-in-Chief of the Mediterranean, took her with him everywhere he

74

could. Her most spectacular strike had been a torpedo-bomber attack on the Italian fleet lying at anchor at Taranto in the heel of Italy, when two Italian battleships had been sunk, another wrecked and beached, and three cruisers put out of action, all in the space of two hours.

Now, her latest job, at the end of a long list, was to provide air cover for the convoy bringing in a consignment of Fulmar and Swordfish aircraft vital to Malta's defence.

But this convoy had to face a new hazard. With the declared aim of "neutralizing Malta" the German Air Force had now elbowed out the Italians and moved a whole *Fliegerkorps* to Sicily. This *Fliegerkorps*, which specialized in attacks on shipping, added up to more than 250 aircraft altogether. By way of opposition to this potent air armada, Malta at that time had two of its original Gladiators and fifteen Hurricane fighters; so it was no wonder that the *Fliegerkorps* at midday on 10 January 1941 could afford to by-pass Malta and to pounce with rare confidence on the convoy. They made their strike when the ships were eighty-five miles west of Malta—very nearly home. Almost from the beginning, they ignored the mass of shipping below them, and concentrated on *Illustrious*.

Forty Stukas were involved, in successive waves which gave no respite to the defence. With precision timing, extreme efficiency and undoubted bravery, they peeled off from a dozen different heights and angles; they dropped their bombs, came down to deck level to press home the attack with machine-gun fire, and soared up and away. At the end of six minutes, *Illustrious* had been smothered by six direct hits and three crippling near-misses. The bombs were not the 500-pounders guessed at when her keel was laid in 1937; they were 1,000 pounders, and they ripped through the flight-deck like a bayonet through a paper parasol.

A squadron of Fulmars was just taking off when the attack began, and the last two planes somehow got airborne through a curtain of spray and smoke, leaving behind a flight-deck completely wrecked, and presently, from the fires within, too hot to walk on.

Illustrious hauled out of line, and began to go in circles, like a dog with its brains bashed out in a road accident. Half her guns were knocked out; her steering-gear was in ruins. Her main hangar, and all the planes inside, were a mass of roaring fire. The two lifts serving it, steel platforms each weighing 300 tons, were welded into meaningless blobs by great tongues of flame.

Steel splinters from this fearful holocaust ripped and tore at anything that lay in their path; while all the time *Illustrious*, with thousands of tons of fuel and ammunition briskly cooking, could have disintegrated at a single stroke. Crippled, and advertising the fact from fifty miles away, she was wide open to attack, and there were still seven perilous hours of daylight left.

When the enemy planes returned, *Illustrious* could only muster half her guns, though miraculously her main engines were untouched. The rest of the fleet closed up round her, concentrating a massive barrage which was almost too tough to penetrate; and *Illustrious*'s own Fulmars, which could not land on the useless deck, circled and fought as long as they could, flew off to Malta to refuel and then streaked back to protect their mother ship.

By 5 p.m., she had made forty-five precious miles nearer home. Yawing wildly and listing from the tons of water on board (a shell splinter had jammed the sprinkler system full on), she steered first with one engine and then another. Smoke and flames billowed from the huge jagged holes all over her hull. Then the Stukas hit her with another 1,000 pound bomb. Like some monstrous homing bird, it plunged straight down the same ruined lift-shaft into the heart of the ship, and started all the fires again.

Illustrious still did not sink, nor stop her agonizing progress, but she took another five hours to make the last forty miles. She entered the Malta channel by moonlight, an unearthly and terrible sight: glowing red within, trailing a pall of smoke behind her, listing, faltering, yet somehow grinding onwards. Though her marvellous construction, and the steel heart of man, had saved this much of the ship, by the time she reached Grand Harbour she had been reduced, inside and out, to a fiery, bloody shambles, and her death-toll made the price of admiralty intolerably high.

THE CITY, after seven months of war, had come to look rather like *Illustrious*, thought Father Salvatore. Many streets were impassable; whole blocks had been gutted, and showed only roofless buildings gaping at the sky. He saw and felt the desolation, as he stumped up the street of steps towards his mother's house; and he saw another kind of desolation, much more sad, in people's faces—the fading of hope, the limbo of faith betrayed.

How could he pass on his own feeling, which had slowly become one of pride: pride that Valletta had been singled out for this punishment because Malta was a base for operations in the centre of the Mediterranean, strategically so important that she must be denied to the enemy, at whatever cost.

Germany, glorying in ferocious strength, had already overrun Belgium, Holland, France, Norway, Poland, Austria, Denmark, and Czecho-Slovakia. If North Africa was now in the balance, and Malta lay directly in her path, the choice was no choice at all. Malta *must* resist, and win at any price.

The bombing had swiftly grown concentrated, and vicious, yet strangely routine. Day bombing, night bombing, *Sunday* bombings —which was held to be sacrilegious indeed—bombing by massed flight, bombing by the single sneak raider: all this had become part of life, to be borne, to be endured.

The bombs were now all high explosive; incendiaries had been tried, but there was nothing much to burn in Malta's simple houses, where even the shelving was likely to be of stone. Though the night-time searchlights were numerous and heartening, the morning after always showed the same inevitable destruction and death. At such a time, there were terrible things to be seen and heard: people with fading voices trapped for ever beneath ruined houses, a sewer bursting open and drowning in slime a shelter full of women and children: a leg-amputation on the pavement: grey dust settling on corpses, on severed limbs, on a lone head presently covered—but too late—by a towel.

Sometimes, very rarely, there were happier stories. There was the tale of the two naughty children who were alone in their house when the warning sounded. They had been told *never* to touch the massive family chest. . . . Their home was utterly destroyed; but two days later, after frantic digging, they were discovered safe and no worse than hungry under the closed lid of the chest. But one such happy ending could not efface the ghastly total. People had seen and heard terrible things. How were the people?

There was a man coming towards Father Salvatore now who might be called typical. This was Manwel Azzopardi, a stonemason of skill and cunning who had recently spent three weeks restoring one of the balustrades in the courtyard of the Palazzo Santo-Nobile, which had been dislodged by nearby bombing.

Manwel had six children and a house in Pieta. His mother, and one of his children, had been killed by bombs; his wife, distraught, had first rushed into the nearest church and tried to drape herself with the altar cloth, then threatened to leave him unless he quit Pieta. So Manwel Azzopardi packed up and left his home.

Now, it seemed, he had returned. A small man with shoulders like the statue of Hercules, Manwel was coming down the street towards Father Salvatore, frowning at his thoughts, and then forgetting the cares of the world as he greeted someone he knew. His little flat tweed cap sat on his head like a muffin on a plate.

They met in the cold morning sunlight on a corner of Old Bakery Street—or what had been Old Bakery Street before the Germans began to dismantle it. On the opposite corner, a restless queue was forming, waiting for one of the five staples of life: bread, milk, pasta, olive oil, or kerosene.

Manwel touched his cap with a grin. "*Bongornu*, Dun Salv!"

"*Bongornu*, Manwel. What are you doing here? Have you come back?"

"No, no. Just for the work. I get the first bus in. When the bus runs." Now Manwel sounded tired and dispirited, like so many other people. "I tell you, Dun Salv, it's no joke being billeted with a lot of strangers. Take the place we're living in. They don't want us, and we don't want them. They're such a *dirty* family." He caught the look on Father Salvatore's face. "I'm sorry, Dun Salv, but some people *are* dirty, and it's no good pretending."

"Perhaps they cannot help it."

"They can help keeping the place like a pigsty! They can help hanging out the washing in the front passage, so you run your face into a wet pair of knickers every time you come through the door!" Father Salvatore, hearing undertones of Manwel's wife

78

in full recrimination, almost smiled. "I'm sorry, Dun Salv," Manwel said again. "I'm in a bad mood this morning. I had to leave the house at five, without a bite to eat. They say there's no more cooking oil till next week. . . . Are you going to visit your mother? Please give her my respects."

"I'll do that. The work you did was really beautiful."

"It's a beautiful house to work in. And don't forget, I'm going to build the altar for you when the time comes. . . . Well, I must get on, Dun Salv. You wouldn't think talking to you could cost money, but it does! There's a miserable timekeeper at the docks who makes a mark on a sheet of paper, if you are even a minute late."

Father Salvatore laughed. "All right. I won't keep you any longer." He touched the other man on the shoulder. "Bless you, Manwel. And life's not really so terrible, is it?"

Manwel Azzopardi grinned back. "If we can't grumble when we feel like it, what's the use of living at all?"

A few minutes later, cheered for no reason at all except his thankfulness for the huge and loving variety of life, Father Salvatore was in his other world, the world of Santo-Nobile.

Despite the burden of war, the Baroness had permitted no change, either in herself or in her great house. At seventy-four, she might have felt older than she should, but this was a fact she would never acknowledge, and thus it did not exist. The folded hands, the black silk dress, the feet neatly crossed on the tapestried footstool—all were just as they had always been: a signal to the present that the past still ruled. So, too, at seven-fifteen she entertained her son to morning coffee.

When the servants had gone, she said: "I'm afraid Gregory is getting old, Salvatore. Did you notice how he closed the door? I believe he actually *stumbled!*"

Father Salvatore sipped his fragrant coffee—that had not changed, either—and looked round the high-ceilinged salon, listened to the deep peace of the courtyard which shut out all the rest of bustling Valletta. "The things that are happening to Malta are enough to disturb anyone. Even old Gregory. Even you."

"Then one has a duty not to be disturbed."

The absolute certainty of her answer was somehow depressing.

79

Life, true life, was not to be measured on this scale of disengagement. Would she have been disturbed by wet underclothes hanging in the entrance hall below? The contrast was so unthinkable that he could never have expressed it openly. Instead he said: "You are lucky to be able to remain so—detached. I wish I could."

As if catching his thought, she answered: "Salvatore, I am *not* stupid. I am not *detached*, either. I know what is going on. It is simply a question of whether one gives in to it. Would you want me to go into hysterics every time a bomb falls?"

"No, of course not. You would never do that, anyway."

They were friends again.

They were also mother and son. "You're looking pale," the Baroness presently announced. It recalled a hundred, a thousand times in the past, when she had said: "You have a cold," or "It is time you went to the dentist," or even "Do you need a laxative?" But it was still an expression of love, intrusive though it sometimes seemed. Now she asked: "Do you get enough sleep Salvatore?"

"Yes, mother."

"In those awful catacombs?"

"They're not awful. They are the blessing of my life." The strange words came out unawares, but he did not want them recalled. "Of course there are disturbances. But we sleep pretty well, and we eat—well, we eat."

In his mother's face there was now an alert look. "What do you mean, disturbances? What sort of disturbances?"

He spread his hands. "Some people want to sleep. Some people need to talk, or even sing. Some people are sad, some are happy, some are even afraid. So—there's always something going on."

"And some people want to drink? Or to make love?"

"Well, yes." It was, from her, an astonishing remark: "Love" he had heard her say countless times, but "make love", never.

"Salvatore, don't look so shocked! I have had three children of my own—remember . . . ? When you said 'disturbances', I thought you meant that sort of behaviour. There has been some talk. . . ."

"Who from?" He knew the answer, and he knew also that she was not going to give it.

"How can I remember? I meet a dozen people every day."

It was a time for honesty. "People behave in the catacomb as they do in their own home. It *is* their own home, quite often. Their only home. But there is always fear, mother. Terrible fear of the war. So they—" He did not know how to phrase it, and it was very important. "So they seize on life, before death seizes on them. The good people are better, the bad people are worse. The drunkards drink more. The people in love are more in love. Those who hate find their hatred turned into loathing." He was almost pleading with her, it was so important. "But they are all God's children. When people talk of bad behaviour, I wonder where they spend their nights. I wonder where is their charity, their compassion. . . . Let me assure you, I have seen *nothing* in the catacomb which God would not forgive."

Now there was silence in the handsome room, the silence of astonishment and deep feeling on both sides. Father Salvatore passed his hand over his face, and felt it leave his forehead wet as well as trembling. He sometimes felt he was becoming possessed by a *daemon* of determination, where the catacomb was concerned. God grant that it was only a small demon, one that a small priest could wrestle with. . . . From a long way away, from the ordered world of Santo-Nobile, he heard her voice:

"I think I am beginning to understand. . . . Is there anything I can do to help, Salvatore? Do you need money for the shelter?"

"You have been generous enough already." But he was a practical priest. "Well, we always need money. I want to buy more beds. Those wicked beds. . . . And material for curtains between them. And a reserve of oil. And powdered milk, if we can find powdered milk. And—but you mustn't laugh—scrubbing brushes."

"Why should I laugh?" The Baroness, whose acquaintance with scrubbing brushes could only have been limited, passed them swiftly by. "Very well. Spend up to five hundred pounds on your beds and your scrubbing brushes, and have the bills sent to me."

"How good you are." It was a magnificent gift, one that he had prayed for. "I can't tell you what a difference this will make. . . . I love you, mother."

"Five hundred pounds' worth?"

Her mischievous eyes recalled a shared memory, as she intended. Once, long ago, when she had rescued him from some appalling schoolboy dilemma with a covert transfer of five shillings, and he had said, dutifully but sincerely, "I love you, mother," she had asked: "Five shillings worth?"

Now he could answer: "Oh much more!" and smile his thanks. It was exactly the same answer as thirty years ago, and not less heartfelt. Indeed gratitude had grown with the years. Just like the money he thought, and knew that if he had said this out loud, she would have been the first to find it funny, and, with equal spirit, the last to admit it.

IT WAS FRANCIS who escorted him to the postern door, instead of old Gregory, and something had changed in Francis. He was walking like a soldier. Near the street door, he slowed his military step. "There is something special I wanted to ask you, Dun Salv. I want to join the Army. The Royal Malta Artillery."

Well, why not? . . . There was enough of war and fighting in the mouldering family journals. It was the footmen of the Palazzo Santo-Nobile, given the promise of all the wine they could drink on every feast day for the rest of their lives, who had put Napoleon's ruffians to ignoble flight. So Father Salvatore simply echoed his own thoughts. "Well, why not? It's an excellent idea."

"Really, Dun Salv?" Francis's eyes were shining. "I was afraid that. . . . I mean, how can I leave the Baroness? I owe her so much. I owe this house so much."

"I am sure that she would not stand in your way. But have you made inquiries? Do they need recruits?"

"Yes. I know all about it already. My cousin is a gun-layer in the Hal Far battery. They shot down a Savoia bomber last week!"

So that was it. "Well, of course, you will be missed here, Francis. But it's not as if you would be leaving the place empty. There are still three footmen, are there not? If you like, I will talk to the Baroness about it first. Then it will be easier."

"If you could, Dun Salv. Thank you very much."

"I could, and I will. . . . Now tell me, does the Baroness still go downstairs when the air-raid warning sounds?"

"Oh yes. She does not like it. She says it is only because she promised you. But we have made the armoury comfortable. She has even slept there sometimes."

"Excellent. I hope the staff will always encourage her to do that. You could even pretend to be afraid yourselves."

"It would not need much pretending." But Francis was smiling; a man could admit to fear, and still conquer it.

Father Salvatore emerged into the streets of Valletta delighted to have paid his call, and for once escaped without meeting that indefatigable churchman, Monsignor Scholti.

He had not.

Bruno Scholti was an element in the urban landscape from quite a long way away. He was advancing up the street towards the Palazzo Santo-Nobile on a wave of ecclesiastical consequence, answering salutes from shopkeepers, pausing briefly to speak to someone on the pavement, bending to pat a child's head, even smiling at dogs.

Monsignor Scholti saw him quite clearly from about twenty yards away. Their eyes met; and it was mortifying in the extreme when Scholti, without a sign of recognition, turned back to the old woman he was talking to. Father Salvatore decided that two could play at that silly game, and crossed the street to hurry by.

It was only then that Monsignor Scholti, with an exaggerated start, called out his name: "Salvu! How nice! I was hoping our paths would meet today!"

What could one do? . . . Father Salvatore stopped, and waited for the other man to cross the street. Scholti's cordial handshake seemed to set the seal on the day's most fortunate encounter.

Monsignor Scholti was another man who, like Francis the footman, had increased in stature with the war. *Fear nothing*, his whole face, body, and bearing seemed to say: *things may be difficult, things may be going badly, things may even appear hopeless, but I, Scholti, the valiant soldier of Christ, am here at your side!*

"And how did you find your mother?" he now asked. "I was telling her, only the other day, that she was looking younger than ever! Between you and me, she was worried about a little domestic matter, to do with—well, it's not important, but I was able to give

83

her the benefit of my own experience. She was like a new woman!"

"That was very kind of you," The day when his mother needed Scholti to advise her on any "domestic matter" would be a catastrophic dawn indeed, but to say so would conflict with his good intentions. "You have so many other things to do."

"My dear Salvu, you have no idea how busy I am!" He gave a benign wave to a couple of passing sailors. "I spent nearly all yesterday at the palace. Just one committee after another. Then there was the Scicluna party in the evening. Not much of a party, when you have to go from one group to another, simply to reassure people that all is well. This morning, guess what?—a working lunch at the palace again! We have to settle the seating arrangements for Solemn High Mass. Such protocol! You really have no idea."

"I'm afraid that I haven't," said Father Salvatore.

"Dear Salvu! You are *so* direct!" But at least Scholti was checked for a moment. "Let me see. . . . Are you on your way to the Debrincats?"

"Eventually. But first I have some calls to make."

"Oh, *really*?" It was clear, for the hundredth time, that Monsignor Scholti had no idea how condescending he could sound. "Now what could those be?"

"I have to buy candles," Father Salvatore answered. "And about two hundred beds. Then I hope to find some curtain material cheap. I need"—he had done a rough sum already—"at least a thousand yards. I suppose you don't know anyone?"

"My dear Salvu, I don't even know about *expensive* curtain material. . . . I was going to say, I haven't seen Lewis Debrincat for some time. But I hear that, for various reasons, he should be extremely grateful to the Baroness. The way that she used her influence was really splendid, from a family point of view."

Father Salvatore, sickened by this sly version of the truth, decided he would have none of it. "I am sure," he said, "that my mother's influence would have counted for *nothing*, if the police thought that Lewis presented any kind of security risk."

"Oh dear, I've annoyed you again." Monsignor Scholti fetched a most convincing sigh. "I was trying so hard to be diplomatic. Let's forget all about it, shall we? Did I hear you say you were buying two hundred beds? *What* a good idea! That must mean that your *catacomb*"—he pronounced the word as if it were halfway between a Rabelaisian joke and a civic blemish—"is full to bursting."

"We often have as many as six hundred people there."

"Really? *Now* I understand why it's so difficult to—well, to supervise them. I mean, you can't be everywhere, can you?"

"I don't want to be everywhere." Father Salvatore had promised, before God, to endure Monsignor Scholti with all the grace due to a superior, but already he knew that he was failing the test he had set himself. "It isn't a matter of supervision. We are all there together, for shelter and for worship. We all have fear in common. So I try to give us all another thing to share. God's help. God's hope."

On a cold morning, on a street corner in Valletta, it sounded too dramatic, too raw in faith. There was silence between them; then Scholti said: "Well, of course, if you are satisfied. . . . Perhaps I should pay you another visit some time."

Father Salvatore was capable only of the minimum answer. "Of course. You will be welcome. You will find it very simple. And rough, I suppose. And humble."

"My dear Salvu, you don't have to tell me anything about humility." The falsity of this was positively choking. But there was worse to come. Scholti's lips slid into a confederate smile. "I would particularly like to be there for your next *performance.*"

It was enough. Burning resentment overcame him. He said, abruptly: "Bruno, I really think I am beginning to hate you," and turned on his heel, and left the other man staring.

Stupid fool, he raged at himself as he began to walk downtown again; idiot, silly child. . . . To allow himself to be provoked was bad enough; but his schoolboy cry of resentment had been utterly shameful. If this was the best he could do under trial, then he might as well exchange his cassock for a clown's rig.

God give me strength, he prayed. God give me humility, and a soul free from pride and pettiness. God give me the sense to see the worth of others, even if I cannot love them.

God give me the pure joy of finding disinfectant for the toilets.

LEWIS DEBRINCAT sat at the head of the family lunch table, fat, sullen, sloppily dressed in a stained grey pullover, collapsed into his high armchair like a bag of assorted *pasta*. It was quite true, what Monsignor Scholti had said of him, and it troubled Father Salvatore even to think of it. Without his mother's influence, Lewis Debrincat would today be in gaol, in common with dozens of other Maltese notables who had declared their hand too publicly to be overlooked.

As a generous compromise, he had been told to keep quiet. His conduct would be noted. . . . It was the best that authority could do for him, and he was lucky. But, being Lewis Debrincat, he was not prepared to accept such luck gracefully. He had to exhibit an air of what the British Army called "dumb insolence".

It was almost as depressing to see how his family reacted to this bitter spirit. Occasionally they could be embarrassed; more often they pretended that Lewis had said nothing out of the ordinary, or even pretended that he was not there. The latter was the case now; his wife was murmuring something to Carmelina the maid—the fatherless Carmelina, whose seven-months-old bereavement had now, helped by the blessed resilience of youth, vanished into the background. Marija, her beautiful face turned inwards towards what might well have been beautiful thoughts, seemed hardly present at the table at all. Pietru had also gone blank.

Suddenly Lewis Debrincat began to address his wine glass in a long, grumbling monologue which could not be ignored. "Is this a free country? . . . Can you go out at night? No, there's a curfew. Can you buy what you want? No, there's this ridiculous rationing. What happens if you go for a drive in the country, *if* you can get the petrol? There's barbed-wire strung all over the place. If that's a free country, then give me—" he paused, and they all knew why; he was going to say "Italy", and it would have been disastrous. But instead he let his chin drop on his chest, and mumbled: "Then give me *anything*. It couldn't be worse."

Silence fell, and persisted. Perhaps lunch would have been gloomy anyway, without Lewis Debrincat to cast a morbid shadow over it. Even in this strong and elegant house, they were living in fear, just as they did in the Cottonera Lines. Fear had been given an added power, just before they went into lunch, when a strange warning had been broadcast urgently on Rediffusion: a curt "instruction for all civilians" to take cover immediately they heard the air-raid sirens, as "special tactics" were to be used.

What did it mean? Father Salvatore, at a loss for a subject, returned to this one, to bridge the gap between the embarrassment of dead silence and a reasonable ending to their meal. "I still wonder what they meant by that warning," he said, to anyone who would listen. "I hope it's not some horrible new weapon."

"Let them play their silly games," Lewis snapped back. "No doubt they'll tell us when the damage has been done."

Pietru suddenly came to life. But it was his Uncle Salvu whom he addressed directly.

"Do you think it means that we've got some new Hurricanes? That they'll be flying all over the place, and the bullets will go smashing into people unless they stay indoors?"

Giovanna protested: "Pietru dear, don't be so blood-thirsty!"

"Oh, I don't *want* it to happen," Pietru answered. "But it could, couldn't it? And, now that the Gladiators are so slow, we *do* need Hurricanes. Hundreds of them! I hope the pilots walk up and down the street, so I can get their autographs and talk to them. There was a pilot yesterday with a *huge* moustache. I'm sure he was a Hurricane pilot. But there were so many people, I couldn't get near enough to ask him."

His father roused himself again. "All I hope is," he said tartly, "if we do get more of these heroes crowding into Valletta, they behave better than the sailors do."

Pietru opened his mouth to speak, and then subsided. Another embarrassed silence fell. It was clear what Lewis was referring to: the undoubted rowdiness and vulgarity which could be expected whenever the Royal Navy liberty boats discharged their cargoes.

Father Salvatore, though he despised drunkenness and abhorred lust, felt that he must say a word for the other side. It was his turn to look at his own wine glass, as he said: "I don't think one should blame all the sailors for what a few of them do when they come ashore. It's difficult for us to realize what they may have been going through, a few hours before. I went on board the *Illustrious*, when she had just come into harbour." He noticed that Marija came to sudden attention as he spoke, though he thought nothing of it at the time. "I've never seen a ship in such a horrible mess, or men so exhausted. That's quite apart from the wounded, and the men killed. That's what you have to remember, when you see sailors walking about in Valletta. They've come ashore to forget. And the things they want to forget are often more terrible than any of us can imagine."

"Well, of course, if you're going to make excuses. . . ." Lewis mumbled, taken aback by the opposition.

Father Salvatore decided he had made his point strongly enough for family consumption. "Still I can't understand why the Germans haven't come back to bomb the *Illustrious*. Even one more bomb could sink her. Yet they've left her alone for five days! It doesn't make sense."

"What does?" Lewis interjected. "It was probably all fixed up years ago. War is just an international racket."

"I hope she gets away all right." He ignored Lewis and looked across the table, at Marija. She was staring at him, her eyes glowing with a transparent warmth and sympathy. What could he have said, to spark such interest?

WHAT FATHER SALVATORE did not know was what had happened to Marija the morning after the arrival of the *Illustrious*, five magic days ago. She had been shopping for her mother in Floriana—sometimes one had to go rather far afield nowadays, to find even the simplest things, which in this case were olive oil, and cheese. She had got them both. In a happy mood, she had crossed the bastions to have a look at the ship which everyone was talking about. What she saw was more awful than anything she could have imagined. Under a haze of dirty, drifting smoke, the *Illustrious* looked more like a ruined factory than a ship. Surely, it would never move again except to settle into its watery grave.

Then, being a girl, with no cares in the world except the silly cares of being a girl, she had looked round her at the people, and found, close by her, the most wonderful, the most beautiful young man she had ever seen in seventeen long years of life.

He was tall, and fair, and slim, and proud. He was in naval uniform which seemed rumpled, as if he had worn it too long without giving it a chance to recover. He was staring at the ship in a special way, a hungry way. But almost immediately—such was the mysterious telegraphy which made the wonderful world go round— he was staring at her instead.

She was very glad, secretly overjoyed, that she just happened to be wearing her new blue dress. She let the young man stare at her for a reasonable number of minutes. Then, without hurrying, she moved away towards a quiet corner of the bastions. Presently he moved also—ah, how brave he was, as well as beautiful— and came directly towards her. It would have been rude not to turn, to see who it was. When she looked up, he was smiling at her, and she was trembling.

He pointed towards *Illustrious*, just visible round the corner, and spoke in a voice so full of happiness that she was almost jealous: "Doesn't she look marvellous!"

"Marvellous" was the last word she had expected to hear; but she was so glad he had spoken to her that she could almost agree. "Yes. . . . Doesn't she? . . . But. . . ." She felt as if she had just run a hundred yards up the slope of Mount Sceberras. "But she looks terrible as well, don't you think? And sad?"

He considered this. Perhaps he was really as nervous as she was: only he was a man, and it didn't show so much. "Did you see her come in last night?" He had a funny, jerky way of speaking.

"No, I didn't." How could she have been on the bastions of Valletta at ten o'clock at night? "It was much too late."

"Oh. . . . Well, I saw her come in, and it was the best sight I ever clapped eyes on." There was something else he had to tell her, and it came out with a rush. "You see, she's my ship."

After that, it was much easier, and wonderfully so. "You mean, you're one of the officers?"

"One of the pilots. Fleet Air Arm." He saw that she was looking at his uniform. "I'm sorry about the suit. But it's not mine. I lost all my kit. It was perfectly all right when I flew off, but when I went back on board this morning, everything was either burned to a crisp or soaked in oil!"

"But what happened? When did you fly off?"

"Just before the bed fell on father." She must have looked puzzled, because he apologized. "Sorry, I mean, just before we were bombed. I was halfway down the flight-deck when they dropped a bomb just in front of the sharp end. Dirty great clouds of spray, falling all over us. Such bad manners. . . . I didn't know whether I was meant to fly, or swim." He grinned. "Anyway, I diced with death for a bit, and then made for your hospitable little island, and then came back to help. But by the time we got there, poor old *Illustrious* was shot full of holes. So here I am, in somebody's third-best suit."

There was silence between them for a moment. In the peace of the Malta bastions, on a sunlit morning, it was almost impossible to realize that this had really happened to him, a few short hours ago, and that he could joke about it, and look at her with such lively admiration, all at the same time. Were there other young men like this in the world? Had her father ever been like this? Had anyone?

Somehow it was important to know every single thing about him. "But what are you doing now?"

"Talking to the most beautiful girl I've ever seen."

She frowned. She did not want him to be like this—silly and flirtatious. She wanted the real young man, whose name she did not even know. "I meant, why are you over here?"

He realized he was not talking the language she wished to hear, and he swiftly changed it. "I wanted to have another look at the ship," he said. "As a matter of fact, I was on my way back from seeing a friend in hospital."

"Is he all right?"

"No. He died." He said it as if death were something that happened every day. "It was probably just as well. He was in a bit of a mess. Like that poor old mess down there."

Marija gasped. "The Germans must be absolutely awful!"

"Oh, I don't know. You've got to see their point of view. Heil Hitler, do unto thy neighbour before he does it unto you. They've got bags of guts, anyway. That pattern-bombing yesterday was something to watch. I just wish they wouldn't machine-gun our chaps coming down in parachutes. Damme, sir, a sitting bird!"

"Do they really do that?"

"With great regularity." But he wasn't really serious, even about such a terrible thing. "We had to work out some jolly smart evasive action. It's called Operation Peter Pan. We slip out of our parachutes"—he made an absurd wriggling motion, like a woman squeezing out of a tight dress, "and they float off into the blue, and while the Germans are shooting them down in flames, we just tiptoe away."

It was so ridiculous that she had to laugh.

"That's better," he said instantly. "You're really pretty when you smile. You're really pretty anyway. Come and have a drink."

The frank approach of the invitation was matched by his face, his lean and alive face, which once again alarmed her. She managed to shake her head. "I'm afraid I can't."

"But I'm really very respectable. I won't—I won't even *look* at you, if you don't want me to. They tell me there are all sorts of good places. The British Empire Snug?—I like the sound of that one. Or Auntie's—surely you'd feel safe at Auntie's?"

"I feel perfectly safe anywhere," she answered severely. It was not true—Auntie's was already notorious—but she really must take charge of herself. "But I must get home to Sliema."

"Can I walk along with you, then? I'll carry that shopping bag," he said helpfully. "My name's Michael Ainslie. Mike."

She said, "I'm Marija Debrincat."

He walked with her nearly all the way home. Their strides could not possibly match, but they seemed to be in step from the very first moment. The nearness of his tall figure was intoxicating. Though he behaved as well as he had promised, his eyes when he turned to look at her were glowing with admiration.

She stopped just short of her house, to say good-bye with a margin of safety. She could not possibly be seen with an escort —particularly such a noticeable one—on her own front doorstep.

"This is it," she told him. "I must hurry. Thank you so much."

He did not argue. "What are my chances of seeing you again? Can I ring you up?"

"It's in the telephone book." Heaven only knew how that could be explained to the family. "Early morning would be best."

He took a step forward, until he was standing almost touching her. His grey-blue eyes flickered over her face, then her breasts, then her face again. He half-raised his hand. What terrible, wonderful thing was going to happen? But suddenly he shook his head, and said: "No. Next time," and the hand dropped away, and he turned, with a gorgeous smile, and was gone.

Next time.

"MARIJA, DEAR!" It was her mother's voice at the lunch table. "Uncle Salvu is speaking to you!"

"Oh!" Marija came to herself, blushing scarlet with embarrassment. The contrast between the dreamy secrecy of her thoughts, and the close, inquisitive inspection which her whole family was now giving her, was mortifying.

"I'm so sorry," she said. "I was thinking of something else."

Father Salvatore smiled. There was something going on—he could tell that—that blush betrayed a moment of crisis. Could it be love? He hoped so. He hoped for many things, including a wise choice. It was time to smooth over the awkward corner.

"What I was trying to do, was to ask if you had seen any of those American drums of egg-powder, on your various shopping trips."

Marija shook her head. The question was so gloriously banal, that she could have kissed her uncle. "No, they seem to have disappeared lately. But Uncle Salvu, what do *you* want egg-powder for?"

He smiled again. "You have never tasted my herb omelette for fifty people—egg-powder, goat's milk, clover leaves, and the tops of turnips, cooked in the lid of a dustbin."

His sister shuddered. "Salvu, you don't eat it yourself, do you?"

"Oh yes! Well—when I am *very* hungry. But of course I serve myself last, and sometimes there is none left."

Lewis Debrincat came to the surface again, after the latest of his long silences. "I think you will find," he said disagreeably, "that your egg-powder will be back in the shops just as soon as there's a fat enough profit to be made out of selling it. You can forget the heroes in their silly little suits. The real battles are fought round a padlocked garage full of egg-powder and Scotch whisky, and the medals are money." He stood up, reasonably steady. "I

93

think that, delicious as it was, this lunch has gone on long enough."

Giovanna Debrincat said good-bye to her brother in the hall. As usual, there was little need for explicit words or explanations.

"Is there anything I can do to help?" Father Salvatore asked.

"No. Really no, Salvu. It just goes on. I've become used to it. Even the drinking. But it's so destructive, such a waste of a man." The fact that she did not say "Waste of a woman" was shining virtue, beyond price. "Oh Salvu, what's the answer? Don't tell me it's prayer, or I shall scream!"

"That's a nice thing to say to a priest."

"It's nice to be able to say it to a brother. . . . All right, Dun Salv, I'll be good. Do you think Marija is in love with someone?"

"I hope so."

"So do I. We need it here."

From a beautiful woman, they were sad words indeed. He touched her arm gently. "You mustn't think like that, Giovanna. The past years have been full of it, and the best will come again."

They said good-bye, and parted. She was still the rock on which this house was founded, and he thanked God for it, even as he prayed God for her strength to endure.

IT WAS JUST AFTER half-past one. Father Salvatore, standing in the thin January sunshine on the steps of the Casa Debrincat, surveyed the deserted seafront, and wondered what to do next.

He still had various shopping errands, but this was the dead hour of commerce, when the shutters went up for the afternoon siesta. So for once with time to spare, he took out his breviary and as he strolled slowly along the pavement towards Sliema Creek, he began to read the Office of the Day. But in spite of this accustomed duty, and the precious pattern of its enforcement, he could not help feeling uneasy.

There was something brooding and dangerous about this silent midday hour. It could have been due to the urgent broadcast from Rediffusion, the barred stillness of the siesta hour—or to the simple presence of *Illustrious*, the hunted refugee that might seal the fate of all around her. . . . He decided, on a sudden impulse, that he must go and take a look at her again: just to bear witness by his attendance that, perilous bait or not, she was welcome to the haven of Grand Harbour for as long as she chose.

A stroke of luck assisted him. He looked up from his breviary to see a small ferry boat about to cast off from Sliema Creek. He knew the man in charge, a roly-poly character with a name to match—Koli Apap. It was this Koli Apap, his jaunty gold-crested cap proclaiming him at least an admiral of the Valletta waterfront, who now hailed him: "Eh! Dun Salv! Are you coming with us?"

"I was going to walk," Father Salvatore said.

"Walk? Walking is for goats!" Koli had clearly taken a glass or two with his midday meal. "You know our motto. We may sink, but we save your feet!" He extended a courtly arm. "Welcome aboard, *Sur Kappillan*. I always feel safe with a priest."

"But does the priest feel safe with you?"

Thus they set out, everyone on board the little wooden ferry boat grinning, enjoying the encounter. Father Salvatore, sitting in the stern-sheets, squeezed between a man with a vast bundle of wicker fish-traps and a bulging woman hugging a fractious child, marvelled once again at the resilient spirit of the Maltese. People had been killed, crossing Grand Harbour on just such a ferry boat as this. People would doubtless be killed again. This might be the very day appointed for it. But rough humour was enough to calm all such fears.

Koli Apap's boat was powered by machinery so ancient that it often seemed to miss a heartbeat between one moment and the next, and their progress across the sunny blue water of the harbour was slow. But such slowness was a gain; for they were plying their way past the history of Malta, bloody and triumphant at the same time, and the names like the stones, cried out for recognition.

They chugged manfully past Dragut Point, where the eighty-year-old corsair Dragut Rais, of evil yet heroic memory, fresh from his gory sacking of the Citadel of Gozo, had set up a battery during the great siege to pound the fortress of St. Elmo into submission. In this he had forfeited his own life, being himself sliced through the skull by a stone splinter from a cannonball.

They passed the mouth of Lazzaretto Creek, where in former days the galleys of the Knights were moored: where now baleful black submarines, which might still prove to be Malta's present succour, were ranged in tiers. They drew near to their goal of Marsamuscetto, a bastion of the island for four hundred years.

It was here too that the Knights, made furious by the decapitation of four comrades, had taken their vengeance by firing back upon the opposing guns the most gruesome cannonade in the annals of war, the still-warm skulls of their Turkish captives. . . .

The ferry was indeed sailing past history; and the moment it landed at Marsamuscetto, a new page of that history began, as bloody as anything in the past; for as the air-raid warning sounded, and as Koli Apap's passengers scurried to safety, the noise of approaching aircraft triggered off a new and frightful sound.

Malta had by now grown used to fearful noises; they lived with noise, as they lived with food rationing, and family upheaval, and death. But what they heard on that day was something scarcely to be imagined. Later it was to be described, officially, as the Box Barrage, a lethal and murderous cube of anti-aircraft shells exploding just above their heads, flung upwards by every shore gun which could fire, and by the guns of *Illustrious* herself.

But on this, their first baptism of desperate defence, it was a sound so shattering that men could only tremble, and crouch close to the ground, as the curtain of steel burst upon the still air like the crack of doom. If their own guns could inflict such punishment, what could the enemy do?

Father Salvatore had known that the enemy would come back for *Illustrious*, and that the punishment it was bound to inflict would be awful; but this shattering assault was beyond imagination. Yet he was still driven to climb to the heights of Valletta, and to watch: to make his way upward like a terrified cat, street by street, shelter by shelter, until *Illustrious*, and the harbour, and the savage slaughter beyond, came into his view.

By then he was trembling uncontrollably. Constantly he had to wipe the sweat and tears from his eyes, in order to witness the punishment raining down upon the twin targets of the enemy: his own big ship, and his own small people.

The Stuka dive bombers, about a hundred of them, were coming in very high from the southeast, circling their target, and then, in spite of the Box Barrage, plummeting down upon it. The successive waves, piloted by young men of superb courage—who could deny that?—dived with an eerie whine, increasing to a monstrous scream as they neared ground level. At the moment when the diving noise became unbearable, the bombs began to fall.

Amid great bursts of spray, the *Illustrious* was hit. Other bombs crashed down on the dockyard, and on the houses and shops, all swiftly pulverized into a great cloud of evil yellow smoke.

The statistics were to come later: 900 homes shattered, 500 people killed or injured in the first hour of the attack; for the watcher ·from the shore, all that could be perceived was a relentless, merciless rain of death. What must it be like, to live or to die in the eye of that hurricane?

Illustrious was hit again, and seemed to stagger. Fierce fires enveloped a merchant ship unloading near by, a ship crammed with ammunition which miraculously did not explode. The harbour became a cauldron of smoke and flame and columns of erupting water. Beyond it, the overspill of bombs was falling upon Cospicua, and the Cottonera Lines, and his own people.

The smell and then the smoke billowed up, spreading a death-like pall across the harbour, blotting out the sun, hiding God's eyes. Nothing which had happened so far, in all the pitiless misery of their war, could compare with what was happening now.

IT TOOK HIM A LONG time to reach the Cottonera Lines. He began his weary pilgrimage, which could only end in grief and horror, on foot. Quickly he found himself, as so often before, caught in a miserable tide of refugees, moving mindlessly in any direction which would take them from certain shock to supposed peace.

It was a relief to get a lift in a British Army ambulance, manned by cheerful and determined young men who said "Hop up, Father!" and "Hold on tight! Fares please!" and even sang, astonishingly: "We're off to see the Wizard, the wonderful Wizard of Oz!" as they rocked along the road. When presently he asked where they were going, the driver, who had blood on his hands and sleeves, answered: "Senglea again. There's been an incident."

In Senglea, an earlier "incident"—that strangely insufficient word out of the Air Raid Precaution Manual—had partly destroyed the beautiful baroque church of Our Lady of Victories, built by La Valette himself at the founding of the city. It had stopped its clock on the instant of destruction, at twenty minutes past two on that January day. For years afterwards, passersby were to be reminded by it of the exact moment when life, for the church and many of its faithful, had ceased to be.

The mutilation and death all around had been increased within the last hour by another monstrous blow from the sky, and Father Salvatore and the ambulance crew—who now lost their merry humour—began to rummage amid the familiar pitiful rubbish-tip of shattered glass, corpses, broken beams, spent shells, dead dogs, cats, poultry and choking layers of dust, for the faint chance of surviving life.

As he worked on, with scores of others, the excruciating noise of the Box Barrage exploded again, hammering upon their bowed heads. The rescuers toiled, their knees and feet often in pools of blood. Father Salvatore was giving all his shocked attention to yet another dying man, under whose shredded clothes was a body so racked with pain that it was like one great open mouth, screaming with agony, when the sound of shots near by disturbed him.

Momentarily he looked round, to see a policeman standing over a dead dog, its bloody muzzle still half-buried in a corpse.

Father Salvatore wept. Then, a few seconds later, the man beneath his hands also achieved death, through the most terrible gateway he had ever witnessed.

When it was over he sat back on his haunches, sick unto dying himself. Then he heard his name called: "Dun Salv! Dun Salv! Have a swig of whisky!"—and he laughed aloud through bitter tears to see a man beside him even madder than himself.

Nero Cassar presented an extraordinary figure, even on that day of violent surprises. He had managed to equip himself with something which looked like a tiny R.A.F. battledress, topped by a tin hat fashioned from a saucepan. He had a sheath knife tucked into the top of one boot, and a swagger-cane in the other. A bottle of whisky and a tin cup completed his equipment.

"Nero!" Father Salvatore exclaimed. He was so glad to see this

lunatic apparition, bouncing out of the flame-flickering darkness, that he could have wept again. "What on earth are you doing here?"

"Looking for you, Dun Salv. And helping, helping. When the bombs began to fall, I elected myself to join the A.R.P. There's no use just sitting still, is there?" Without waiting for an answer he glanced down at the tortured figure lying at their feet. "Well, we can save the whisky on that one, can't we?"

"He is on his way to heaven, Nero," Father Salvatore said reprovingly. Half-deafened, they were both shouting at each other. "Think of his soul. Pray for it."

A curious look—half-cynical, half-sad—came over Nero's face. "God must be busy listening tonight."

"But He is never *too* busy."

"I hope not." There was a mutter of distant guns, and then the hideous sound of the barrage erupted once more. "Here they come again!" Nero shouted. "We'd be better off in the catacomb, Dun Salv. And they need you there. That's why I wanted to find you. People are half-mad with worry, all screaming at each other."

Father Salvatore looked round him. There was certainly little more to be done here: the wounds had all been bound up, and the dead speeded towards eternity. Sadly, he turned towards the Cottonera Lines.

As they reached the great rock face, they could hear shouting and screaming and weeping, dogs barking, sheep bleating, children crying, women beseeching help, men calling for silence. Father Salvatore could also hear prayers amid the clamour.

Prayers were always welcome to his ears, but not these prayers, infected with a desperate fear. He walked out of the shadows as briskly as he could, flogging a tired body and a confused mind to make the best entrance at his command. He was greeted with sudden silence, then a gasp of horror. Dishevelled, bloodstained and exhausted, he must have seemed a living proof that Death lay in wait for all who ventured outside.

He blessed them, and made the sign of the cross, as if to prove his credentials. He bent his knee to the altar, with its magnificent gold crucifix and gleaming altar cloth—both of them his mother's gift.

Then he climbed the steps to the stone pulpit which Rafel had built for him, spread his hands on either side of Nero's microphone and looked down upon his people.

It could have been a scene from the Inferno, brought up to date by the evil devices of man. Under the vaulted ceiling, smoky and filled with shadows, men and women, children and dogs, were huddled together in what seemed the last stages of despair.

The crash of a bomb nearby, and the shudder of the earth under their feet, released fresh screams, fresh panic. He saw the huge Rafel wrestling with a man who insanely tried to fight another. He saw Nero hugging a tormented child to his narrow chest. He, Father Salvatore, must also play his part. This was the night for it. But whom should he speak of?

It must be someone near to their present ordeal; someone who had seen the Blessed Saviour, and could humbly pass on His message of peace; someone who knew the fear of death, yet had conquered death; someone who had survived shipwreck and misery and fury from the skies. *Someone who had brought hope and faith to this very island.*

HEXAMERON II

In the Year of Our Lord, 60, An Illustrious Gift from the Sea

Father Salvatore bent down and blew fiercely through the microphone. The crude blast of his breath brought silence at last. Then his voice rang clearly through the loudspeakers, and echoed through the caverns beyond: "There was once a man who said—and we should be proud to say it too: 'I have fought a good fight, I have finished my course, I have kept the faith.'

"The man of whom I speak said also: 'Now abideth faith, hope, charity, these three; but the greatest of these is charity.'"

The aeroplanes, the three little planes which had saved them! . . . *There was subdued laughter at this. There must be a story coming, a story of Malta, a story for themselves alone. Then Father Salvatore added, with that special inflexion which heralded one of his small, off-duty jokes: "This man was the most illus-trious ever to arrive in Malta, though it cost the wreck of a fine ship to bring him here."*

Illustrious. . . . Of course! . . .

"Saint Paul—and there are no prizes for guessing Saint Paul—was a little man, like me, and he was seasick. Four weeks from today we celebrate the shipwreck which threw him up on to the rocks in our own St. Paul's Bay. He came ashore. . . ."

He came ashore, bruised, half-drowned, shivering with deadly ague, after the most fearful voyage in a life which had subjected him to many such ordeals. He gave thanks to his master, Jesus, for his escape, though he knew that death still lay in store for him in Rome; and to Rome he must go, as a bound prisoner who had appealed for final trial before Caesar himself.

What had brought him to Malta, at the end of a long, cruel, and glorious life, was strange to him, though crystal clear to God because God had sketched the plan. Paul accepted all things, and regretted nothing except the evil days when he was a fiery little Pharisee, a bigot who had excelled in hunting down Christian souls. But that was before he saw the light.

It was Saint Luke, telling the story, who called it "a light from heaven" bursting upon Paul on the road to Damascus, a light which struck him blind for the next three days, while a voice demanded: "Why persecutest thou me?" A light which made him the most potent missionary the world has ever seen, a tireless traveller for Christ, from Athens to Corinth, and from Antioch to Palestine. He preached the gospel, he wrestled with men's souls; he was loved by many, mobbed by many more, spat upon, and scourged by Roman lictors, and thrown into prison.

Paul was never well-fitted for such fierce ordeals, nor for the close human contacts on which so much depended. He was small and ugly, with bushy eyebrows joined together above a big hooked nose; he was nearly bald, and his short crooked legs carried him awkwardly. He had what he himself called a thorn or stake in the flesh, which humiliated him every day of his life. Its exact nature has remained doubtful. A stammer perhaps, or erysipelas, or even epilepsy. Yet, persistently, it was said that "sometimes he had the face of an angel". *This man?* Yes, this small, sick, ugly, awkward man, this magical man. Perhaps it was such angelic glimpses of glory, as well as his sweet reason and his burning faith, which brought in the converts.

Certainly, as he travelled, he made many converts, men and women, Jew and Gentile. With this success came an avalanche of anger from the Jews, who could not forgive him for preaching the Messiah, not only to the chosen, but to any Gentile dog or pagan rascal who would listen. If Christ was the Messiah, said the Jews—and they often said it in that violent pride of race which, after all their travail, one could understand, if not forgive—then He was the Jews' Messiah, not the public property of any infidel who happened to be passing. If it was not true, then the man who proclaimed it was a vile blasphemer, and it was a duty and a pleasure to slake the thirsty earth with his blood.

They hounded him wherever he travelled; they spied on him, and sent secret intelligence of where he was going, so that a mob, or a riot, or a ferocious inquisition was always waiting for him. These were tempestuous and frightening years; often he must have wondered why he ever left Tarsus, where he was born to all the privileges of Roman citizenship, where he had a good trade—tent-making in summer, sail-making in winter. He was uplifted only by his faith in Christ, solaced only by the converts he made, and their abounding love. Whenever he had to say farewell—and his tireless travelling involved more farewells than any man could count—the local Christians, full of foreboding that Paul must always be going to his death, first begged him not to leave, and then came down to the seashore in a body to see him off.

"What mean ye to weep, and to break my heart?" Saint Paul would chide, only to be overcome by weeping himself. Then he would set sail: ever onwards, towards his final appointment.

Presently the Jews booked that final appointment. Paul was in Jerusalem, in the very footsteps of his Master; the orthodox Jews, driven to frenzy by his presence on such hallowed territory, staged a gigantic riot at one of his public appearances, a well-drilled mob tearing their clothes, throwing dust in the air, and shrieking: "Away with such a fellow from the earth! Kill him!"

The Roman commander, Claudius Lysias, took the simple way out, which was to arrest Paul as the cause of this disgraceful uproar, and threaten him with scourging if he did not clear out. Paul pleaded his Roman citizenship, which meant that he could not be scourged or crucified. Lysias knew that if he were released the Jews would pounce. A lynching party was lying in wait for Paul, bound by a solemn oath neither to eat nor drink until they had done him to death. That would look *very* bad in the half-yearly dispatches to Rome.

Since it was impossible to smuggle out such a rare prize, Lysias gave Paul an armed escort tough enough to hack a pathway through any opposition, and sent him to the Procurator Antonius Felix of Caesarea, sixty-two miles away up the coast.

If Claudius Lysias was a prudent career-soldier, Antonius Felix, on whom Paul had been palmed off, was a venal, jumped-up coward. He kept Paul in prison for the next two years, officially "deferring his verdict", though the suspicion that he was hoping for a bribe in return for Paul's release was common gossip. And when the time came for Felix to be relieved as governor, "to show the Jews a pleasure", he pocketed the spoils of office and left the prisoner still in custody.

The man who took over as Procurator was in total contrast with his predecessor. He was Porcius Festus, an upright and honest man. As soon as he had time he sent for Paul. He examined him, and his accusers, in great detail. He decided that Paul must be sent back to Jerusalem to be tried. When this dire verdict was announced Paul again pleaded his Roman citizenship. He appealed to Caesar, and thus he had to be sent off by the first available ship. Ageing, battered by his enemies, sustained only by faith, he must embark on his last voyage, for Rome, where he would be on trial for his life: where he was to lose that life, indeed, at the hands of the demented tyrant Nero.

Paul began his journey in a small coasting vessel, but on the south coast of Turkey they transferred to an Alexandrian corn-ship. By modern standards she was tiny—less than a hundred feet long; but at that time she was the very best that could be built for the deep-water carrying trade.

On sailing-day, the ship's complement was set down as: sailors, one hundred: soldiers, one hundred: prisoners, seventy-six. The party was in the command of one Julius, a centurion whose word was law. They embarked on a voyage as stormy and perilous as anything in Paul's own perilous life.

Bleak winter was well advanced, and any merchant captain with sense kept his ship snug in harbour between mid-November and the tenth day of March. But a Roman grain-ship had a time-table to follow, and a Roman centurion had his orders. They sailed in accordance with both; traditional fears proved well-founded; they plunged straightway into desperate trouble.

They used every trick of seamanship, in grey days and evil black nights, to ward off the blows of the fearful sea. They reduced sail to a patch of canvas, just enough to keep the ship from slewing broadside-on to the waves. They lightened her as much as possible, by throwing most of the spare gear overboard, and half the cargo. When the planks started to gape, they bound them round with ropes, and tightened them on the windlass, to try to hold the hull together. They kept pace with the leaks by furious bailing.

All the time, they were in terror of the unknown. The ship, even under a kerchief of sailcloth, was surging westward down the Mediterranean, helpless and half-waterlogged. Ahead lay rocks and islands, the shoals and quicksands of North Africa, or even—who could tell?—the unspeakable void beyond the Pillars of Hercules.

Paul rose to the occasion as he had risen to so many others, with courage, love, and faith. This little man moved among them like a giant. He told them the ship was *not* going to sink. They were *not* going to drown. Soon they would be safe on land. *He had been told so by the Lord.* He believed it; they must believe it also.

No one—not even the experienced master of the ship—knew where they were. They had not had a sight of the sun, nor of a single star, for two weeks. When the sailors' ears picked up the dreadful sound of breakers ahead, crashing down on some unknown shore, the shore might have been Sicily, or North Africa, or Spain, or some territory not yet named.

It was night, pitch-dark night, screaming night. They put out four stern anchors, and prayed for daylight.

Just after six o'clock, a faint lifting of the gloom behind them told them that dawn was at hand. It was not much of an improvement, but at least they could glimpse, through the murk, a line of wicked breakers smashing against the coastline of a land they did not know.

There was no hope of saving the ship now; they must run her aground, and trust to the gods, or Paul's own god, to bring them safely to land.

They hoisted the mainsail, loosed the rudder bands, and drove straight for the beach. The stem struck the sandbar with a rending crash. The crippled timbers cracked and splintered, the stern towered above the waves, and she began to break up. Where-upon, soldiers drew their swords, and shouted "Kill the prisoners!" According to the rulebook, they were right. If the ship was breaking up, then the prisoners were about to escape. Escaping prisoners could be killed—must be killed—on sight.

It was time for Julius the centurion to act. He drew his own sword—and he was a good man with a sword, none better—and stood in their way. He did it, Luke said, because he wished to save Paul's life. As his soldiers fell back, he ordered: "No killing! Everybody overboard! Jump for your lives, and swim!"

One by one they left the ruined ship. Struggling in the raging surf, they slowly fought their way to land, the rain lashing down on their bobbing heads. At last they reached the rocks and clambered up, bruised, bleeding, but alive!

Every last soul was saved, as the saint had told them.

In the shelter of the cliffs of this bare, silent land from which all living things appeared to have been swept, a marvel-lous peace descended. Then, as Paul rose from his prayers, and set about comforting his companions, the inhabitants came out to discover what the sea had brought.

They gave the shivering mariners a kindly welcome. Their first thought was to light a fire from the plentiful driftwood now piling up on the beach. Paul helped them, and as he was adding a bundle of sticks to the flames, a snake jumped out and fastened on his hand. The Maltese were aghast. "Undoubtedly this man is a murderer," they muttered among themselves. "Though he has escaped the sea, yet vengeance suffereth him not to live." Yet when Paul shook the snake off into the fire, and they saw that Paul did not swell up and die, the Maltese changed their tune, and said that he was a god.

Paul had no time for that sort of veneration, though at least it turned an uncertain moment into a happy one, and if indeed the

snake was poisonous, then it was the last one ever to be seen on the island.

Julius the centurion now reported formally to the Roman governor's palace. In two hundred years of rule the Romans had transformed Malta into a sophisticated community, and the governor lived in considerable style. The ship had been wrecked, reported Julius, but all the prisoners were held in reasonable security in barracks; except for one called Paul of Tarsus. "That troublemaker?" Governor Publius was taken aback, and he showed it with patrician emphasis. "We've heard more than enough about Paul!" He looked at Julius with a frosty eye. "What makes him different from all the other riff-raff?"

But Julius had had to deal with governors, consuls, senators, generals before. They were all the same, they just needed a nudge in the right direction. "Sir, he's a bit more than a prisoner. He's been a great help to me, during the last few weeks. He kept everyone cheerful. Quite a character. Very persuasive. I think you'd like to talk to him."

"*Here,* in my palace?"

The governor was turning patrician again, and Julius produced a more formal argument. "We're likely to be here for two or three months. I think that headquarters would be grateful if you kept a special eye on him. He might say something worth reporting."

"Oh. . . . Intelligence, eh? Political?"

"Just so, sir. Political and religious."

"All right. . . ." Perhaps it might be interesting, after all. Life in Malta was comfortable and pleasant, but one did feel out of things. If this fellow Paul had one or two good stories to tell, confidential stuff about Judaea, it might make them sit up in Rome. "You'd better bring him to see me. . . . As a matter of fact," he said, with the faint surprise of many governors in the same situation, "I've really got very little to do this morning."

Thus it was that Paul made himself known to "the chief man of the island", as Luke described him. By now, it should not seem astonishing that within the next three months, Paul lodged with Governor Publius, talked with him, converted him and many others to Christianity, and, just before he left, consecrated him as the first Christian bishop of Malta.

Then Julius the centurion reported that it was time to go. Another Alexandrian corn-ship, which had wintered in the island, was due to sail. They must all be on their way. Once again, for Paul, there was a desolate farewell; he had to say to his new Christian friends: "Why are you crying? Do you want to break my heart?" But this time he did not weep. His last good-bye, his last journey, must show a steadfast face and faith.

His faith remained, centuries after he died for it. He had brought to Malta the first news of Jesus Christ its Saviour; and his bravery, his resilience, his capacity to resist earthly torments, gave the island its most priceless example.

Though few on earth could be saints, yet all could be men.

THEY HAD HARDLY *been aware of the thunder outside. Then a breathless bloodstained man burst into the catacomb, and panted for help. There were people buried alive nearby. The rescue workers could not get through. The bombs were still falling.*

At the words, more than fifty rose to their feet, and crowded towards the exit tunnel. It was these brave volunteers, with Father Salvatore at their head, who went out into the fearsome darkness once more, and so continued steadfast in the faith of their forefathers.

The Hopeful Day of Father Salvatore
26 July 1941

Father Salvatore loved his little cell, where night after night he drifted into exhausted sleep, where morning after morning he woke to the sounds and smells of the catacombs, and to a new day of terrors and happiness and the love of God for man.

The cell was ten feet by six, and bare to a degree which would have horrified his mother. He made his bed on a stone slab which had once roofed the grave of one of the long-dead brothers. A crucifix guarded his head: an oil-lamp gave him smoky light at night: through the open archway of the door, pale daylight filtered through. Two pegs furnished his wardrobe, and a stone pot his washbasin. That was all. But the cell was never his prison. It was his cradle, in which, by God's grace, he had been newly born to guardian priesthood. It was sanctified by the small niche just below the crucifix, where many a requiem candle must have burned in the dim past. Here he had placed the private joy of his life, the heart of his devotion: the mahogany box containing certain sacred relics which were the fruits of pious travel, the precious souvenirs of a true pilgrim. For more than twenty years, he had never slept outside their blessed aura.

Today he awoke early, before the first thin bell, the best that authority would allow, sounded the call for Mass. Already he could feel, from the prickly discomfort under his worn blanket, that this would be another day of blinding heat.

Of course, the new day could only be like yesterday, and the four hundred yesterdays since their war began. It was astonishing to think that they had lived for more than a year in the catacombs, and had seen them grow from a tomb ripped open to a refuge made secure: had seen themselves—or many of them—grow in the same degree. By now they were better men, better women, even better children. Any humans, subjected to three or four air raids a day for the best or worst part of a year, must inevitably change; they would either rise or fall. His people, his Maltese, had risen.

They had risen above blows which especially wounded. Apart from the damage to be seen all over Malta, there were particular hurts which drove home the fact of total war. It hurt, intimately, when the little church of St. Publius had been half-ruined at a single stroke. It hurt when a cinema was hit, and a hundred people died in the midst of their innocent enjoyment. It hurt when village *festas* were banned and church bells could not be rung except to sound an alarm. It hurt to see their countryside so disciplined, the signposts all erased, and open spaces which might be used for invasion landing-grounds defiled by concrete blocks.

But they had risen above such things. They had even come to grumbling terms with the dreary rationing, which made every day a secondary battlefield for the housewife. What could a woman do to promote the joy of family life, when sugar, coffee, matches, and soap were all strictly rationed: when butter, cheese, milk, chocolate, and pasta were often unobtainable: when vegetables and fruit were scarce: when a lot of rubbish like potato *purée* was mixed into the bread, to make up a reasonably-sized loaf?

It was explained, time and again, that the convoys could not get through. To the north, Greece and Crete had fallen: to the south, the Italians were back in Libya. The island was stuck between

Sicily and Tunis. The nearest help, Alexandria and Gibraltar, were each a thousand miles out of range; so when ships did manage to get through, more often than not they were bombed and sunk before they could unload.

The only question was, how long could this last? They were all a year older already. How *was* the war going?

There were no answers: only rumours, and the general knowledge that there were always two hundred and fifty German bombers in Sicily, sixty miles away, waiting to pounce on anything that moved. Apart from that, it was just stories of tanks racing up and down the northern coast of Africa, now winning, now losing; of a new name, Rommel, and a new enemy, the Afrika Korps, both seemingly invincible: of all Europe crushed under the heel of Germany, of slaughter in the North Atlantic and terrible damage to the heart of London: and finally, of the threat of invasion to their very own homeland!

Yet against all such fear, there was still hope. If, in spite of frenzied efforts to destroy her, the *Illustrious* could get safely away, then anything could happen.

Though it was six months ago now, that story still shone with pride, and it deserved to. Maltese dockworkers by the thousand had toiled all round the clock, for fourteen solid days and nights, to get the poor wreck ready for sea; and this in spite of a continuous rain of bombs which not only hit the ship, but which plastered the dock area and left behind it acres of wasteland where not a single building survived, nor one stone upon another.

Finally, *Illustrious* steamed secretly out of Grand Harbour under her own power, cloaked by darkness. But she sailed to such purpose, with her hull and machinery so valiantly patched up, that she outstripped her own destroyer escort, and safely reached Alexandria, on a happy dawn only two days later.

Father Salvatore was one of the hundreds who watched her leave. It seemed like the biggest conjuring trick in the world. One moment she was there, towering upward like a castle which ruled all their lives and took all their sweating labour; and then, with a few softly called orders, the great black shadow moved away into deeper darkness, and there was not a trace to be seen. It was the proudest moment he could ever remember. With such triumphs for the human spirit, how could Malta lose the war?

The tinny bell, for the half-past-four Mass, sounded nearby. It was a fine thing to have a dependable sacristan—even though, this morning, Rafel seemed to be ringing awkwardly; the ragged sound more like a child playing with a new Christmas toy than a solemn call to worship.

Father Salvatore stretched, feeling his toes aching as they uncurled, and he thought: it is more than time for a new pair of boots, but how can I find them, now that Vincenzu the old cobbler is dead?

As he got down from his high stone bed, dressed, and left his cell, he felt bound to admit that though he loved all these people, these better people, love could not blind the eye nor muffle the ear to the sights and sounds of cramped humanity. Love could not plug the nose.

His practical mind dwelt on the smell, and as usual turned away again. The first thing one noticed, unfortunately, about the catacombs was the smell of them, but there was nothing to be done about it. In this hot July weather, the motionless, loaded air must always bear down on them. The catacombs could not be ventilated, without weakening the shelter they provided. Better to pant, and suffer, and live, than breathe the open air and die.

He approached his altar for his private devotions before he began the Mass. Here to his surprise, he was met, not by Rafel, but Nero, holding in his hand the bell-of-office of the sacristan.

"*Bongu*, Dun Salv." Nero greeted him cheerfully enough, but with hesitation in his face. He looked down at the bell, firmly muffled by his thumb. "I'm sorry about the rotten noise I made."

"But what's happened, Nero? Where is Rafel?"

Nero avoided his eye again. Nero's mouth was actually trembling, as if he feared what he had to say, what he had to do to someone he loved. "Rafel has gone. He has left."

"I don't understand." But Father Salvatore did understand, with a bitter pang of bereavement.

"Rafel had to go back home, to Gozo." The dwarf seemed almost to be grovelling on the stone floor, he was so sad, so ashamed. "He had to be with his mother. He said he did not believe in the catacombs any more. He had met a man who told him that what you were doing was forbidden."

"Forbidden? What man is this?"

"I thought you would know." And then, seeing Father Salvatore's face as stricken as his own at this Judas stroke, Nero cried out: "It doesn't matter! Let him go! I can do everything!"

With that, Father Salvatore had to be content. Gradually he became absorbed, first in the formality and then in the joy of the Mass. Nero tolled his little bell at the right moments. The faithful supported them both; it became, as usual, a purge for the spirit and a glimpse of glory. All was well, between God and man.

But then, as soon as it was over, guns began to bark almost over their heads. Father Salvatore did not like to be interrupted between the miracle of communion and his re-engagement with humanity. But now the moment became lost in the brazen voice of war. He said: "Nero, something is happening," and ran out to see what it was.

IT WAS VERY DIFFICULT to decide what in fact had happened, or was happening, or would happen next. Sunrise brought nothing but confusion and doubt. The sound of gunfire, which had started at a quarter to five, continued for about half an hour and then abruptly ceased. But there had been no air raid. Father Salvatore, waiting at French Creek for a ferryboat which did not come, heard a dozen stories. He could credit none of them.

"It was the invasion from Sicily. Thousands of ships! They say there were landing-craft as big as houses."

"No, no! It was an air raid. They were after the big convoy."

"But they didn't drop any bombs."

"It must have been *something*. All the searchlights were on."

"But they shone the searchlights *along* the water! Why?"

Then old Angelo arrived, urging his *dghajsa* towards the quay like a mad rocking-horse. As usual, he had the whole story.

"I saw it all," he told his audience. "I was just starting out from the Customs House. You wouldn't believe what I saw!"

"That's the first true word today."

113

Angelo ignored the jibe and the laughter which followed it. "You can laugh. But I *know*! It was hundreds of little boats coming in from the sea. They were all blown up. First by the guns, and then by the fighters. I tell you, I was right in the middle of it! I thought I would be sunk myself." His whiskers bristled fiercely. "You could have *trodden* on the bullets!"

Astonishingly, old Angelo's story was somewhere near the truth.

It had been a good try, a very good try indeed. The target was a convoy of six ships, of immense value to hard-pressed Malta, which had just reached harbour after a ferocious fight stretching half across the Mediterranean. The Italians decided to destroy these six ships where they lay, in the farthest corner, and under the guns of a harbour which, ringed by protection nets, had become one of the hardest in the world to crack.

A curious kind of mother-ship, called *Diana*, set sail from Sicily. She was playing mother to eighteen Italian craft of an even more curious breed. They were one-man jobs: small motor launches with a torpedo-head as a bow, an engine in the middle, and a brave sailor in the stern whose job it was to aim the boat at its target, activate the torpedo, and then jump overboard before the impact.

The choice of these death-or-glory boys, whose gallantry was beyond dispute, was thus death by their own torpedoes, death by drowning, death by pot-shot from the shore, or capture and imprisonment for the rest of the war.

As she neared Malta the *Diana* was tracked by radar to a point nine miles north of Fort St. Elmo. There, just at daybreak, she launched her eighteen turbulent children, turned round, and made for home again. She was radar-tracked doing this as well. But the lethal little bundles speeding towards Grand Harbour were too small to be picked up on the defence screen.

Perhaps they should have made their approach shortly *before* dawn; but perhaps, equally, without light of any kind, they could never have steered towards their target. In any event, an alert gunner spotted one of them coming towards his battery on Fort St. Elmo in the pale eastern glow between night and day.

Wisely he decided to believe his eyes. The crash-alarm sounded, and the coastal guns, manned by bored gunners who had shot at nothing since the war began, now jumped into delighted action.

The leading torpedo-boat hit the bridge between the two arms of the breakwater—perhaps on purpose—and blew up with a huge explosion which partially blocked the entrance. As the shore searchlights came on, the second boat was hit; then the next, at a hundred yards range. After that the rest of the flotilla, zigzagging wildly in a sea now floodlit from a dozen angles, were picked off one by one.

The harbour was never breached, and out of eighteen starters in this killing steeplechase there were no survivors. Hurricane fighters disposed of the last four as they retreated—they had nowhere to retreat to, anyway. One boat was captured, and towed into Malta as a war trophy. Three prisoners were taken.

The prize which had escaped this attack was rich. Besides thousands of fighting men, the six-vessel convoy carried 65,000 tons of supplies to relieve the straitened island, the first worthwhile supplies for nearly thirteen weeks. Frozen meat (2,000 tons), edible oils (2,000 tons), three months' supply of sugar, coffee, fats, and tea: 10,000 tons of ammunition: spare submarine propellers, spare Hurricane engines, hundreds of anti-aircraft guns—such was Malta's desperate shopping list, and it had been delivered just on time. Of the brave effort to deny it, only splinters of wood, oil patches, three prisoners, and a slightly damaged breakwater were left to tell the tale.

FATHER SALVATORE was late for his morning visit to his mother, and he walked swiftly uphill from the Customs House steps where old Angelo, who had rowed so slowly because he talked so much, had finally put him ashore.

On that triumphant morning, however, everyone wanted to talk to everyone else; a priest in haste was not excepted from the universal need for happy human contact. There was a wonderful lightness and good humour in the air. Indeed it was the first expression of pride and hope he could remember since the war began. A man, a stranger, said: "You must have been praying hard, *Sur Kappillan*!" Another man, a shopkeeper, shouted, "So much for the Italian navy! Now for the Germans!"

Only one sadness nagged him, in all this celebration: the desertion of Rafel. He had known that this must come, but it was still a shock and it would remain so for a long time. That being so, he could logically put it aside, to consider later.

He entered the Palazzo through the postern gate. A tottering Gregory let him in, after a long wait—and this was a sad reminder of decay. The major-domo should not really be answering the door; and an old man, past eighty-three and ailing, should not do so in any case. But Francis had gone to the army, and another footman had also left to help a widowed mother in the fields. There had been a necessary scaling-down of style. Two whole wings of the house had been closed. Formal entertaining was out of place.

Beyond doubt, two things only were important in war: the winning of it, and the death it cost. The high quality of life, enshrined in one house, could not be listed among the real dead. Death was bloodshed, not dustsheets, or the end of dinner parties for sixty guests. Yet in the midst of global uproar, one might still spare a thought for such small areas of mourning.

He could spare a thought also for Gregory. He touched the old man on the shoulder. "*Tkun imbierek*. . . . Gregory, you should *not* be answering the door. One of the girls could do it."

"What? A girl to answer the door at the Palazzo?" Gregory was horrified—or was he only pretending to be horrified, and thus acknowledging, ruefully, the decay of the house?

One of the difficulties with talking to the very old was that one underestimated their awareness—and their sense of humour. He had always remembered his very first death—that was how he had phrased it, as with trembling hands and the great doubt of the novice he had anointed the lips of an old woman slipping away from life as if from a family party which had gone on long enough. He had thought that she was already dead, so calm was the grey-white face. Then the anointed lips had opened, and he bent his head to hear what she might say. Some holy thought?—some last confession?—some confused memory of a life of travail? Not so. . . . Her eyes remained shut, but her lips were smiling. "You did that very well . . . for a young chap. . . ."

On which brave and blessed farewell, she had died.

Old Gregory, another survivor of the same quality, led the way slowly across the central courtyard. He stumbled on the stone flags, and Father Salvatore put out a hand to steady him. They were in the harsh sunlight of a very hot morning, and gently he guided the old man into the shade of the portico.

"You've walked quite far enough, Gregory. Now go back to your room, and have a little rest."

"But I must conduct you to the Baroness," Gregory protested.

"I am the only visitor you need not conduct. . . . Now, will you be good, or must a priest order you?"

"If you say so, Dun Salv."

Father Salvatore waited until the old man walked away, and then made for the staircase leading to his mother's apartments. The first thing he heard, as he paused outside the door, was a man's voice. The sonorous, fruity accents were unmistakable. He had been forestalled, on his traditional visiting day, by the last man in the world he would have chosen. It was really intolerable. His rebellious thoughts unconquered, he opened the door and entered.

His mother, facing the door, smiled at his entrance; Monsignor Scholti, however, turned with an affected start, as if some important business had been interrupted in spite of strict orders to the contrary. When Father Salvatore advanced to greet his mother, Scholti did not even give ground, but remained where he was at the side of the chair.

"You are so late, Salvatore," the Baroness complained, as soon as he had kissed her. "And Monsignor Scholti came early."

"So I see. . . . I'm very sorry. There were all sorts of excitements down at the harbour, but no boat to take me across." He nodded to the other man. "Good morning, Bruno."

Scholti gave him a curt nod. His mother said, "Well, sit down. The coffee is still hot, though it tastes perfectly terrible. These girls haven't the faintest idea how to make it properly."

She sounded so unlike her normal self that he looked at her more closely. She had become frail during the past few months, and her face had that inner pallor which he had come to associate with the margins of mortality. Though she sat as straight as ever, it was now the straightness of self-discipline, not of natural habit.

117

"I'm sure the coffee will be excellent, as usual," he said. "You must cheer up, mother. We have so much to be thankful for."

"It's easy to say that." Scholti's reproving tone revived all Father Salvatore's rebellious mood. "But your mother has a great deal to worry her. She has had bad news from Paris."

Father Salvatore gave all his attention to his mother. "Was the news from Benedict?"

"It was *about* Benedict," the Baroness answered sharply. She was very agitated—an astonishing reaction from her. "Your brother has been distinguishing himself on a truly magnificent scale!"

"Please tell me. What has he been doing?"

"Only entertaining Göring and half his staff at Maxim's!"

Father Salvatore felt like laughing. Of course it was disgraceful that the heir of the Santo-Nobiles should do such a thing, but the heir of the Santo-Nobiles had been misbehaving, in the full glare of publicity, for over twenty years, and there was scarcely anything he could now do which would seem in any way extraordinary.

The Baroness had no such indulgent thoughts. "I have it in mind to disinherit him! Instantly!"

Father Salvatore could only murmur: "Legally, it would be almost impossible."

The Baroness seemed to detect the fact that her son was not taking this very seriously. "Salvatore, have you no pride?"

"I try not to have. It is a sin."

Scholti said stiffly: "We are not talking of *sins*. There is absolutely no harm in family pride."

Father Salvatore had had enough of Scholti. "That sounds like a very interesting Maltese heresy."

Monsignor Scholti glared at him. The remark had been undeniably impudent. But for the first time in many months, Father Salvatore felt supremely careless. It must be the utter rout of the Italian motorboats at the hands of the Maltese gunners. The vision of the elegant Benedict, the product of first-class tailoring and second-class morality, plying Hermann Göring with vintage champagne in the plush opulence of Maxim's was really hilarious, compared with Malta's doleful rationing. Still, he knew that he owed his mother more than a light-hearted verdict. "Of course I am truly sorry that you should be worried about Benedict. But I imagine that the situation in Paris, under the occupation, is very difficult. I wonder how certain of the Maltese would react, if the Germans were installed in San Anton Palace?"

"Are you making excuses for your brother's treachery?" Scholti said grandly.

"Yes."

His mother, who had been watching him, broke in. Her voice was almost plaintive. "But *why*, Salvatore? I thought you would be as shocked as I am. And think of the disgrace!"

"The disgrace is Benedict's, not ours. Benedict can no longer shock me. Can he shock you?"

"He can go too far."

"Mother, I am quite certain that he has gone too far already, on the only path which really matters. This last sin is mere feebleness, mere vanity." He leaned over, and clasped his mother's hand, so wasted, so white. It made his own feel like a peasant's paw. "The only bad thing is the way it has hurt you."

"You believe that I should forgive him?"

"I believe that you should understand him, and show compassion."

"*Well!* . . ." Scholti began, on a scandalized note.

"It is also a family matter." What was prompting him to such bravado? It must be the Italian boats again. "So we must look on the bright side. Did you hear about the torpedo-boat raid?"

They had heard about the torpedo-boat raid. Monsignor Scholti had heard *all* about it. "It was of course the beginning of the invasion," he declared. "But I am told that they will think twice before trying again. Their fleet was utterly smashed!"

Father Salvatore let him talk on. The change of subject was all that he wanted; the wild suppositions, the pretence of inside information, did not matter. Even when, at the end, Monsignor Scholti said "I am sure your mother is tired," and rose to go, clearly intending to take Salvatore with him at the same time, such presumption did not seem important. He made his farewell as if it were nothing out of the ordinary, glad to see that his mother now seemed more relaxed, more reconciled to her dire news from Paris.

He said: "If I may, I will telephone you from Giovanna's," and left their proper intimacy till later.

Monsignor Scholti, however, had not finished with his side of things. He had only been controlling his displeasure.

"I did not wish to speak of it before your mother," he said, with a formidable change of manner, as soon as they were outside the postern door. "She has suffered enough already. But your remark about heresy was really unforgiveable."

"It was a joke, Bruno."

"Not to me. You seem to forget that I am your superior."

"Only in rank." It was hopeless: he could not take things seriously today. "No, no, I withdraw that. You are my superior in every way. In rank, in looks, in social graces, in access to official secrets. You have the ear of his Lordship—"

"*Salvu*—" Scholti began furiously.

"You also have the ear of my sacristan."

For once, Scholti was taken aback. "What do you mean by that?"

"I think you know. You have been talking to Rafel, haven't you?"

"We met by chance in the street. That is all."

"It seems to have been enough. Was it you who made him go back to Gozo? Did you tell him what I was doing was wrong?"

"He told *me!*" Scholti suddenly launched into a violent attack on Father Salvatore's permissive attitude to sexual misbehaviour: his tolerance of noise and wild parties: his carelessness over money matters: his laxity in religious observance: his ridiculous "performances" which took the place of a proper homily. He had even called St. Paul "an ugly old man with bow legs". . . . "Apparently I cannot save you from corruption, Salvu," Monsignor Scholti ended, on a note of doom. "But at least I can rescue an innocent like Rafel Vella from being contaminated!"

It was ridiculous and pathetic. Father Salvatore could not even bear to answer back. The charges were baseless, in the context of the catacombs. "Which way are you going, Bruno?" he asked.

"*What?* Is that all you have to say?"

"Yes. I forgive you . . . Which way are you going?"

Scholti gestured uncertainly. "Down there, I suppose."

"Then I am going up here. Good-bye. God bless you."

Presently he found himself back on the bastions again, free as the air under the warm sunshine. But now came a surprise of a different sort. The first person he recognized, among a throng of chattering cheerful people still engrossed in the morning's victory, was his niece Marija.

She was alone with two tall young men in uniform. They all stood close together, and they were laughing. But when she turned to look up at the sailor, Marija's face was so utterly blissful that its beauty gained tenfold, transformed as if by magic.

As he walked towards them—both as an uncle and a priest, he must look into this—Father Salvatore realized that there was in fact true magic in the air. Indeed, he had never before seen Marija like this: never observed in her such shining eyes, such happy freedom, such an open avowal of life and love.

PIETRU PAWL HAD ASKED, for the third time: "What are we waiting here for? There's nothing to see," before Marija decided on desperate remedies. She just had to stay on the bastions, and Pietru had to stay with her, for her mother said that she was not to wander about town alone. Finally she said: "Can you keep a secret?"

"That depends."

"Promise you won't tell anyone." While she spoke, Marija's eyes were still searching the long approach to the bastions. "Not anyone in the whole world, and I'll give you—I'll give you—"

"You'll give me what?"

Her voice suddenly changed, from desperation to triumphant happiness. "I'll give you absolutely *nothing!*" she said, and raised her hand to wave.

It was Michael Ainslie, splendid in uniform, beautiful as this day and a hundred days like it. . . . He smiled as he saw her, and strode swiftly past the people who separated them. He saluted.

What did girls do when they were saluted? As far as Marija was concerned, all they could manage was a silly, joyous smile. Pietru, immensely impressed, saluted back, his hand ripping up to his forelock as if it bore all the brass insignia in the world.

"I'm terribly sorry I'm late," Michael Ainslie said. "But I've got quite a good excuse."

"It doesn't matter," Marija answered, and indeed it now mattered less than anything else in all her life so far. "Oh—this is my brother Pietru."

Michael held out his hand. "I'm Michael Ainslie."

Pietru, wordless, shook hands. His eyes were taking in every detail of the uniform: the beautiful doeskin cloth, the two gold stripes with the little A in the circle, the gold buttons, the peaked cap with the gleaming white cover, the glossy black halfboots. He had never been so near to such gorgeous perfection.

Marija strove to catch up with reality. "What did you mean when you said you had a good excuse?"

He turned towards her, and his pleasure in doing so was obvious. "Well, as a matter of fact—and do stop me if you've heard this one before—I was sinking an Italian E-boat."

"Michael!"

"Believe it or not, a man woke me up and said 'Get dressed, Ainslie, get into that Hurricane, and *get weaving!* There's a funny-looking boat with a red-white-and-green flag due north of your bedstead. Sink it!' You know, the man was right!"

"But did you really sink it?"

"Subject to confirmation, as they say when they may be telling lies, the score in Ainslie versus Mussolini is now one-nil."

Pietru surfaced breathlessly. "Did you say a *Hurricane?*"

"Yes. Mark Two." Michael checked himself. "You are now in possession of a military secret known only to the enemy." He bent down, and whispered fiercely in Pietru's ear: "*Don't leave the country!*"

Pietru, utterly captivated, lost no time in consolidating this marvellous friendship. "But aren't you a sailor?"

"A flying sailor. That's rather like a tame duck. As soon as we get scared enough, we take to the air and, flying round in ever-decreasing circles—" but he did not want to finish it. "I'm shore-based now, anyway. Are you interested in flying?"

"Oh yes! Specially the Fleet Air Arm!" The questions flooded over. What was the difference between a Hurricane and one of the new Seafires? What was it like to take off from an aircraft-carrier? Was it easy to get into the Navy? How did one find out if one was colour-blind? Marija rescued him. "Pietru, *hanini*," she said. "Don't you want to go and buy an ice-cream?"

"What, *now*?" He turned back to Michael. "Is it true that—"

"Pietru," Michael said, with a reasonable air of authority.

"Yes, sir?"

"A word in your ear."

It was very adroitly done, out of earshot and almost out of sight. When Michael returned, after a couple of sentences and what looked like a handshake, he was alone.

"Where did he go?" Marija asked.

"I said I wanted to talk to you alone, and here was half a crown to prove it."

"What did he say?"

Michael laughed. "He said: 'I am baffled, Watson, baffled. But thank you all the same.' Then he took the money, and charged off. . . . That's quite a lad. How old is he?"

"Fourteen."

"Good lord! When I was fourteen I'd only just given up knitting." He was becoming marvellously relaxed, and so was she. It did not matter what they said, nor how silly and vulnerable they were.

"What *did* you knit?"

"Grey scarves for old age pensioners. Only my sisters had to cast on and off for me. I did the middle bit. If they were both away, or we had a row, that scarf could be nine feet long."

"Did you often have rows?"

"Oh yes. Sisters can give you hell. Do you give Pietru hell?"

"That's not an expression we use."

"Are you religious?"

"Well, of course."

"I'm not. I rely on Saint Michael and all Ainslies."

It was a moment before she could take it in. "That's not a nice thing to say."

"I thought it was rather clever. . . . Oh, you're so beautiful

123

when you're shocked." Now he had taken hold of her hand instead of her arm, and an important frontier had been crossed. It was incredible to think that they were, at last, alone. It was only the fourth time in six awful months.

She could have recited them all by heart, with places faithfully described and hours measured by the minute-hand of joy.

After that first time, Michael had rung her up early next morning, as they had planned; and somehow, by juggling with a shopping trip and a vague appointment with a girl cousin, she had managed to meet him in Floriana, and have coffee in an obscure café. But it was not as good as they had hoped.

He was still terribly worried about his ship, and didn't know when she was going to sail, or how long he might be away. It was almost as if he didn't know why he was sitting talking to her. They parted in secret despair which neither could yet admit. It had set the sad, heart-rending pattern of love in wartime.

He had sailed away without warning, breaking another appointment with no word of good-bye; harsh security dictated *that* piece of the pattern, as it dictated so many others. There then followed a miserable separation of two whole months. He wrote ambiguous, cheerful notes—he was better with spoken words than on paper, and his handwriting was disgraceful—and she never knew where he was, to the nearest five thousand miles.

Suddenly he came back to Malta—but it was only for half a day, and it was a horrible meeting. He had been strung up to the point of insanity, and rather drunk as well. He had tried to kiss her almost straight away, and she had been silly about it.

She had cried for nights afterwards. But tears could not bring him back, nor the lost kisses either. Another long separation, of nearly four months, star-crossed their lives again. She was now sure that he would be killed. Then, fantastically, he had rung up last night. He was *not* dead. He was ashore in Malta! Land-based! He ought to be free next morning, "unless there's a flap". Could they meet at that point on the bastions where they had first seen each other?

What other answer could there be but Yes? And now he was next to her, and within reach at last.

124

He was asking: "What was that you called Pietru?"

"*Hanini?* It means—well, 'darling' is the nearest."

"Can I call you *hanini?*"

"Of course not!"

"I think I will."

A most intrusive voice, much too near to them, broke a magic moment.

"What ho!" it said. "Is this how the flying Jack Tars relax? I think I'll swap uniforms!"

They turned from each other, not without an effort, and faced the invasion. A tall young soldier was standing in front of them, grinning all over a freckled face. He had red hair, and a sharp pointed nose, inquisitive and aristocratic at the same time. He was almost overwhelmingly smart, his uniform enhanced by the gold-tasselled aiguillettes of an aide-de-camp.

"Ian," Michael Ainslie said, without enthusiasm.

"Hello, Mike! I hear you distinguished yourself this morning." He was staring at Marija. "But not half as much as now. Who's this absolutely ravishing girl?"

Michael introduced Captain Ian Ross in a voice so grumpy that Marija could have laughed, if she had not felt the same about the intrusion.

"What are you doing up here, Ian? Or is it the army's day off?"

"As a matter of fact I've been touring all the gun-sites with our gallant Governor. He wanted to say 'Well done' to the chaps. I must say they deserved it. There was some mighty shooting this morning. I've never seen gunners so pleased with themselves." Then, glancing over Marija's shoulder, "Don't look now," he cautioned. "But that funny little black beetle seems to know you."

Marija turned. "Oh, he's my uncle," she said. Ross suddenly looked totally embarrassed.

She introduced them coolly and efficiently, though her heart sank at Uncle Salvu's *very* guarded look. Then Ross, who had not recovered from his *gaffe*, took himself off with the minimum of delay, and the three of them were left. She prayed that there would not be too many questions just yet. It was going to take hours to think of the answers.

The first question was easy. "Are you here alone, Marija?"

"No, no." Her reply came, perhaps, a little too quickly. "Pietru is with me. He just went off to buy something."

"H'm." It explained nothing, and Father Salvatore felt bound to pursue the subject. "So you met—"

"We've met before." Marija said bravely. It was all going to come out anyway. "Michael is stationed in Malta now."

Michael. . . . In spite of lawful suspicions, Father Salvatore found himself irresistibly drawn towards the splendid young man with the alarmingly attractive smile. "So you're in the Navy?" he said, for want of a better probe.

"Fleet Air Arm, sir," Michael answered. "I was here in *Illustrious*, originally."

"O-o-oh. . . ." Things fell neatly into place. "*Illustrious*. . . ." The young man looked honest and open: not dangerous, except in the way that all the explosive young were dangerous. Father Salvatore decided to relax his role of inquisitor. He said: "It was really amazing that the ship went away so quickly, from what I saw of her."

To Marija's relief, Michael and Uncle Salvu now got on very well. Michael was deferential: the word "sir" reappeared every few moments. They talked about the ship, and convoys, and rationing in Malta. Then, for no reason at all, the subject was boots.

"If you really want a new pair, sir, I could fix it with the R.A.F. The erks—I mean the aircraftmen wear the kind you like." Michael looked down, politely yet dubiously, at Father Salvatore's feet. "But they're a bit *bulbous*. Wouldn't you prefer—" and he raised his trouser leg to display his slim half-Wellingtons.

"No, I want the ordinary kind," Father Salvatore answered. "Big toecaps, and laces and good thick soles."

"What size do you take?"

Father Salvatore did not know. Maltese bootmakers in this particular line did not make sizes, only big, medium, and small. He and Michael, linking arms, measured their feet side by side, Marija delighting in the absurd picture, and decided on size nine. While they were still smiling at their ingenuity, Pietru reappeared.

"Uncle Salvu! Are you *dancing*?"

"No Peter Paul, I am not dancing." Father Salvatore straightened up, and smoothed his ruffled cassock. "But I see you have been eating." Crumbs and a ring of milky white round his mouth betrayed the gluttonous boy. "You know it will spoil your lunch."

"Not mine. I only had two *pasti* and some ice-cream."

Father Salvatore sighed. "I don't know where you get your money from." For some reason this seemed to amuse everyone else inordinately, and looking from one smiling face to another he felt so close to youthful happiness that he could only see it as a privilege. Details could come later. He looked at his watch. "It's nearly time we were on our way. Peter Paul, will you go and find us a *karrozzin*, and we'll ride home in style."

When Pietru was gone, Father Salvatore shook his head. "I'm sorry to cut short this meeting," he told Michael, "but today is our family lunch day."

"Yes, I know."

There was a lot this young man seemed to know. Perhaps that was as it should be: it gave whatever was going on—and he was still a long way from discovering even the rudiments of this—a certain honesty. He looked from Marija to Michael Ainslie, and back again. What he saw, in their nervous, electric, private entrancement made his next move easy to determine.

"I think I'll just make sure that Peter Paul is doing what I want." He pointed to the lower street-level behind them. "Meet us down there. Shall we say, in two minutes?"

They joined him again in five, which was a reasonable extension. Pietru had picked a fine *karrozzin*, with polished brasswork, gleaming leather, tossing plumes. Marija and Michael walked down from the bastion, studiously apart, looking sad and happy and expectant, all at the same time. Young lovers could do this, old priests could not. Father Salvatore held out his hand.

"Good-bye, and good luck."

"Thank you, sir. I hope we meet again sometime."

"I wouldn't be at all surprised."

Michael saluted them all, smiled in the vague direction of Marija, and was gone almost before they realized it.

Pietru was very impressed. "Uncle Salvu! He called you 'sir'."

"That's because I'm older."

"Well, of course. But still. . . . He's a Hurricane pilot! . . . Can I ride on the front seat with the driver?"

"I think that's a very good idea."

To the clip-clop of the hooves, Father Salvatore, sitting beside his niece beneath the tasselled canopy, and out of earshot of anyone else, said, "*Now*. What is all *this* about?"

"Dear Uncle Salvu"—Marija was at her most appealing, "*please* don't be angry with me."

"Why should I be angry, Marija? Is it something sinful?"

The startled look in her face was a joy to see. "No, no! How could it be?"

"Deceit is sinful. Have you told your mother about this meeting?"

"Well, no . . . I didn't want to worry her. Not that there's anything to worry about. . . . *You* won't say anything, will you? Not just yet."

"I need to know more. How many times have you met him?"

She told him, and for him it was another sort of joy, as their *karrozzin* wound its way onward at a gallant pace, to listen to her meticulous accounting, to hear the why and wherefore of chance meetings which became milestones of excitement and awakening. Father Salvatore had heard many such stories, within the confessional and outside it; what distinguished Marija's account was its purity. She wished to obey, she wished to love and give, she wished to *know*. It rejoiced him, as it would have rejoiced her mother.

Marija returned, at the end, to the violent preoccupation of the young. "But I *do* want it to be a secret. *Please* trust me."

"I trust you, if you trust yourself. Do you love Michael?"

"I don't know. *We* don't know, not yet. But it feels like it. Is it wrong?"

It feels like it. . . . Is it wrong? . . . Here she had given him a glimpse of unknown territory, forsworn by a priest. What it felt like, to be in love, he had never known and, after the first few turbulent years, had never wished to discover. If marriage was, as the Church enjoined, a great mystery, then love itself was the final enigma, to which the simple and the lucky might find a key, the greedy and the lustful never. What could he tell Marija, so tempting and tempted, trembling with such delight on the verge of divine discovery—what could he tell such a girl?

He woke to hear her say: "Did you like him? He liked you *terribly*. He said you were absolutely wizard!"

"Good gracious!"

"But *did* you like him?" Her lovely eyes beseeched him; for her, there could be nothing more important.

"Well, it was only a short meeting, wasn't it?"

"But still. . . ."

"I liked his uniform. And his feet are smaller than mine."

"Oh, *Uncle Salvu!*"

He put his hand firmly on hers. "I'm bound to say that I thought he was a very fine young man. Perhaps *just* good enough for you."

Her answering eyes were so joyous that, moved suddenly by emotions never to be shared, he had to turn away to hide his own.

FAMILY LUNCH WAS as much fun as it should always have been. To begin with, there was a signal blessing, announced by Giovanna Debrincat as soon as she greeted her brother.

"Gigi is so sorry he can't be here. He had to go to a meeting."

Unworthily pleased, Father Salvatore said that he was sorry to miss his brother-in-law. After that, he settled down, alone with Giovanna and the children, to enjoy himself. Underlying all their happiness was the morning's news of the Italian "defeat"; and this framework of hope ordained a memorable day.

With the head of the family absent, Giovanna was composed and contented. Marija was silly with happiness, and surfaced only to advertise the fact; Pietru was bursting with news, and presently with food.

"We met a Hurricane pilot this morning," he announced, between mouthfuls of cannelloni. "Only he was in the Navy."

Giovanna said: "That's nice, dear."

"He was terrific. And he's going to give Uncle some boots."

"We were talking," Father Salvatore interposed, "and I just

happened to mention boots, and he said he could get me a new pair from the R.A.F. I don't know whether he'll remember."

"I'm sure he'll remember," Marija said.

"I'm sure he'll remember you," Pietru muttered.

"Now, Pietru."

Giovanna looked from one to the other. "Am I supposed to understand all this?"

"Of course not," Father Salvatore assured her. "These are but wild and whirling words."

"Who said that?"

"Horatio—in Hamlet." He smoothed the way. "Hamlet also said, 'O! that this too too solid flesh would melt', and that's exactly how I shall feel at the end of this wonderful lunch."

They were enjoying their coffee out on the patio when Carmelina appeared, full of important news.

"Excuse me, Dun Salv. There's a man to see you."

They all trooped out into the hall. An R.A.F. dispatch rider in a blue-and-white-striped crash helmet, grinned all over his face as he proffered Father Salvatore a brown paper parcel.

"Well, thank you very much," said Father Salvatore. "Er . . ."

"No charge," said the dispatch rider. He executed an impressive salute, and a foot-slamming about-turn. Then he marched out. He must have winked at Carmelina as he passed, since she dissolved into helpless giggles.

It was like Christmas. Unwrapped and displayed on the patio table, the boots were everything which had been promised, gleaming black, with bulging toecaps, and soles like planks.

Surrounded by admiring helpers, Father Salvatore tried them on. "They're perfect," he said. "They should last for years."

Giovanna looked round her family, aware of all sorts of mysterious undertones. But she knew them to be benevolent, and therefore acceptable. "Well," she said, "You must have made quite a hit with this pilot."

"Oh, I think we did. . . ." Father Salvatore was sitting down again, but he was not going to take the boots off. "What a happy day. You know, I think I shall go for a walk."

He had already decided exactly the walk he wanted to take.

130

THE ONE AND ONLY railway system which Malta had ever known opened in 1883 and closed for ever in 1931. It boasted ten steam-engines (two to each train, because of the gradient), ran seven times a day on a single line from Valletta, through the Floriana Tunnel, and, after rising to six hundred feet with the aid of sandboxes and those two puffing engines, ended its journey in another tunnel under the hilltop citadel of Mdina.

Father Salvatore had always loved that railway. After getting a lift to the outskirts of Santa Vennera in an army lorry full of rowdy gunners boasting of their part in that morning's exercise, he set out on foot again. He found the disused railway track running beside a country road, and began his journey, slowly and gently, uphill to distant Mdina. His mind was at peace, his spirit buoyant, and his boots seven-league.

There were traces of the vanished railroad still: discarded rails and the rusted iron ties which had once bolted them down: the stone chippings which had made their firm bed: and at one point the ruins of an ancient barrel, from which the coal dust had spilled out to make a black circle among the weeds.

It was a peerless day, the blue arc of the sky a perfect frame for the citadel of Mdina which could be seen crowning the hilltop far ahead. As he walked he wondered who among his family was as happy as he.

It was not a comforting tally. His father lay at peace in his sailor's grave. His mother was old and troubled. Giovanna was not happy. Lewis was not happy. Inconstant Benedict, far away in Paris, perhaps was. Pietru, yes. Marija, yes and no.

Marija the young and vulnerable, with all the tearing passions of love and life still before her. *Somehow she must be helped.* Father Salvatore had liked that young man instantly. When the moment came, he must tell Giovanna about him *in the right way*. That still left Lewis, the jealous father who, he suspected, would never be reconciled to a suitor from the camp of the enemy.

He was now topping the crest of the hill, reaching the end of the line as the railway itself had reached the end of its life, in 1931. For it had not been able to survive a succession of crises, ranging from a rise in the price of coal to a trade recession which meant that the poor and the not-so-poor were forced to walk instead of ride. It had been a sad, sick year when Malta was not only desperately poor but tormented by political and religious strife as well. It was the unhappiest year of his priesthood.

The year before was, or should have been, election year. He could remember, even now, reading out the pastoral letter which had forbidden the faithful to vote for one of the parties, as a grave sin, and instructing himself to refuse the sacraments even to its party workers. A British protest to the Holy See had received an inflexible reply. The election had been cancelled, the constitution suspended, and Malta returned to a long paternal servitude, under the colonial power of Britain.

Religion and politics. . . . He prayed that so gross a conflict would never happen again. This was not why he had become a priest, to drag his feet through a muddy temporal stream. He had become a priest, against all the hopes of his family, because . . . because. . . .

He tried to be honest here, as he had always tried. He had become a priest, instead of a sailor like his father, for reasons which were grounded only in shame. He had become a priest because, at the age of sixteen, he had taken a terrified vow to do so, if a certain girl did not find herself with child. He would be chaste for ever afterwards, if only. . . .

God had spared her, and him, and thus enrolled him in His ministry. By the time that the girl, released from her fearful burden of guilt, had married someone else, he had already kept his vow. He could tell no one about it, not even his astonished family; only his confessor. For himself, there had been nothing but silence, and the humility and glory of service.

There were many paths to God. His had been sin, and redemption, and faithful dedication, for ever afterwards.

Walking through the great and timeless gate of the citadel of Mdina, built on the site of the old city of Melita, he took refuge from the broiling sun within the cool caverns of streets so narrow that it was possible to reach out from the upper floors of one house and touch the hand of someone opposite. In the whole of this sleepy hour, he met no one except a single mendicant friar, dusty and sandalled. Father Salvatore raised his hand in blessing, and the friar, a spare and shabby man whose white cloak was threadbare, smiled in answer.

As he walked slowly back to the main gate, feeling his new boots beginning to pinch at last, he remembered Rafel Vella. Since the morning, he had put the matter out of his mind, except to realize, that the problem must eventually be faced. Now that he was prepared to face it, he discovered to his astonishment that it did not matter at all.

There were many reasons. On the practical side, little Nero could do the work as well as Rafel, perhaps better, spurred by boundless energy, freed from such worries as beset Rafel all the time. For the rest, it was sad, but it was not the end of the world. All sorts of things could happen. Perhaps Rafel's wife would follow him to Gozo. Perhaps Rafel, after a brief experiment, would change his mind. Perhaps the old lady would die. Perhaps it was, after all, best as it was.

Father Salvatore sighed, and smiled, and walked on down the hill towards the plains of Attard where, of all unlikely things, roses bloomed. If roses could bloom in the parched soil of Malta, he thought, then so could charity and hope, and acceptance of all things fearful and strange.

He had scarcely gone a quarter of a mile, on feet which now seemed to be under a private inquisition from the pinching irons of new leather, when he was given a lift by a farmer taking the last of his onion crop to the storage place at Attard.

This was a most cheerful man, brown as a wine barrel, full of his many blessings. All was well with his world: the onion bags which pressed against Father Salvatore's back were bulging, the price was good, the Italians were on the run, the war would soon be over and then Malta would be run by the farmers and the Labour Party. It was all planned.

"Planned by God," he added piously, with a side glance at Father Salvatore's dusty cassock. Even as an afterthought, that seemed to be good news too.

As the farmer set him down, with a hearty farewell, at the end of the avenue of huge trees which led to San Anton Palace, a car swept by him and turned into the entrance. He had a glimpse of a Union Jack on a small flagstaff, of a compact grey man sitting in the back, and a young man in uniform by his side. Then the young soldier looked back, and after a moment the car stopped.

A trim figure walked back towards him, his gold tassels swinging in perfect tempo. It was Captain Ross, the aide-de-camp who had seemed so unaccountably ill-at-ease when they had met that morning.

Ross saluted. "Sir," he said formally, "His Excellency would be delighted if you would come in for a cup of tea."

Father Salvatore knew the Governor. He also knew the great house well, and honoured it as a focus of Maltese history which had housed sixteen Grand Masters and twenty-seven governors. Noble in proportion and set amid orange groves, it remained after three hundred years the very signature of pastoral ease and elegance. Now this magnificence was occupied by a markedly austere governor, who received Father Salvatore in a small salon, under the portrait of another admired warrior, Alexander Ball, Nelson's most trusted captain and the first Civil Commissioner of Malta after the British succeeded the French.

General Dobbie was a grey man, grey all over, with a grey bristle on top. Between his truly enormous ears was a lined face, on which a terrible exhaustion had begun to carve its mark. But he was politeness itself to his guest: politeness, with overtones of a religious rectitude which was not going to pass unnoticed for want of a word in season.

"You may or may not know that I belong to the Plymouth Brethren," he said. Father Salvatore did know. "Their *principal* article of faith—" and he expounded briefly and cogently the faith of a Plymouth Brother, which seemed to reject Church government and Church hierarchy of any kind, any drinking, smoking, dancing: yet allowed anyone to get up and expound the faith as long as he was inspired by zeal, piety, Calvinism, rejection of worldly pleasures, and a taste for "household baptism".

"This may seem rather strange to you," General Dobbie concluded.

Father Salvatore was enjoying his tea, and could not possibly be ungrateful. He said that it was always interesting to hear a different point of view.

"I'm glad you said that," the Governor interrupted him. His grey face was almost lively, "it means we're on the same team."

This very large assumption slipped by, as he dealt with the rightness of their cause. Father Salvatore listened, and nodded, and wiggled his toes which were now comfortably at ease. It would be unfair to dismiss Dobbie as a bigot, accurate to call him a devout bulldog for his faith—which was unquestionably the only true gospel. Dobbie reminded him of another stern soldier of Christ, Oliver Cromwell. Cromwell had once admonished some unruly parliamentarians: "I beseech you, in the bowels of Christ, think it possible you may be mistaken!" There was no record that he had ever said it to himself. Yet Cromwell had also said: "Put your trust in God, and keep your powder dry!"—an endearing gloss on Holy Scripture. General Dobbie was endearing in the same way. Manifestly he was always right, and his battles inevitably commendable to God; but he was not hesitating to work himself to death to prove it.

"We put up a splendid show this morning," he said, and once more the weary face awoke to pleasure and pride. "Absolutely splendid! The chaps were right on their toes, and we hit them for six! I believe it will happen again and again, until in God's good time . . .!"

God's good time passed in a steady flow of facts and figures. The exposition was fascinating. One plan slotted neatly into the next, until the whole grand design was marching irresistibly onward. A wall-map was referred to. An attack *here*, a holding operation *there*. Scandinavia neutralized. North Africa cleared of the enemy—this was where Malta was so important.

Father Salvatore listened, deeply impressed. Captain Ross stared out of the windows at the avenues of oleander, now blazing pink and white and red in the last brave display of summer.

Presently it was time to go. The Governor, now overwhelmingly tired, handled it with the dispatch of a man who *must* take a rest before the next task. "Ian, arrange for a car, will you please? We can't have Father Salvatore tiring himself out. . . . Good-bye, Father. Please remember me to your mother."

Outside, under the massive pillared portico, Captain Ross saw him into the official car. Father Salvatore thanked him. "I enjoyed that very much. The Governor was so *inspiring*. . . ."

"He has that effect," Captain Ross answered.

Then Father Salvatore, in the big black car with the soldier-driver at the wheel, rode in style round the harbour, and back to the Cottonera Lines.

The catacombs, at seven o'clock on that hot summer evening, were in a boisterous ferment. As soon as his imposing car drew up, Father Salvatore was surrounded by a laughing mob which almost carried him into the cool twilight within. Obviously wine had been circulating freely, but something more had prompted this explosion of good humour. It was hope, hope long deferred by the months of their ordeal. Excited questions greeted him. He was asked, a dozen times: "Is the war really over?"

Then suddenly Nero came trotting out from a dark passageway. As he caught sight of Father Salvatore he jumped in the air and capered round the rock grotto. People watching laughed; and one called out: "Steady, Nero! Save your strength for the wedding." Then Nero burst out with his news: "Dun Salv, I think I've found a girl!"

"But that's excellent." The beaming face crowning the shrunken body was irresistible. "Who is she?"

"Oh, just a girl. But she says she'll marry me. She's not very pretty."

"That doesn't matter. How old is she?"

"Perhaps twenty-seven."

"Have you spoken to her family?"

"Not yet." For a moment the dwarf looked sad. "They don't think much of me. You know how it is. Can I bring her to see you, Dun Salv? Then you could tell them I'm all right. Because she *does* want to marry me."

"I'll do everything I can to help."

"That's wonderful!" The small despised cripple of nineteen became the confident lover again. "Do you remember I once said— when I was talking about finding a girl—"

"I remember everything you said, Nero."

"Well, she's more than five feet tall!" With that vital item of news, he had told enough of his triumph, and swiftly turned the conversation. "Everything's ready for Mass, Dun Salv."

"Splendid, I knew I could trust you."

"Will you speak tonight?"

"Yes."

"Have you got a happy story for us?"

"A very happy story."

HEXAMERON III

A.D. 1090 Count Roger, of Blessed Memory

Such was the joy and excitement that it took them nearly an hour to settle down. When the time came to speak, he disdained formality and entered into their mood as closely as he could.

"Uliedi—*children*—I do not wonder that you feel like children tonight. Today has been a wonderful day, and it would be silly to forget it, even in church. It would be ungrateful as well. Such wonderful days come from God, and from our own strong arms; and this one has come after many terrible months. We should never forget that the wonderful days and the terrible days have all happened before. They are as old as man himself in Malta. There was a time when Malta was miserable and afraid, not for days or months but for whole centuries.

When the Roman empire was destroyed by the Vandals and the Goths, the longest night in the world came down. Barbarians governed our island. The Saracens came, and stayed two hundred and twenty years. They were Moslem Arabs, and they ruled all the known world from Persia to Spain. Malta they used only as a garrison, despising us, and reduced it to ruin and neglect. Then at last a man came, a Christian soldier, to change our history for ever; and on every fourth day of November since the year 1090 we have said a Mass for that man's soul, in the cathedral church of Mdina.

"This Christian soldier arrived from Sicily. . . ."

FRESH FROM RIDDING the whole of southern Italy and Sicily of the Arab invader, he had a reputation as a fierce, invincible conqueror. But he had no need to conquer Malta. He had long been expected, and hoped for, and (by a few) prayed for.

From the moment that Roger the Norman, Count of Sicily, set foot on a dry beach in northern Malta, he was welcomed as its saviour.

As its saviour, this Christian soldier looked the part. He marched through the shallows and up onto the foreshore as if he owned every foot of the ground. He was attended by thirteen knights and many other men—all equipped like himself in chain mail the like of which had never been seen on the island. Leaving the cover of rocks, the people gathered on the shore to gaze at this tall man, at the long shield shaped like a kite, and the great two-edged sword which completed his massive armament.

Where the sea met the land, Count Roger stopped and looked about him, while his knights and soldiers spread out on either side, their weapons at the ready. But nothing stirred. Who could attack such an iron-clad man? Who would wish to? Finally he made the gesture they had been waiting for. He reached up his hand, and swept off his helmet.

A murmur went up from the crowd. This was a new face altogether, cheerful and ruddy. The sunlight glistened on his fair hair, and on his red-gold beard. Though he was fifty-nine, he

looked younger, and full of life. This was the man for them.

Count Roger threw back his head. He spoke a single phrase: "I take possession of this land."

A man from the crowd came forward, the head man of the village, one Joseph Bin-Said. Bin-Said was accustomed to rule his small kingdom, but not to govern such a moment as this. He made gestures of peace and humility, spreading out his hands to show that he was not armed.

He said: "You are welcome, lord. We will not fight you." And in ones and twos the crowd came forward to kneel in homage and to accept their ruler.

COUNT ROGER had taken possession of many lands, like all the rest of his eleven brothers. Of the father, the progenitor of this clan, little was known except his name—Tancred d'Hauteville—and the fact that he married twice and produced five sons by his first wife and seven by his second. There were daughters as well.

Father Tancred, who must have had problems of family precedence, domestic jealousy, and even plain housekeeping, sent all his sons to seek their fortunes in Italy, which in honest terms meant that they were dispatched with a modest purse and a pat on the back to steal, plunder, and generally to make their way in a world of robber barons, warring popes, and humble, persuadable people.

Many of the Norman barons had originally been welcomed in Italy, as papal allies against the infidel, since their prime object had seemed to be the expulsion of the Moslem Saracens from Catholic territory. They came to be hated for their rapacity, their malice, their flint-hearted butchery, and their forgotten vows.

Roger the Norman was not such a man. He kept his dream of the crusade in view all the time. It was this which brought him at last to the shores of Malta, where a remnant of Saracen rule was ripe for overthrow. He did not especially want the island. Why should he, when he had spent nineteen years in conquering all Sicily, which was fertile and could be immensely prosperous? He wanted Malta, dry and poor Malta, to be restored to the Faith. That was all, and that was absolute.

Now, while the small waves lapped at the heels of his escort, and the crowd waited fearfully in the sun, Count Roger spoke to Bin-Said. "I am here with a message of peace. Christ our Saviour said, 'I come not to bring peace, but a sword.' Well, I bring both!" He was smiling still, but the red-gold beard jutted out like a rock as he spoke. "Yet I have peace in my heart, not war."

Bin-Said, already under the spell of this man, answered: "Lord, no one in this village will oppose you."

"Do you swear?"

"Yes, lord, I swear."

Over his shoulder, Count Roger called out an order, and his soldiers began to assemble, a handful to each of his knights, all led by a standard-bearer with the red-and-white quartered flag. "We march to the citadel. How far is it away?"

"Some four miles." Bin-Said took the wisest decision of his life. "Lord, can we march with you? I have nearly a hundred men."

"You can march behind us," Count Roger answered. "If I need help, I will remember you. . . ."

Bin-Said's eyes were on the flag of the Hautevilles, gleaming proudly in the sunshine. "If only we had a banner to march with. . . ."

"I will give you a banner," Count Roger answered promptly. "Your very own banner." He beckoned, and the standard-bearer brought the flag to his side. Count Roger reached up, took the standard with its squares of red and white, and tore it down the middle. Then he handed the strip of cloth, now reduced to one red square and one white, to Bin-Said. "Here is your flag, and I charge you, never stain it save with your own blood. Now hoist it up, and march!" (This was the flag of today, the red and white flag which flew all over the island, from the heights of Valletta to the police-station at St. Paul's Bay).

The dispirited Saracen garrison, of just two hundred men, had been doing nothing in Mdina for years on end, just sitting there waiting for their pensions. It was no match for Count Roger, his knights, his swordsmen and crossbowmen, and his fiery spirit. He took the citadel without stratagem; he simply arrived before its ramparts, sent a priest in as an envoy under a flag of truce, declared that he would put every man to the sword who did not surrender before sundown, and presently marched in.

He found the church of Publius in sad decay. Half of it had fallen down; there were no worshippers, because the Faith, persecuted and derided, was now only a faint memory from the distant past.

The church was his first care. "Build it again," he told Joseph Bin-Said, who had become a trusted ally. Bin-Said had his own

141

reputation; he also had villagers skilled in stonework, friends who were glassblowers, silversmiths, carpenters, and lampmakers; he had sisters who could sew an altar cloth like a band of angels. The cathedral church of St. Publius rose from the ruins like a declaration of faith. Count Roger finished it off with a pair of carved gates made of Irish bog-oak, black and solid as a ship's timbers, which he had picked up on his wanderings as a young man and now installed in their last home.

The church, and the newly ordained bishopric, crowned an act of apostleship which Malta had been awaiting a long dark time. For this reason alone was the Mass said for Roger's soul, a Mass which outlived his rule by at least eight hundred years.

But he did far more than this. He rescued a desolate and wasted island from the worst kind of overlord—the kind which did nothing with its prize except occupy it and tax it to death. From the sloth of centuries, Malta woke to enterprise and activity.

There was only one attempt, by a force of Saracen corsairs, to overthrow him, and he drove this off with disdainful ease. Yet he could not have done so if he had not been trusted, and respected, and even loved by the islanders he had come to rule.

He set Joseph Bin-Said to prepare the defences. What Bin-Said and his people set up was no massive earthwork. Instead, about fifty feet out from the shore, where the bay began to shelve, they planted boulders, and between them wedged a long line of upright stakes. To the stakes, which just broke the surface of the water, they fastened the simplest of all island snares, a net.

A man in a hurry would take it to be some fishing device, used by stupid islanders. It was more.

Daylight came, and with it the enemy, a squadron of ten galleys speeding towards the shore. Behind their cover of rocks, the defenders watched them. The boats fanned out on a broad front. The rowers cheered themselves on with shouts and cries. Men at the stern-posts beat gongs and cracked whips, while soldiers stood ready to jump and wade ashore. Then, still moving at their best speed, the galleys reached the line of the stakes.

Chaos came. At almost the same moment, the leading rowers in each boat found their oars trapped in the underwater net.

They lost their stroke, and fell in heaps, while their companions in the stern rowed bravely on, until they themselves were caught.

The fleet came to a stop. Cries of Saracen rage filled the air. Boats were milling about, crashing into each other. It was like some holiday frolic.

The defenders laughed, and then began to shoot.

It was all planned. First a volley of stones from a corps of expert sling-men came crashing down on the boats. Next a shower of crossbow arrows flighted towards the *mêlée*, and found flesh and turned it into meat. Then another volley of stones stirred the bloody water into a cauldron of smashed wood and despairing swimmers. Then there was a pause.

Count Roger's men, and Bin-Said's own small band of club-wielding villagers, were ready to charge. But there was nothing left for them to repel. The wrecked boats stayed where they were, hopelessly entangled; the last gasping swimmer was picked off by marksmen. No war-galley grounded on the beach, and the only man who set foot on the shores of Malta did so in death.

Count Roger had set his mark on Malta for ever. Sometimes its faith wavered, but, like the Mass for Roger's soul, it was never forgotten. After the Normans came other nations, Germans and French and Spaniards, who coveted the island for their several needs. Only one nation, however, was there to stay, the Maltese: who could be as proud and happy, on a latter day, as when Count Roger first gave them their flag, restored their church and put the imprint of lusty manhood and the pride of a nation on a people who had long despaired of either.

The Christmas Day of Father Salvatore
25 December 1941

Marija Debrincat awoke in a strange bed. She was spending the night with her grandmother, to help in preparation for the grand family lunch-party on Christmas Day.

She awoke saying "Michael" out loud, just as she had gone to sleep saying "Michael." They had progressed a long way since their first shy loving; now it was an acknowledged love, and an acknowledged tempest in the blood also. He was often away on missions which cancelled their plans without warning; when he came back, they always contrived to fly into each other's arms, with a readiness which made it terribly difficult to remember the rules.

She wanted to talk to somebody about it, really talk. Not to other girls, who were either prim or silly or with bad minds. Not to her mother, who could know nothing of love. She talked finally to the only person she could trust, her Uncle Salvu. But it was so difficult. He had been sweet, and reassuring, yet not very helpful. There were rules, he insisted—she must know this already. If she was falling in love with Michael, and he with her, and all things were properly arranged, then they might marry. Afterwards, love itself—making love—was sanctified.

So there only remained confusion and a little shame. It was something she had to solve by herself. Michael was naughty because he was a man, and couldn't help it. She must be good, because she was a girl, the shrine of purity. It was dull, being a shrine. Perhaps she was just a bad girl after all. . . . Midnight Mass, a few hours earlier, had been a woeful performance. All the time her thoughts had strayed. Try as she would, she could only think of him. He was up there, flying somewhere in the black night: nearer to the Star of Bethlehem than anyone in the church. Nearer to the Birth, nearer to death.

It was love in war, uncertain and beset by unmentionable fears. Marriage was not yet even a word between them. The family was aware of him, but only on a careful plane of non-involvement.

But he *was* coming to lunch. It was the least they could do, her darling mother had announced, with the straightest of faces, to entertain a British serviceman at Christmas, when he was lonely and far from home.

Cold morning light was slipping through the curtains. It was seven o'clock, and Christmas at last. A knock on the door brought a maid, with hot chocolate and a cheerful greeting.

"*Bon gornu, Sinjurina Marija. Il-Milied it-tajjeb!*"

"Good morning. Happy Christmas," said Marija.

The smell of the chocolate was enough to re-christen the day. They *never* had hot chocolate at home. . . . She took a first sip, while the maid drew back the curtains, letting in light which, to judge by a glimpse of clear sky, would shortly turn to sunshine.

Marija had licked the last drops of chocolate by the time the maid had tidied up the room.

"Is the Baroness awake yet, do you know?" she asked.

"Oh yes, *sinjurina*. She's been up since five o'clock."

"Heavens! I must go and help her."

The Baroness Santo-Nobile had indeed been up and about since before dawn on a cold winter morning. Disdaining to wake anyone so early, she had put an end to fitful sleep by making up her mind to get up and dress herself; an exercise which would have been simple if she had not been plagued by rheumatism and a high-necked black dress with a regiment of buttons.

This Christmas morning was a day she had been secretly dreading, yet proudly announcing as "the usual family lunch". Lunch for twenty-six had once been a simple matter of giving orders. This time, it had taken the best part of an exhausting month to organize. It was a task for fifteen servants, and she had only four, and one of them, old Gregory, was, to his infinite shame, ill in bed.

"But I shall get up for the lunch, madame," he assured her, time and again. "You can count on me."

She counted on herself. Rooms were opened up, cleaned, dusted, polished. Fortunately, Francis the footman, on leave for the holiday, was giving up the whole of his time off to help, and the chef had already brought in his family to assist: tradesmen's aunts, gardeners' second cousins—all were co-opted and set to their tasks, which ranged from unwinding the silver-settings from their green baize cocoons to pounding the brandy-butter sauce to the perfect creamy consistency of her grandmother's recipe.

She drove all these helpers with a steely will, and herself most harshly of all. It was thus that her granddaughter Marija found her, at half-past seven on Christmas morning, moving heavy chairs around the lunch table.

"Grandmother!" Marija said. "*You* shouldn't be doing that."

"And why not, pray?"

"Because I'm here!"

The sight of the little old woman, in her severe black dress, straining at a heavy armchair with paper-thin hands, was almost shameful. Her grandmother seemed about to explode into a cutting dismissal of this interference; then, suddenly, she smiled, and sat down at the head of her empty table and said: "You're a dear girl, Marija. A happy Christmas. Come and kiss me."

When Marija touched the parchment cheek, she found that the Baroness was trembling. She sat down by her grandmother's side, and for a moment they were composed in silence: the old woman and the young, at the head of a vista of mahogany and crested silver platters.

I shall never have a table like this, Marija thought. It did not matter. It only mattered that she would never have another grandmother like this. "Have you had your tea?" she asked. "Can I get you anything?"

"Not tea," the Baroness answered. "Not coffee, either. On Christmas morning, I would like something a little *stronger*. If you will please open that corner cupboard"—she nodded towards a walnut cabinet, "you will find a decanter of brandy, and some glasses."

The glasses were tiny, all of different colours, small jewels of polished crystal. Marija chose a green one, filled it with brandy, and brought it back to her grandmother. Between sips, her grandmother asked: "How old are you, Marija?"

"Eighteen."

"I am seventy-five. . . . When I was your age I had just met your grandfather."

Marija waited.

"My family did not like him," the Baroness went on, "or rather, they liked him very much—everybody liked him—but they did not like the idea of my marrying an English sailor. So we did not get married until I was twenty-three."

"But that was five years!"

"Five years," her grandmother repeated, her voice beautifully calm and measured. "But we were quite sure of ourselves, so it did not really matter." She took another sip of her brandy. "Of course, it *mattered* tremendously, but in those days it was natural to do as one was told, so we did not think it was so terrible."

"But what did you do?"

"We loved each other, and we waited." The Baroness, normally so stiff and upright, leaned against the high back of her chair. She was almost lounging, if so absurd a word could be applied to her. "Now—tell me about this young man who is coming to lunch."

Marija, confused by the sudden change of subject, decided to take the easiest course. She told her—everything. At the start it was terrifying, and embarrassing, yet once she was launched it was easy. She said exactly what had happened, and how, and what the future held, or could hold. She kept nothing back. There was no need to. The gulf of the years proved to be no gulf at all. It melted away in tender trust.

It was impossible to tell exactly what her grandmother was thinking. Sometimes she nodded, but for the most part she had a judge's look: the look of wisdom and maturity which waits for all the facts before considering a verdict. At the end, silence fell like a graceful curtain.

Finally the Baroness said: "Your Uncle Salvatore says that Michael is very good-looking."

"Oh, yes! But he doesn't—I mean, it isn't really important to him. He doesn't *use* it, like lots of men try to do."

The Baroness sipped her brandy. "You say that he has never proposed marriage?"

"Not really. Well, not at all."

"But he wants to—to love you."

"Yes. At least, I think so. But when I say no, of course not, it's impossible, he doesn't seem to want to any more."

"Ah. . . . Then I think he will propose. . . . Has he given you a Christmas present?"

Marija smiled. "Yes, a motorcycle man brought it last night. I just opened it. It's a pot of strawberry jam. I know it sounds silly. But we can't *get* strawberry jam!"

"Silly presents are the best. . . . Hugo—your grandfather— once gave me a little bunch of carrots, tied up with navy-blue ribbon."

"*Carrots?*"

"Certainly. He wanted me to be able to see him in the dark."

"Did you love him very much, grandmother?"

A change came over the Baroness, one of the swift changes of old age. Feeling flooded in, affecting her face and her manner most movingly; memory became real, memory became *today*.

"We adored each other equally from the moment we met. He was a fine-looking man. . . . And I was a great beauty. Why should I not say so? . . . As I told you, we had to wait five years to get married. When my turn came, I made your mother wait four years, but there were other reasons for that. . . . Now it may be that you cannot marry for quite a long time also. Sailors are always being sent away, sometimes to the other side of the world. Perhaps your father will object. He has a right to do so, but we will deal with that when the time comes."

In a heart-stopping moment of realization, Marija understood what her grandmother was really saying.

"*Grandmother!* Do you mean you don't mind?"

In a strangely small voice, the Baroness answered: "Do you really think I would object to your marrying an English sailor?" Then, to top all the surprises of the morning her frail face seemed to crumple, and she was in tears.

Marija had never seen her grandmother like this, nor even imagined that it could be possible. She wanted to take the old woman in her arms, but she knew that this would have been utterly wrong. The pride of privacy must always be respected.

She got up, and occupied herself at the corner cupboard, rearranging the glasses. Not until she heard, behind her, a sound of delicate nose-blowing did she turn round.

It was as if it had never happened. "And now," the Baroness said, "let us go back to Christmas Day, and our troublesome lunch party. Oh, how I wish my dearest son were here."

IN THE COLD AND DRAUGHTY tenement which was the catacomb of the Cottonera Lines, her dearest son was putting in an ordinary morning's work. Christmas Day made no difference to this; it was just another day, and that was the strangest thing about it. This, the second Christmas of their war, was a Christmas under siege, and the siege, with its attendant miseries, ruled their lives; the day was simply the twenty-fifth of December, and, for the first time that he could remember, no one was really bothering about it.

There were no Christmas decorations—who had money for that? Presents?—well, presents were for happier days. A special meal?—the special meal here was likely to be Father Salvatore's Widow's Soup, the soup of the poor, which he had promised to serve sometime during the evening. Wine?—a man was lucky to get a cup of clean water in this smelly old ruin!

Father Salvatore made his rounds. "Prowling", they called it, but with affectionate meaning. If Dun Salv did not prowl, God knows what certain people would be up to. He helped an old man, shivering in a bitterly cold room, to get some warmth back into his legs, chafing them until they turned from faint blue to pale yellow. He told another man, *No*, he could *not* store rabbit dung inside the catacombs. The air was foul enough already.

He praised, with warm words and a full heart, a little girl who was patiently fashioning a Christmas crib from matchsticks and bits of torn paper.

Then he heard a long-drawn-out cry, from one of the high galleries. A girl was in labour, as she had been since the dawn of yesterday. She lay in a tumbled bed, surrounded by old women in black, who crouched like a ring of crows round a dying sheep, by staring children, constantly shooed out of the room and as constantly filtering back again, by a distracted husband, by a calm and competent nun who was the girl's sister, by a mother-in-law whose complaint never varied—she had always said the girl's hips were too narrow, and no one had paid any attention, and now by Father Salvatore, who sidled into the room like any fearful child, and privately wished that someone would shoo him out again.

The pious pictures of Christ in the manger had *this* foundation, and no other.

Silence fell as he approached the bed. "Help her, Dun Salv!" someone whispered, as if he could lay on hands, and bring calm and peace to this racked and wrenching body. He knelt, and prayed, and took the girl's hand. "Concetta. Can you hear me?"

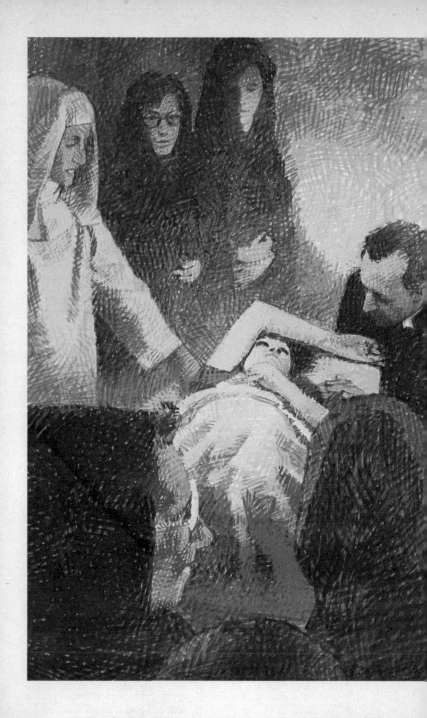

The cloudy eyes opened wide, and then closed again. "It must be a big one, Dun Salv."

"Big and strong. A child you can be proud of. . . . It's not too late to go to hospital."

"Never!" Concetta was actually smiling, in the midst of her torture. "I want to have it in the catacombs. That's where it started!"

He stayed for twenty minutes, while gradually the straining ceased, and calm returned. Her hour was not yet. . . . When he came down again, he found himself wondering, fancifully, if the child, in spite of the pain it was inflicting, was not right after all. This was a poor time to be born in Malta.

This cruel siege, in its short life of nineteen months, had already grown old in sin and misery. Nothing now was new; it was only worse. There had been a short respite in the bombing, while Germany turned her fury on Russia, but it had all started again on 2 December, and they had suffered nearly six raids a day during the month. Two good convoys had got safely through in September; now, because of ferocious reaction to this success, nothing more was planned, and rationing was harsher than ever.

Meanwhile, their nearest land-battle raged up and down North Africa. One thing was certain. Malta was contributing vitally to this battle, and was being punished for it. It was being punished just for being *there*, astride the Axis supply lines from Europe to Africa, and maintaining such a striking force of Blenheim bombers that it could cut these supplies by anything up to seventy per cent. It was being punished for simply trying to stay alive. A Government grant of nearly half a million pounds kept the price of essential food down. But one could not eat money, and where was the food anyway? The rationing scale sank steadily downward, and the spirits of the men with it.

There was one ray of hope, though it came from a long way away. The Japanese attack on Pearl Harbour had brought the Americans into the war at last. They *must* be allies worth having, even though the day had clearly been a day of disaster also.

In the meantime, an egg cost God-knew-what; there were queues for everything, from bread to paraffin; and petrol was so scarce that horsedrawn trams had reappeared. What would come next? Swapping a sheep for a house? Queueing for coffins?

Even the energetic little Nero was looking depressed when Father Salvatore met him near the entrance to the catacombs. Nero had gone out at first light to scour the shops for something worthwhile to put into the promised Widow's Soup. "Leave it to me, Dun Salv!" he had said, by a way of farewell, and added: "I'll get something, even if I have to dress up as a Carmelite and beg!"

But the estimated six hundred people who would attend this Christmas feast needed seventy-five gallons of soup (Father Salvatore was becoming used to such monstrous sums); and seventy-five gallons, even if thickened with mountainous crusts of bread, demanded a mountain of other ingredients. Nero, from the look on his face, had procured no more than a molehill.

"I've done the best I can, Dun Salv," he reported. "But it's mostly *rikotta*—I know people don't like it as much as sheep's cheese, but they don't have to pay for it. So—fifty cottage cheeses, quite big ones, and about a dozen sheep's. Plenty of rabbit bones, to make a bit of juice. But only thirty eggs. I tell you, I could have gone bankrupt buying eggs!"

"Thirty eggs," Father Salvatore repeated, doubtfully. Thirty eggs between six hundred people was not a recipe that sounded very much like Christmas.

"We can make them look more, Dun Salv, I'll boil them hard, and then slice them up into rings. They'll float on top of the drums, and there you are—eggs for everyone."

"I suppose that will have to do."

"I'm sorry, Dun Salv. But I did get a big bundle of herbs— well, they're weeds really, but they must taste of *something*. Plenty of bread, if you can call it bread—I call it sawdust and potato mush, myself. But"—there was something important coming—"I bought a whole sack of dried beans. Well, it wasn't quite full; the rats got there first. But it was cheap, and it'll give the soup a bit of body!"

"Nero, you've done very well," Father Salvatore assured him, and it was true. Against the background of their lives, Nero's assorted wares were riches indeed. If only this wasn't their entire

Christmas feast. . . . "I'm sure we'll manage to make a fine soup. . . .
Everyone realizes how difficult it is. . . . What a pity your fiancée
can't be here tonight."

Nero shrugged his small strong shoulders. "You know how it is.
Her mother doesn't trust me after dark. I suppose it's a compliment
really. I'd rather have a few insults. . . . But it's taking such a time!
Do you think we'll ever get this wedding settled?"

It was a difficult question. Father Salvatore had met the big
ugly girl, Teresa Grima, when she visited the catacombs. At twenty-
seven, she was a thickset peasant girl, vacant of face, to whom the
word "love" seemed as remote as the words "elegance" or "tender-
ness". She towered above Nero, whose delight in this, as in everything else about her, was pathetically fierce. But if she was in love
with him, it had never been advertised by a single gesture.

"She has a good heart, I know," Father Salvatore had assured
the prospective bridegroom. He hoped, in spite of all appearances,
that this was true. It was certain that Teresa seemed to have
nothing else, and that her parents had not even this commendation.
They were stubborn and selfish, and relentlessly engaged in giving
poor Nero the most miserable time of his life.

Teresa was the last of their seven children to be unmarried and
to live at home; and they were going to preserve this status against
all hazards. The father worked his fields hard enough, but he had
only Teresa to help him. The mother was given to fainting fits;
upon Teresa therefore devolved much of the household also. The
idea of Teresa taking even one day off was enough to give Mrs.
Grima a very bad spell indeed.

The old folks had four lines of defence: Teresa was perfectly
content as she was: she could not be spared: Nero Cassar was "not
good enough": and they could not afford the dowry. They had been
ringing the changes on this malevolent strategy for the past five
months, without the slightest sign of weakening.

Father Salvatore could willingly have bashed their stupid,
mulish heads together. But a priest could not interfere in the sacred
area of family and marriage ties. So the matter remained. They
agreed that there could be an engagement—of a sort. They had
grudgingly admitted that *if* Mr. Grima could get full-time help on

153

the farm, and *if* Mrs. Grima could afford a maid, and *if* her delicate
health improved, and *if* the matter of the dowry was waived, then
there might be a chance of marriage. They could have added: And
if Nero Cassar grew another eighteen inches, and turned out to be a
millionaire. It was a complete deadlock, and poor little Nero was
the frustrated loser in the middle.

Now Father Salvatore said "You mustn't give up hope, Nero.
These difficulties often happen."

Nero stretched out his arms in a gesture of despair. "I'm so
afraid Teresa will cool off, if this arguing goes on much longer.
It's not as if she was so . . . so. . . ." He searched for a word, and did
not find it. He moved nearer to Father Salvatore, and dropped his
voice. "Dun Salv, what can I do to make her more interested?"

"How do you mean, interested?"

"In love. Kissing, if you like. When I try to kiss her, she always
makes some excuse. Either it's too light, or it's too dark, or someone will see us, or that sort of thing will have to wait till we're
married. But what's wrong with kissing?"

There were all sorts of answers, all sorts of insults to a dwarf
who wanted to marry a girl of normal size—a girl who might once
have dreamed of something different, and be now resigned to
nothing at all. He gave a feeble reply: "There can be too much
kissing."

"But there's none at all! Three times, in five months! A monk
could do better! I'm sorry, Dun Salv, but you know what I mean."
He moved even closer, lowering his voice again, so that Father
Salvatore had to bend his head to stay in communication. "You
understand these things. Everyone says you know so much about—
about everything." He drew a deep breath, the breath of despair
and intimate longing. "How can I make Teresa really *want* to
marry me?"

Not for the first time Father Salvatore found himself full of
misgivings at the topic of their conversation. Sex was not of his
world; it could not be, it must not be; he should be able to say,
to any inquirer: "Do not ask me that—I am a priest."

Yet, absurdly, it was *because* he was a priest that people plagued
him with such questions. There was something ridiculous, even

indecent, about a celibate giving advice to married couples; or instructing engaged lovers in the permissible limits of a caress.

He recalled dear little Marija, and her problems, and her humble appeal for help. To her, as to Nero, he had wanted to say, in despair: "Don't ask me. I know nothing of love." Now he could only dismiss Nero with: "Love will grow between you. It does not need any tricks. Have faith."

It was a dusty, cowardly answer. Father Salvatore knew in his melancholy heart that he had just celebrated this, the first and dearest morning of every Christian year, with that most un-Christian of all human acts—passing by on the other side.

THOUGH IT WAS NEVER like the great occasions of the past, the Christmas lunch-party at the Palazzo Santo-Nobile was, to begin with, a cheerful and rather moving occasion. It was good to see the splendid house restored to something like its past magnificence, to know that it stood like a rock against war, and an elegant refuge against the drabness of their siege. Though by the end the party had become a disaster, its start was memorable.

Father Salvatore, in his best black cassock and still-handsome boots, arrived late, to find a distinguished company already assembled. The Governor, and his *aide-de-camp*, Captain Ian Ross, led the field, as far as temporal power was concerned; his Lordship the Bishop of Malta, flanked by Monsignor Scholti, stood surety for the spiritual arm; the Admiral who commanded the dockyard, and the Air Vice-Marshal who held an umbrella over it, were matched by the Mother Superior of the Baroness's favourite convent, and the best-behaved orphan from the home which the Santo-Nobiles had maintained since the days of Charles II, when the problem of bastardy had attracted fashionable attention.

Lewis Debrincat and his family headed a sprinkling of Debrincat relatives, while the numbers were made up by some members of Malta's shrunken diplomatic corps, and by Michael Ainslie who, desperately tired after a night's flying and slightly bemused by all the "hot brass", clung to Marija's side like a homesick limpet.

Father Salvatore found them all gathered round the family crib which had enthralled at least ten generations of Santo-Nobile children. The figures were silver, silver of a marvellous vitality, telling their story under the glow of minute branched candlesticks which lit the stable scene with a miraculous, loving warmth.

After this had been duly admired, the company moved to the nearby Christmas tree, under which were presents for all, and Father Salvatore took the opportunity to greet his mother.

"You are so late, Salvatore," she told him as he kissed her. "What have you been doing?"

"Making soup."

"You will get a better soup here!"

"I don't doubt it." He stood back, still holding her wafer-light hand. "A happy Christmas, mother. You're looking wonderful."

But it was not true. In successive weeks he had been forced to notice how worn she had become, and what an effort it was for her to maintain her straight back and proud carriage. "I hope you haven't been doing too much, getting ready for the party," he said.

"Don't fuss, Salvatore," she said immediately. "Of course, there was a good deal to do, but I'm not a helpless old woman yet." She looked round the great salon, her eyes in the pale face full of a fierce satisfaction. "Have you spoken to the bishop yet?"

"No. You first, everyone else afterwards."

"That is *not* the way to get preferment." But she sounded pleased. Her hand reached out for the polished black stick, propped against the arm of her chair. "Help me up, Salvatore." He could not recall ever having heard her say this before. "I must see that my guests have everything they want. . . . That young man of Marija's is really extraordinarily handsome. . . . Please go and speak to the bishop *now*. I know that he wanted to talk to you."

She moved away, leaning unobtrusively on her stick, halting but still upright. He knew that he need have no fears for her spirit, on this morning at least. She was in her element. . . . He took a glass of sherry from the vast silver salver with which Francis was slowly circling the room, greeted him warmly, and set off in the direction of the Bishop of Malta.

Inevitably, he was intercepted, by Monsignor Scholti.

They had not met for nearly a month, since Scholti had paid a memorable visit to the catacombs. It had been one of those nights

156

when everything had been at its most earthy. There had been four different birthday parties, presently combining into one ribald, singing, dancing celebration. Scholti, who began his visit with portly good-humour, had become perceptibly more withdrawn; his smile grew thin and presently vanished altogether, as bursts of laughter alternated with cursing: as shadowy young figures were seen to be intertwined, in shameless display: as a chicken was chased and cornered within sight of the altar: as a chorus of groans greeted the news that one of the toilets was overflowing *again*: and especially as Father Salvatore, rising to make an announcement about next morning's early Mass, was cheered as if he were a visiting film star.

When rather sooner than planned, he had escorted Monsignor Scholti to his car, Father Salvatore said: "I'm sorry. They were a bit out of hand tonight."

"I agree." Scholti glanced back. The robust voices of the laity could still be heard. "Do you really say Mass *there*?"

On this Christmas morning, however, Scholti had regained all his poise. He greeted Father Salvatore with full-scale aplomb, sure of his place on his own ground, with a bishop to prove it. "Salvu! At last! I was afraid you were not going to join us."

"Good morning, Bruno. A happy Christmas."

"What? Yes, of course. And *what* a happy Christmas! What a joy to see this house as it ought to be. You must agree to that."

Father Salvatore sipped his sherry, eyeing the other man over the brim of the glass. "Why should I not agree?"

Scholti smiled, without calling on his eyes for help. "Well, you must admit that when we last met it was in rather different circumstances. I thought perhaps that your tastes might have changed."

"I am more at home in the catacombs, if that's what you mean."

"But how *can* you be? Oh, I admit there is pastoral work to be done there. A great deal, if I may say so, judging by some of the behaviour I saw. But the *prestige* of the Church is also important. The need to maintain standards. The *quality* of priesthood."

"I do the work I want. No one can be happier than a man who is allowed to do that."

"That is rather the point, isn't it?" Scholti said tartly. "At the moment, you are *allowed* to conduct this rather extraordinary assembly, this *circus*. But it is somewhat irregular, don't you think?"

"Oh come, Bruno!" Now Father Salvatore was irritated, in spite of noble Christmas resolutions. "The catacomb is not a circus. It's simply a large air-raid shelter where I try to take care of people, and celebrate Mass twice a day. Why should that not be allowed? In fact"—he looked at the other man sharply, "why did you use the word 'allowed' at all? Are you trying to—" he could not put it into words: the idea that his work might be curtailed was too appalling to contemplate. "What *are* you trying to do, Bruno?"

"*I* trying?" Scholti's large brown eyes opened very wide indeed. "Nothing at all, except to help you to the best of my small ability. The question is, what are *you* trying to do?"

"The best I can. With my small ability."

"No man can do more. . . . Would you like me to take you to the bishop?"

"No. When the bishop is a guest in the house where I was born, I do not need any passport." He turned on his heel and made for the other side of the room.

That much-loved old man, Monsignor Dom Maurus Caruana, had been Bishop of Malta for the last twenty-six years, and his gentle dignity came as an immediate balm to Father Salvatore's troubled spirit from the moment he bent to kiss the bishop's ring.

"My dear Salvu!" the bishop said. "How good it is to see you again! And you look so well. From something Bruno Scholti said, I thought you had been over-tiring yourself, and needed a rest."

There were many tempting answers to be made, but Father Salvatore resisted all of them. "I would like a rest," he admitted. "I think we all would. But that doesn't mean that we shall take one."

"Well said," the bishop smiled his approval. "War is the great test of man. Perhaps it is meant to be." He noticed Father Salvatore's puzzled expression, and smiled again. "Am I being too serious, for such a pleasant occasion as this? I can't help recalling that I became bishop in the middle of another war. It was about that time that I first met you. Do you remember?"

158

"Yes, *Eccellenza*."

"You were still at seminary, but you came back from Rome for a holiday. What year was that?"

"Nineteen seventeen." Already Father Salvatore felt marvellously healed by this contact. Was this what was meant by "a good shepherd"? He could almost feel the abundance of grace and kindliness flowing from one soul to another. "I was twenty-two."

"And I was fifty." The old man was recalling the past with pleasure. "But that young seminarian became a parish priest."

"And still is."

"Some regrets, my son?"

"Never!"

The old man nodded. "It is comforting to be certain. . . . But even certainty has its pitfalls. . . . There is one thing I want to say to you, and Christmas morning is a good time to say it. I gave my permission for your church in the catacombs. . . . From the reports I have had of it—some good reports, some not so good—it has grown in a way I did not expect. . . . Do something for me, Salvu. Search your conscience, and see if your work has not enlarged *you* rather than the Church and the Faith. You understand?"

"Yes, my lord!" When a bishop of this quality said, "Do something for me", with such infinite kindness, how could a priest feel afraid? "If I have made mistakes—" he did not know how to finish.

"Then I trust you to discover them." The old man, whose sharp eyes had been on Salvatore's face, turned away, apparently satisfied. "I spoke to you like this," he went on, even as he looked round the room, "in your own house, on Christmas morning, because I wanted to mark the difference between a talk with a friend and an interview in my palace. You understand that too?"

"Yes, *Eccellenza*. Thank you."

"Then the homily is ended." What extraordinary things he could say. The Bishop's eyes, moving from person to person, was caught by something which amused him. He nodded: "Whatever we may feel about the troubles and the weariness of war, there's one young man at least who is having a happy Christmas."

When Father Salvatore followed the bishop's glance he saw Pietru, who had fallen wildly in love with one of his Christmas presents, and was going round the room wanting the whole world to admire it.

This was a very large model, some three feet in wing-span, of a Hurricane fighter plane, complete to the last detail, gleaming with polished metal and freshly painted roundels.

Other eyes besides the bishop's were following Pietru's progress as he swooped from guest to guest. "You are a darling," Marija said to Michael. "How did you ever find such a thing?"

"It took two of our armourers the best part of a month to produce that little item. The war came to a total stop—didn't you notice?"

"You mean it was specially made?"

"Rivet by rivet." He was not even glancing in her direction, but he said: "You look different today."

"How different?"

"More beautiful. *Most* beautiful . . ."

With the expert connivance of the young they submerged, as far as they could, into a private world of delight, while all round them, as the trays of drinks circulated, the sound of conversation rose and fell. The hour of the *apéritif* seemed unusually long, but at the moment it did not matter: the occasion was happy, the surroundings magnificent, and the delay acceptable.

Lewis Debrincat, however, had already become a centre of embarrassment and irritation to almost everyone in the room. "Gigi Debrincat is in a bad mood," was the most generous comment, accompanied by shrugs which indicated that no one would very much care if Gigi Debrincat sank without trace in the depths of the courtyard well. It seemed to be established that he could not bear the sight of anyone in uniform. He was not interested in any of his relatives: he had made good, they had not. He had been curtly formal with the Governor, and derisive with Father Salvatore— "Your holier-than-thou brother," he commented to his wife, and added: "That takes a bit of doing, I can tell you," for all to hear.

It was the ever-loyal Giovanna who bore the brunt of all this boorish impudence. She never left his side for a moment. Continually on the defensive, she softened such casual insults as she could with a smile and a turned phrase. It was the public role of devoted wife, and the private one of nurse-companion to a sick nuisance.

Time passed. The noise-level in the room still maintained a satisfactory pitch, but it faltered now and then as people glanced at their watches. The Baroness signalled vexedly to Francis the footman. They conferred for a moment, and then Francis turned and left the room. The trays of drinks circulated yet again, and a tired drone of conversation picked up once more.

Finally, at ten minutes to two—fifty minutes late—when Governor Dobbie was even consulting Ian Ross about his next appointment, and Father Salvatore was considering a personal foray to the kitchen to find out what was going on, the double doors at the end of the salon opened and Gregory appeared.

All eyes turned on him; to many of those present, he was a lifelong friend, and for everybody else a respected institution. Though handsomely dressed, from buckled shoes to high winged collar, he looked undeniably mad; his eyes glittered in a face hectically flushed and he peered about him as if he had no notion where he was. Finally he caught sight of the Baroness, and bowed low. Then he said, in a weird cracked voice: "Dinner is served, your royal highness."

Emilia Santo-Nobile was not a royal highness, and this was lunch, not dinner; the twin *gaffes* had a sad effect of dissolution on the company. A few laughed nervously; most pretended not to have heard. But the Baroness had been born for such moments. If her knuckles turned white as they clenched over her stick, there were few to see and none to comment. All she said was: "Thank you, Gregory." Then turning to the Governor, "Your Excellency, shall we go in?"

On Sir William Dobbie's arm she led the way, as erect and proud as if she were in truth royal, and took her seat at a table of such splendid elegance that she might well have expected that the next hour, at least, would go smoothly.

But terrible things were to happen—terrible by Santo-Nobile custom—which were to reduce the lunch party to a shambles. Gregory made no further appearance. Francis, though immensely efficient in a military fashion, had not the style of a butler; and he was supported by footmen whose ill-fitting liveries advertised the fact that they did not belong to the household, and by maids whose energy and cheerfulness were only a minor substitute for skill.

A loud crash signalled the entrance of the sauce which was to be served with the avocado. As all eyes turned in the direction of the sound, the whispered "*Gesu, Marija!*" of the girl responsible diverted attention back again to the bishop, in whose department this mishap had suddenly been placed. The moment passed, since His Lordship was magnificent in diplomatic deafness, and there were three other sauceboats borne by three other girls, equally sprightly, more adroit. But the sauce itself, succumbing to long delay, had curdled. It set the pattern of all that was to follow.

Some wine was brought in, but at a signal from the Baroness was taken out again: it was red, which could not be acceptable either with the avocado now being politely abandoned by the guests, nor the soup, nor the fish which was to follow. The soup proved intolerably sour, though blandished by an occasional homely thumb as it was served; and when the fish course finally arrived, there was not enough to go round, and those at the bottom end of the table were left with empty plates. The giant turkey which replaced it after a long interval was so overcooked that the white meat was scarcely distinguishable from the dark.

There was no longer any room for pretence that the lunch party was a normal occasion, far less a superior one; and for the Baroness, flanked by the Governor and the bishop, it was impossible to maintain the appearance of composure. She was reduced nearly to tears. Her two table companions talked, compassionately, to the people on their other side.

The iced sherbert, when it arrived, was a warm and watery disaster. The champagne which should have accompanied it was served just as everyone had finished. They then waited for the Christmas pudding. Vague sounds of commotion came from the kitchens.

At last the double doors swung open again, and Francis appeared, bearing the flaming offering on a fluted silver salver. Unfortunately its entrance happened to coincide with an almighty sneeze from one of Lewis Debrincat's relatives, a jolly bald sausage of a man called Cousin Lawrence. The force of this seemed to blow out both the brandy flames and all the candles surrounding the dish, though it must have been due to the slight draught from the open doorway. This instant fire-extinguisher was too much for the company. As Francis, coughing and spluttering through wreaths of candle-smoke, struggled to maintain his composure, the room dissolved into helpless laughter.

The excellence of the pudding itself, of which there was plenty for all, and the *richesse* of silver trinkets accompanying it, went some way towards restoring calm; and by the time the port had gone round the table—*one* glass for the ladies, after which they would withdraw—the Baroness had reasonable hope that lunch would end without further embarrassment.

But she was doomed to yet another lamentable breakdown. It was her son-in-law who set the seal of disaster on a happy Christmas Day.

Lewis Debrincat had been drinking his way through lunch, with a determination which resisted all attempts to interest him in food. He drank whatever was placed before him, and on occasion even snapped his fingers for more. Sinking lower and lower in his chair, he was, by the time the port was going round, almost incapably drunk. He drank thirstily of the port, which was several years older than himself, and then—a monstrous breach of etiquette—reached across for the decanter as it passed down the other side of the table, and poured himself a second glass. No one remarked on this: it was only Gigi Debrincat doing as he liked. Then, under all their eyes, his face turned pale and sweaty, and he levered himself up and made a stumbling rush for the door. The crashing slam of this could not mask the gross sound of retching, nor the splash of vomit on the tiled floor outside.

An urgent whisper at Father Salvatore's side broke into the most painful silence of his life. To see his mother so shocked, his sister in tears and the children scarlet with shame. . . . He turned quickly. It was Francis.

"Dun Salv! Dun Salv! Can you come, please. It's Mr. Gregory, Dun Salv. Please come and see him. But quickly!"

Father Salvatore rose instantly. "Have you called a doctor?"

163

"The doctor has been here for an hour." Astonishingly, the eyes of Francis, the soldier, the only true stalwart in the house, were bright with tears. "It is for you now."

SAFELY AT PEACE, far away from the awful adult world, Marija Debrincat and Michael Ainslie lay in a fold of the hills above the cliffs of Dingli, on the southwest coast of the island. They were there because they had to be there. Fugitives from the terrible Christmas gathering, they had chosen, as if to solace all the wounds of the day, the most superb view of the whole of Malta.

Behind them were the cream-coloured stone battlements of the Verdala Palace; and at their feet the sheer eight-hundred-foot drop of the cliffs, a breathtaking view of the island's western coastline, and the tiny islet of Filfla. In the evening sun, it had all the magic of longed-for tranquillity. Here they managed to forget the awful lunch, and to be at peace again—complete and loving peace. But even in this pastoral paradise, doubts and mysteries returned to confuse them both.

There was some kissing at first: not as much as Marija had expected, or hoped, or prepared for. But strangely, it was not what he wanted.

After a first hungry embrace he had drawn back, and turned his attention again to the view. Was he angry? Was he bored? Was he having second thoughts about that shameful lunch party?

It seemed that he was only tired.

"I'm sorry, *hanini*," he said presently. He was sitting a little apart from her, sucking a dry blade of grass and staring up at the pale sky. "I'm not much good today. . . . I was doing some horrid things last night." His head fell back, and this time it lay securely in her lap. He snuggled down, and she had to bend over him to hear what he said: he was muttering indistinctly, almost talking in his sleep. "I must have killed some people. Soon it will be their turn to kill. Fair's fair. . . . It's just arithmetic, with a bit of blood on it. . . . I can tell you one thing, though"—and his voice sounded far away, and near at the same time—"too many of our sailors are being killed. Unless we're very careful, we might lose this contest."

Then he fell asleep.

In the annals of naval slaughter, the last half of that year was indeed nowhere more cruel than in the Middle Sea round Malta. Returning from a ferrying job to Malta, the aircraft-carrier, *Ark Royal* had been torpedoed and sunk within a few miles of Gibraltar. Shortly afterwards, the old battleship *Barham* was also sunk, 862 men drowned out of a ship's company of 1,312. Then two other battleships, *Queen Elizabeth* and *Valiant*, were limpet-mined in Alexandria Harbour, and the cruiser *Galatea* was torpedoed and sunk in the same area. Lastly, another fleet ran into some mines off Tripoli, and the bill for that was two cruisers, *Penelope* and *Aurora* damaged near to sinking, the destroyer *Kandahar* blown in half, and the cruiser *Neptune* left for dead in the centre of the minefield, with *one* survivor (four days on a raft) remaining out of its entire crew.

Thus the whole top *echelon* of the Eastern Mediterranean Fleet had been eliminated, within the space of two months. For those who had to tot up this grisly arithmetic, it was a debit sum beyond belief; and for Malta the most desperate setback of all time.

It was early evening dusk when Michael fell asleep, and the moment of sunset when he woke again. During all that brief half-hour, Marija, cradling his head in her lap, gazed down at him, and thought, and loved, and finally wept.

She had started, when she knew he was asleep, by examining his face inch by inch. He was so beautiful, but so desperately tired, like all the airmen, all the sailors. It had become the face of an exhausted child, too thin for happiness, lined where it should not yet be lined, fragile when he was really so strong.

He had said, a little time ago: "Too many of our sailors are being killed," and the unspoken thought was that one of these sailors would be himself. She thought of all the sad and aching hazards of war pressing in on them, and it was then that she began to cry. A tear fell on his face, and he woke. He woke swiftly, as he must often do in these troubled times. He sat up, and looked about him, and then at her.

His face had changed instantly as he woke, gaining strength. He was not an exhausted child at all; he was a rarely handsome young pilot who had been taking a nap. "Isn't that beautiful?" he said, nodding towards the last half of the vanishing sun. "And aren't you beautiful, too? Will you marry me?"

Her heart stopped, and started again. "What?"

"You heard. . . ." He leaned over and kissed her tenderly. "Marija, don't look so surprised. It's not very flattering. . . . Yes, of course I was going to try to make love to you, but this seems a better idea. It *is* a better idea, isn't it? Will you, please?"

TRUDGING WEARILY towards the Cottonera Lines as night fell, and yet another air raid ended, Father Salvatore had time to think, and time to mourn as well. That afternoon he had closed Gregory's eyes with a painful feeling that his own span of life would never be quite the same again. He had lost an old friend—indeed, his oldest friend—and to see the wasted body at peace could only bring a flood of memories.

His recollections, even during the last anointment, were of Gregory the small boy's steed: Gregory the benevolent moneylender when times were hard: Gregory the stern adviser on deportment; and especially of that Gregory who had been the first to kiss his hand, with undreamed-of humility, when Father Salvatore had returned to the Palazzo Santo-Nobile as an ordained priest.

Gregory had no other family save the one he served, and the bereavement would fall hardest on the Baroness, whose day had been wretched enough already. Father Salvatore could not think without embarrassment of the lunch party. But where did such things come on the true scale of misery? The wounds, which seemed mortal, were only the faint shadow of a thousand more terrible wounds. A dried-up turkey? Some avocado spoiled? This was not Malta's war, nor even the smallest part of its real ordeal.

On dusty tired feet he was now passing something which *was* part of Malta's war. On the edge of the Marsa Harbour a bomb had hit a winter boathouse full to the roof with boats, fishing-gear, ropes and cordage, oil drums, oars, barrels of pitch: all the stored necessaries of fishermen and ferrymen.

The mass was burning briskly, surrounded by a smoky ring of sad-faced men whose livelihood had been lost. But more had been lost; another small circle, with bowed heads, stood round the dead laid out on the ground. There were five of them, neatly ranged on the quayside, waiting for their last transport. Malta had grown very orderly in such disposal.

Since there was a young priest kneeling among them, and all else was still, Father Salvatore knew that he could not be of service. He passed on, with a prayer, and plodded towards Cospicua, his spirits lower than ever. This was the war—nothing else, and nothing less: bloodshed and destruction, heartbreak and death. Could it really be Christmas night, the birthday of the Saviour of the world? Could God give so marvellously, and then take away again with such cruel change of mind?

He came within sight of the Cottonera Lines, and found, for the first time, that he was dreading this return. He had promised himself that he would "speak" tonight, but was it wise to do so? The bishop had given him a kindly but clear warning: not to exceed his province; not to play God, nor his prophet. What *could* he speak of, anyway, on such a wicked Witches' Sabbath as this?

As soon as he had passed through the masked portals of the catacomb, and found the comforting warmth and light within, he was greeted—as had happened on the very first night—by the cry of a child. For a moment he was confused, unable to relate it to anything he had been expecting. Then he remembered. It must be Concetta's new baby. Her travail must be over. Glory be to God for another safe delivery, on Christmas Day itself.

It was little Nero who confirmed the news. "It's a boy, Dun Salv! Huge! Nineteen pounds!"

"Nero, it *cannot* be nineteen pounds."

"Well, nine pounds. Fat as butter, and nearly as big as me. They're going to call it Salvatore."

An old man died, a child was born. It was as if the day had been saved after all. He was suddenly overjoyed. "That's wonderful news, Nero. I must go and see Concetta. How is she?"

"Full of life! She wants to have another one!"

There was a throng of people pushing about all round them, securing their places for the evening, and a savoury smell of cooking. "How is the soup, Nero?"

"Going well. I found a bit more stuff to put in it. The old skin-

167

flint Tony Mizzi came through with two dozen eggs at the last minute. And I got some more cheese from the canteen."

Concetta's baby, the newest citizen of the catacombs, wailed again. . . . Father Salvatore knew now that, come what may, he must speak tonight of hope, and beyond hope, self-help. However deadly or depressing the evidence to the contrary, there was one certain truth—that no siege could last for ever. Indeed he would remind them that another siege of long ago, on this very same ground, *because it had been valiantly withstood*, had ended so suddenly that the men and women of Malta found themselves laughing for joy almost before they ceased to cry.

HEXAMERON IV

A.D. 1565 The Greatest Siege

When he faced his flock, meagrely fed and resigned to the end of Christmas without great hopes of the next dawn, Father Salvatore knew that, to raise their spirits, to make them comprehend what the greatest siege of all had really been like, he should start with the men, the fabulous men. . . .

THE MOST FABULOUS MAN of all, at that moment of history, and the most feared, was Suleiman the Magnificent, Sultan of Turkey: conqueror of Belgrade, of Rhodes, of Aden and Algiers, of Budapest and Baghdad: scourge of all things Christian. He had not been called "the Magnificent" by fawning courtiers, but by reluctant admirers who had felt either the bite of his sword or the cutting edge of his genius for lawmaking and lawkeeping.

He was now an old man, but still ferociously determined that his rule and the Mohammedan faith should prevail. Of all the men barring his way in the Middle Sea, the most capable and the most hated by the Turks were those other warriors called the Knights Hospitallers of St. John of Jerusalem. Sultan Suleiman had been twenty-nine when he had expelled this Order from its base in Rhodes; he was seventy-one when he took his oath to expel them from Malta also. Impressed by their bravery, he had allowed the Knights to leave Rhodes with generous honours of war, bearing their arms—but he would not make that mistake again.

The Order had started, in the long-ago of five centuries, as a small company of stretcher-bearers, caring for those Christian pilgrims who, dying of fatigue or poverty, had managed to drag their wretched limbs to the Holy Sepulchre of Jerusalem. Presently it became necessary to found a hospital for these sick waifs; the hospital was dedicated to St. John the Baptist, and the staff—the Hospitaller Brothers of St. John of Jerusalem—to vows of chastity, poverty, and obedience.

From Hospitallers they perforce became fighting men, pledged to defend the pilgrims on their journey (a nightmare of violence and theft as soon as they neared the Holy Land). After the sack of Jerusalem by Saladin the Knights Hospitallers first tried Cyprus and were driven out; then they took Rhodes from the Saracens, and kept it for two hundred and twelve years. Expelled by Suleiman after a bloody six-month siege, they wandered another seven years before the Emperor Charles V of Spain, the then owner of Malta, gave them the island to make of it an impregnable naval base, to be the frontier of Christendom.

Now when the Turkish battle-squadrons—31,000 men in 180 ships—set out against Malta, the Knights were led by another warrior in the seventy-second year of his life, the French Grand Master Jean Parisot de la Valette. The enemy force was enough to daunt, without shame, a garrison whose fighting élite numbered 641 knights with about 8,000 troops, but if the Grand Master had a single doubt about the outcome, it did not show in his bearing. Beneath the blood-red emblem of the Order, the four barbed arrowheads whose points met in the middle to form the Maltese Cross, his heart, like his valiant sword, was already worthy of eternal honour.

The Knights were organized in the eight *langues* or tongues of their various fatherlands: three of these were French, and the rest came from Aragon, Castile, Italy, Germany, and England. Drawn from the noblest families of Europe, volunteers for Christ, the Knights were quartered separately, and often luxuriously, in the various *auberges* which they had built in the narrow streets of Birgu and Senglea. The eight *langues* were kept apart to avoid quarrelling, and it proved an effective safeguard. Indeed in Malta, Knights belonging to nations on terms of traditional and ferocious hatred towards each other managed to live in perfect concord.

The Order had never forgotten its origins, nor its mainspring in human pity. The first of its cares, on reaching Malta, was to build a hospital; the first of its rules was that *all* young Knights, of whatever degree, must perform their share of nursing the sick—a menial and unpleasant task as far from the normal life of a nobleman as cleaning out his own stables.

Its parallel task was to maintain the cult of physical excellence essential for fighting men. This was their whole tradition: strength, speed, tenacity, and a nimble cunning; and every day of their lives was devoted to it. They even exercised in heavy armour, yet fought in light, to gain extra agility when it came to the test.

So trained, and armed, and inspired, the Knights had settled down to police their half of the Mediterranean, and to ravage the other half, Suleiman's half. The provocation was intolerable, and now they were preparing for what must be the answer, the assault on an island which Suleiman, dreaming and waking, loathed as a nest of impudent vipers.

All that need be said of the Turks was that they matched the Knights in bravery, in their ferocious determination to overthrow their enemy, and in their devotion to their faith. To this must be joined a capricious brutality which guaranteed that a man would fight to the death rather than fall into their hands alive. Ranged beside them also was a splendid and subtle rogue, the Corsair Dragut Rais, Pasha of Tripoli, with his fleet of fifteen war galleys, 1,500 men, and an array of monstrous siege guns. Being eighty years of age, he completed a glittering array of supreme commanders, three men whose worth as fighting men was pure gold, and whose combined age at that time was two hundred and twenty-two years.

Against all these visitors, to a greater or lesser degree, were the people of Malta. They had hardly swallowed the Knights, being unable to spit them out, and now yet another tyrant was on his way to conquer and enslave their island. When in heaven's name would it end? To the very last man, whether noble or humble, they had heard this song before, and they were chokingly sick of it.

After the Normans, there had been the Angevins, a sort of French-English crossbreed. After the Angevins came the Aragonese, and after them the Castilians—both Spanish, and as cruel and proud as Lucifer himself. Then some foreign emperor, without a word to anyone, had presented their island to the Knights of St. John. As if at a signal, the Maltese went to ground, rolling up in a ball like a hedgehog, playing dead until the storm was over. They had not been consulted? They would do *nothing*!

Then suddenly the climate changed. The breath of rumour stirred, and became something like a hurricane. This was no ordinary foe whose sails were now soiling the horizon. The Turks, it was said, would take every last man, woman, and child into slavery; they practised loathsome tortures, not for gain, not for information, but for simple pleasure. What would happen if these cruel wolves from the east became their new lords? No Knight, however overbearing, could be as bad as such monsters!

On a certain morning, the Maltese began to come forward, and to help. They begged to do so: they begged to be allowed to do anything—anything which would prepare the island for its ordeal. Before a week was out, they were working side by side with the Knights, labouring fiercely to fortify their homeland.

Forts and watchtowers were completed, including one, St. Elmo, on Mount Sceberras itself; walls and barricades soaring to thirty feet were thrown up; gun-emplacements were fashioned as fast as men could run from one vantage point to another. Behind each fort a great ditch was dug, cutting it off from assault on the landward side.

Nature had given Malta a superb harbour; men now strove to turn it into a fortress. The Maltese, who knew more than anyone about the working of their native rock, were the first to give strength and sinew to this dream of an impregnable stronghold.

But it was the Maltese fishermen of Birgu who put the finishing touch to the harbour defences. Across the mouth of the deepest creek, between Senglea and St. Angelo, they planned a chain boom. One end of the boom was secured on the Senglea side. Then, link by link, the chain—more than two hundred yards long—was fed out across the harbour mouth, and married to a giant capstan on St. Angelo Fort. It lay on the seabed until all the fleet of galleys had come to their final berths, where they must stay until the siege was over. Then a thousand men, in relays, bent their backs to the capstan-bars tautening the chain, raising it to water-level. Underneath it, Maltese swimmers threaded more than forty pontoons and rafts, and made them fast: completing a floating iron rampart, the cunning of which could not be matched in all the Middle Sea.

Now the inner harbour was secure. The forts on either side were as strong as they would ever be. The granaries were bulging with grain, the underground cisterns with clay water-jars, and the stables with animals driven in. Outside this fortress, and that of St. Elmo, the land had been stripped bare of its last peacetime crop, and the wells poisoned. All had been done that could be done; now a man could only wait, and receive the comfort of the sacraments, and perfect his weapons, and pray.

Thus it was that on the fifteenth day of May Malta awoke to the thunder of guns.

THE GREAT SIEGE failed, and it failed because the island's valiant garrisons would not give up. No matter what was done to them or to their fortress, they would not surrender, though wave after wave of furious attackers stormed the walls, treading the corpses of their drugged holy men who had died in the belief that they would meet that night in paradise. This bridge of bodies was not enough foothold for the shrieking, surging regiments of Turks; but a carpet of their own dead was platform enough for the beleaguered Knights.

When the old corsair Dragut Rais arrived, two weeks late, and saw what was being done by the Turkish commanders, he spoke his mind without delay.

"All your plans are wrong," he told them. "You will never take St. Elmo, nor any of the other forts, by a simple land attack. Bring up heavy guns, and bash them to pieces first! *Then* make your advance, and they will fall like rotten fruit."

Under Dragut's expert eye, the Turks put a battery of their

largest cannon on Tigne Point, a mere five hundred yards from St. Elmo: another on the slopes of Mount Sceberras: and a third on Gallows Point on the southeast side. From there they began to smash St. Elmo to pieces, while Dragut settled down to watch. Like many old men, he was sleepless; like very few old men, he was tough and enduring. No silken tents or cool evening sherbet or plump grapes for him. He shared his soldiers' rations, and at night slept briefly by the guns, under the stars, on a stone bed.

From three points of the compass the guns hammered away, hour after hour, day after day, at the small fort with the hastily built walls and the handful of defenders inside. One special mark was selected each day, and on this the avalanche of shot crashed without ceasing, until stone became powder, and bastions were reduced to shapeless rubble.

A man inside, a Maltese who lived to tell the tale, counted more than six thousand cannonballs which found their mark on the defences between the dawn of one day and the dusk of the same evening.

Time and again, Dragut judged that the moment had come for an attack, and Mustapha Pasha, the Turkish field commander, sent in his hordes to throw themselves against the great bastions of St. Elmo. Time and again Mustapha surveyed moats and ditches full of corpses of his irreplaceable élite, and said that it could not yet be done, and Dragut resumed the fiery weight of the cannonade.

There came a day when the Knights inside St. Elmo, which was no longer a fort but a heap of stone, believed that they could do no more. Their defences were gone. Their numbers had been decimated. The wounded lay and suffered agonies in their own blood. Outside the walls—if mounds of shuddering, blood-soaked rubbish could be called walls—the stench of decaying bodies, of the sandwiched heaps of Turkish dead, was almost suffocating.

They sent, by a Maltese swimmer, a respectful message to La Valette across the harbour. St. Elmo, they told him, was now useless. They had once numbered 118; they were now sixty, most of them wounded, all exhausted. Since they were unlikely to last out another day, could they not make a final sally, and try to fight their way out?

It was not cowardice; it was brave common sense. But the Grand Master had his own timetable, and his own stern code of discipline. He was waiting for promised reinforcements from the Viceroy of Sicily, and every day, every hour, that St. Elmo could survive was a golden hope for all Malta. He sent back an icy answer indeed: the garrison, under its vow of obedience and valour, was *not* to make any attempt to leave the fort. St. Elmo was to be held to the last Knight. With humble apologies, the defenders returned to their duty, Dragut Rais to his smoking guns, and Mustapha to unleash, once more, his demented legions.

The Knights of St. Elmo, whose last commander was the Aragonese Melchior de Monserrat, held on to their fort with matchless bravery for an incredible thirteen days more. Melchior had seen his brother Antonio killed by an arrow a few days earlier; it may have been this, as much as his knightly devotion, which drove him to such a fury of resistance before he forfeited his own life to a musket-shot, in the last hour of St. Elmo's ghastly twilight.

It came—it was bound to come—to a bloody end. As the last attack, which continued for six hours, rose to its climax, even the wounded were carried to their battle stations, and set down like bloodstained dummies. All were confessed, and received absolution; then they fought, with a maniac, steely will, and if a man propped up in a crumbling corner of a wall could manage to swing a broadsword for the last time, that was what he did.

Dragut Rais did not see the last assault, nor its triumph; he was slowly dying of a fearful wound. Five days earlier he had been directing his guns for a final cannonade. "Aim lower," he signalled to the battery behind him. "You are overshooting the walls." They took him at his word. A Turkish cannonball crashed into the trench where he stood, and a sliver of stone sliced into his skull so that (to quote the man standing by him) "his brains spilled out from his mouth and nostrils", and he fell.

Dragut Rais breathed his last as the fort was taken. A last wall was breached, and suddenly there were no more men left to stand and bear arms. Nine prisoners were snatched for ransom. Five Maltese soldiers dived off St. Elmo Point and swam for their lives. Within moments, the rest of the garrison was dead.

St. Elmo was the key to Maltese victory. Though the fort was rubble, and inside were the corpses of 1,300 defenders, the delay in taking it was fatal to the Turkish plan. Eight thousand of them had been killed, and instead of the promised four or five days St. Elmo had held out for thirty-one. Neither the time lost, nor the men

thrown away, were ever made good. As Mustapha mourned the monstrous total of his own dead, he could only say: "If the daughter cost us so much, what will be the price of the mother?"

The mother was St. Angelo. The Knights of St. Angelo, having watched St. Elmo die, took a fresh oath that their fortress would live, and they kept it.

La Valette, the grave and handsome old warrior with the weight of the whole island on his shoulders, had two frontiers to guard: the ditch behind St. Angelo fort, and the harbour defences themselves. The harbour side remained impregnable, and the ditch was held against every device, whether it was bombardment, or fiery hoops launched against the walls, or men massed in their thousands who threw their bodies at the ramparts, content to form a bridge of the dead which would serve for the last assault by living comrades.

On one day a gigantic mine, planted after weeks of tunnelling by Turkish gunners under a part of the defences, went up with a roar, leaving a gaping hole in the ramparts. Through this the attackers immediately began to pour, while the defenders were still dazed by the explosion. It was the moment when St. Angelo came nearest to ruin, but La Valette was ready for it. As with all great captains, he could recognize a fatal hour, when danger had to be grasped, before the strength for grasping failed for ever. He advanced into the breach himself, at the head of a small band of men which swelled to hundreds as his heroic figure was identified. Under the lash of their furious energy, the ramparts were swept clear of the enemy, the breach sealed, and the city saved.

It was such exploits as these which ensured the blind loyalty with which he was followed, even in the darkest hour. If the old Grand Master could do it, then shame on the man who did not try! . . . This feeling spread beyond the garrison, down to the slum-dwellers and the fishermen of the waterfront, and the women who had to share all the horrors of siege. For throughout the long ordeal, Maltese men, women and children toiled to repair the walls; they hurled stones at the attackers, carried away the dead, tended the wounded, and had the pleasure of pouring cauldrons of boiling water over the ramparts to scald infidel heads. Many were fighting men themselves: many were faithful unto death; and no single Maltese ever deserted to the enemy.

Suddenly the rumours of help from the slow-moving Viceroy of Sicily became fact. A force of 9,000 men landed at Mellieha Bay. For the Turks, it was the last straw. Exhaustion and disease had spread their wings like monstrous spectres; the remorseless toll of their dead could no longer be endured. They faltered, and turned to run helter-skelter for the ships, to sail away, in utter rout.

Suddenly there were no invincible Turks left in Malta. The gates of the forts were pushed open, and the inhabitants streamed out.

Though they must mourn their dead bitterly—250 Knights and 7,000 others killed, out of a garrison of 9,000—they could turn to rejoicing at what they had done to the enemy. A bare 10,000 Turks were left alive, fleeing for home to face the wrath of their Sultan and the laughter of the world; and there remained Malta, unbroken, unchained, where they need only remember glory.

The Worst Day of Father Salvatore
10 May 1942

That spring morning, Father Salvatore came with a heavy heart to visit his mother. He came from the prison where his brother-in-law had been under lock and key since the previous night.

Lewis Debrincat, at last, had gone too far.

The story was a remarkably silly one, even by Lewis's own standards of furtive enmity towards the war effort. He and certain of his friends had formed a club to send food parcels and other creature comforts to German and Italian prisoners of war imprisoned in Malta. In theory, it was not such a terrible idea; it could even be seen as humane and charitable. But before long something happened that was not charitable at all but clearly treasonable. An Italian pilot, bailing out from an aircraft in flames, disappeared altogether. He was seen to land in a remote part of the island, but all that was to be found was a buried parachute, and a trail leading to a fishing-boat missing from Marfa harbour. The enemy pilot, in fact, had been hidden, and then helped to escape.

Lewis himself, under questioning, made one revealing slip. Asked about the possible motives of those involved, he made a jaunty joke: "I suppose they did it for the Chianti!"

A grim-faced security man interjected: "What Chianti?"

"I mean, for Chianti. Like an Italian bribe."

"But you said, *the* Chianti."

"What difference does that make?"

It made a great deal. The buried parachute had been wrapped round a Chianti bottle, now empty, which the Italian pilot, a young man of spirit, had grabbed just before he bailed out. Nothing about it had been mentioned before.

Though this was not hanging evidence, it was enough. Lewis had been warned about his conduct, long ago: he was promptly arrested, and interned; it was the first order of its kind signed by the new Governor of Malta, Lord Gort.

When Father Salvatore, by privileged permission hard to obtain, entered the prison cell, he found Lewis lying on the stone shelf which was his bed, covered by a coarse grey blanket like the poorest shroud in the world. One could only feel sorry for such derelict humanity, and appalled by all the evidence of disrepute—the dank cell, the foul-smelling bucket in the corner, the door which a visitor had been ordered to leave open, the staring sentry. . . . He advanced a few steps into the room, and touched Lewis on the chest.

Perhaps Lewis, weary of intrusion, had only been feigning sleep, for he opened his eyes immediately. He hunched his shoulders, and the blanket fell away, to reveal a sweat-stained undershirt. He swung his legs, and sat up on the stone bed. "*Bongornu, Sur Kappillan.*" His voice was low, his face indifferent. "Have you come to see the condemned man? . . . I said that to you, two years ago. Remember?"

"Yes, I remember. And I said: 'No one has condemned you'."

"You would hardly say that now."

"How are you, Lewis?"

"Worse than yesterday, better than tomorrow." But he did not sound sad about it: these were facts, not complaints.

"Is there anything you want?"

"No."

"Can I take any messages for you?"

"No." He raised his eyes for the first time and they were astonishingly gentle. "Just say that you saw me, and that I am—as you see me." Suddenly Lewis drew the blanket round his shoulders, and lay down again. "I'm sorry, Salvu. I don't want to talk to anyone any more."

178

"I understand. I'll say good-bye. God bless you."

"Thank you."

Whether it was thanks for the blessing of God, or thanks for coming, Father Salvatore did not know. With a last glance at what had now become a formless grey sack again, he backed out of the cell. As he left the prison he thought: How strange—I liked him more today than I ever did before.

HIS MOTHER'S HOUSE had shrunk until it was a shadow of all it had ever been. Rooms were dust-sheeted and closed off; the two larger wings of the house now locked and barred.

Old Gregory was dead; Francis had rejoined his regiment; two maids, a chef, and an ancient gardener who could not keep pace with spring, were all that was left of an establishment which had formerly numbered sixteen. The Baroness lived and slept downstairs in the armoury, where her cherished four-poster bed had been reassembled after a week's painstaking carpentry. ("I wish to die where I was born" was all the reason required for this.) Only the shape of the great house remained to bear witness to four centuries of merit and magnificence.

As with the house, so with its noble occupant. Father Salvatore, who in former days had never ceased to wonder at his mother's spirit and strength, could only mourn what had befallen her. She had shrunk with the house; she was old, and in poor health. The ebony stick which she had once despised as an enemy was now an essential friend.

When he greeted her in the armoury, which was now no more than a lavishly appointed bed-sitting room, she seemed possessed by a single woe. "This coffee!" she exclaimed pettishly. Though poured from the same silver pot into the same blue-and-gold fluted cups, it was indeed tasteless and gritty, like all the coffee in Malta. "Surely there must be some way of getting proper coffee beans?"

"I'm afraid they're not importing them any more."

"But who decides these things? When I think of the old days, when one only had to mention something like that to one of the equerries. . . ." She sipped again, and made a wry face. "Well, tell me, how is that traitor, my son-in-law?"

It was a matter to be faced. "I've just come from seeing him. Lewis is quite—" the absurd word could not be changed, "quite happy. I suppose he expected it—even wanted it. . . ."

"Prison? How can that be? He is worse than Benedict, with all his nonsense in Paris. What a generation!"

"You mustn't distress yourself, mother."

"I am not *distressed*. I am *very angry*." How sad that the words, which once could have made the hearer stand in fear of what might come next, were now only sounds, empty and futile. "Lewis must be mad! I always knew it. I knew it when he made that disgusting scene at Christmas. What will happen to him, Salvatore?"

He had already worked this out, from his modest knowledge of the law. "At the best, he will be interned for the rest of the war. At the worst—if he is brought to trial and found guilty—he might spend fifteen years in prison."

"This would never have happened if Sir William Dobbie were still Governor. Well, I can do nothing for him now, even if I wanted to. I have not even met this Lord Gort."

"I expect he's busy, like everyone else."

"But he must hold some sort of reception. There was always a *levée* for a new governor. When Lord Plumer arrived—"

Father Salvatore put his hand up to his face, in an involuntary gesture of weariness. With all the love in the world, he could only feel that his mother's complaints were trivial and selfish. People were *hungry* in Malta; people were giving up hope under the merciless pressures of the bombing which was beating their brains out, and the hunt for scraps of food which sickened all appetite. *That* was Malta, 1942. Nothing else. Not proper coffee beans, nor governors' *levées*, nor even Lewis Debrincat and his treachery. People did not die of disgrace. They died because they could no longer live.

Something of this sad despair must have shown in his face, for the Baroness suddenly asked: "Is anything the matter, Salvatore? Are you unwell? Are you getting enough sleep? Enough to eat?"

"Oh yes."

"You really need a proper rest. And I'm not the only one who thinks so."

He smiled. "Who else thinks so?"

"The bishop. He is quite sure you are wearing yourself out."

"Why should he think that? He can't know much about me."

"I can assure you, he knows a great deal. You are becoming quite famous, you know."

"At last?"

"It is not a joke, Salvatore. Sooner or later you will—" she stopped suddenly. It was clear that she had been going to quote a certain remark, and had then decided against it. Instead she finished: "Sooner or later you must have a real rest."

He was not going to venture further. Whatever the bishop said about him must somehow be kept at bay; and the best way of doing that was to know nothing.

"I don't want to rest before we can all rest." He stood up. "I'm afraid I must go, mother. There are quite a lot of things to do. And we have our first wedding later today. Remember? Nero and his bride are so grateful for your generous gift of wine."

She seemed, in a brief instant, to gather her strength. As he bent to kiss her, she said: "Give my love to Giovanna, and the children. You will know what to say to them—better than I do, perhaps." Her face had a beseeching look which he had never seen before. "I'm silly sometimes, aren't I? You must forgive me."

He was deeply moved. "There is nothing to forgive."

"There is something every day. But Salvatore—"

"What?"

"If you *are* going shopping, and you hear of any coffee beans—"

It was a brave joke: so much so that, even as he left the armoury, he found himself wondering: How wonderful if somewhere in the island, a forgotten sack of this rarity was only waiting to be liberated. . . .

HE SPENT THE REST of the morning in shopping—scavenging would have been a better word—not for coffee beans, but for the meagre necessities of life: for the powdered milk which the children must have, for olive oil—or anything resembling olive oil—which would make dry food eatable, for pasta however coarse or mouldy. The food situation had now become so desperate that it had overtaken even the bombing as the worst misery of their lives.

During the last few days the newspapers had been full of the arrival of a new Governor. The "Cromwellian soldier", as Churchill called Sir William Dobbie, had worn himself out in the defence of his island; he was also losing heart, as his last dispatches showed. These gave warning that "the very worst may happen if we cannot replenish our vital needs, especially flour and ammunition, and that very soon. . . . It is a question of survival."

Churchill's judgement was that the man, if not the island, was headed for a breakdown, and he replaced him with Lord Gort. Gort had considerable personal *panache*. He was a Field-Marshal, and a lord. He had a string of names—John Standish Surtees Prendergast Vereker, sixth Viscount Gort—and a string of magnificent medals to match: the Victoria Cross, the Distinguished Service Order, the Military Cross, and nine Mentions in Dispatches. In addition, he brought to the island a medal of its own: the George Cross, awarded to the whole of Malta three weeks earlier, with a citation from King George VI which did not overstate the case: *To honour her brave people I award the George Cross to the island fortress of Malta, to bear witness to a heroism and devotion that will long be famous in history.*

Even the Russians, not given to praising their allies, sent their congratulations at the same time. But when Lord Gort made his first tour of Valletta, he was greeted, on certain street corners, by men who stood in silence and rubbed their bellies. They were giving him, not an insult, not a threat; just a message: "We cannot eat the George Cross."

It was a fact—stated by Dobbie, confirmed by Gort—that Malta was now within a few weeks of starvation and defeat. There was almost no sugar, cooking-oil, or flour. There was no butter, no jam, and no potatoes until the next harvest. Even bread—plain bread, the staple of life—was now a luxury; from the three loaves a day which were a working man's natural expectation, the allowance was now half a loaf. By an inevitable process of strangulation, one shortage led to another. There was no more coal, so the power stations faltered. People turned from electricity to kerosene, and presently there was none of that either. After that it was wood and candles, until these in turn ran out; and then it was cold food, and bed at sunset.

There was a time when snails became popular, and then they too disappeared. "How do they run so fast?" was a sour joke indeed, for stranger things than snails had a habit of disappearing. When a bomb fell near a man driving a horse-and-cart through Kalkara, the horse was killed by stray splinters. The man, after taking shelter, went off to get help; and when he came back, the horse was not be be seen. An eatable horse was worth a princely forty pounds.

What was being done about this famine? The best that could be. Since supplies from outside were no longer reaching Malta, except in small packets by submarine and small cargoes from the occasional ship which passed the blockade: since even food boats from Gozo were mined or sunk by low-flying planes: since little more could be grown on an island which had not been self-supporting since Napoleon, every scrap of food had to be hoarded, and fairly shared out.

Bread every day, kerosene every fortnight—though only enough for four hot meals. Then communal "Victory Kitchens" were established—"So that we can all starve equally", as the grim saying went. With the help of the Army (itself on half-rations) these fed 200,000 people a day. Often for three people the meal would be three thin sausages, and fifteen peas; or soup with beans, or a slice of corned beef.

How did people really live, in their wrecked and beleaguered island? They lived very small. They grew weaker from lack of food; they suffered from scabies. Throughout that summer there was a widespread typhoid epidemic, a product of broken sewage pipes, contaminated reservoirs, and the use of raw excrement to irrigate fields during a "Grow More Food" campaign. Shelter life bred verminous children. The crash of bombs led to ruined eardrums. The use of ear-plugs made for a brooding family despair.

Even when they found something to cook, many bombed-out families had nothing better than rough stoves carved out of stone, and with these they made the most of that dwindling kerosene ration. Putting tins of water on the roof, they let the heat of the sun bring it halfway to boiling-point, and a piece of string stuck in a kerosene bottle furnished a light of sorts.

The rations for the Three Cities were brought across Grand Harbour from Valletta by *dghajjes* which often, on the return journey, carried corpses for burial. The obscenity of this grisly trade seemed, after a while, as normal as any other bargain.

Father Salvatore, touring the shops of Valletta, was feeling something less than human. As with thousands of others, it was brought home to him once again that he was now only a troublesome statistic, a unit of consumption. It would be better if he disappeared off the face of the island.

He had a shopping-list—of things that Nero said they *must* have, things that other people had begged him to try for, things he had thought of himself. But he might as well have let the slips of paper blow away on the wind for all the use they were to him.

But there was still good nature to be seen, and friendly greetings to be heard, and courage in adversity, and humour among hungry men as they compared the number of holes remaining to be tightened in their belts. It was enough to make Father Salvatore praise God, and to persist in his forlorn search.

He was determined to find something special for the wedding feast. They had the cake already, saved and scrimped for, built up from hoarded flour, eggs begged one by one from every hen-owner he could trace, sugar even hammered from empty bags which could still surrender a grain or two. They had the wine also, a magnificent 140-gallon butt of it, brewed from the sweet muscat grapes in the Santo-Nobile vineyards near Mdina, and sent by the Baroness "to bless the marriage".

But "Please find something special for us!" Nero had repeated, as they said good-bye at dawn. "Even if it's only enough for two. We can't get married on Widow's Soup!" So he kept on with his search, acknowledging secretly that part of this persistence was a cowardly wish to delay his next appointment. Lunch at the Casa Debrincat was not, on this particular morning, something one hurried to.

In the end he succeeded. Picking his way, on aching feet, down

lower town, through the mean slit of St. Nicholas Street which had
at its end that enchanting glimpse of blue water, he came upon
a young man he knew. This was Wenzu Tonna, who ran a general
shop, and was one of the affluent heirs of this war.

Wenzu was a fat, sharp-eyed young man in stained overalls. He
stood outside the flapping bamboo curtain of his shop door and
smiled equally at all passersby. He did not look like an angel, but
he proved to be one.

"Have you got anything for me today?" asked Father Salvatore.

"It depends what you want, Dun Salv. But if I said 'Nothing',
I wouldn't be telling a lie."

Father Salvatore went through his list once more. For rationed
goods he had the coupons, collected from all over the catacombs;
for anything else, he had hope. But the answer, like all the earlier
answers of the day, never varied. Wenzu spread his hands, in the
familiar gesture of despair. He had nothing, on or off the ration,
which had not gone to his customers already.

The priest, as one Maltese to another, persisted. There was something in Wenzu's manner which indicated an area of negotiation.
"Well, have you anything *special*? I want it for the wedding."

Wenzu's eyes opened wide. "A wedding? What wedding is this?"

"My sacristan is getting married this afternoon."

"I hope they'll both be happy. As happy as anyone can be,
these days. I wish I could do something for them."

"I'm sure you could, if you tried."

"All I've got is a tin of biscuits. They're called dog-biscuits.
It's a special import: you don't often see them here." He noted
Father Salvatore's face, and spread his hands again. "Yes, I know
it sounds funny, Dun Salv. But if you put a bit of jam on top—"

"Have you any jam?"

"Not a spoonful."

"Then it's no use." It would have been no use anyway. Dog-
biscuits. . . . But even now he would not give up, and he had one
card left to play. He turned as if to go, and then turned back. "Do
you still make wine, Wenzu?"

As soon as he said it, he knew that it was a good card, a genuine
Maltese bargaining card, the kind that opened a crack in a closing

door. He knew this because Wenzu, who had been looking straight at him, now looked sideways up the street as if some strange curiosity had caught his attention. Then his head came round again, and he was wary. "I make a little wine," Wenzu answered. "Just for the family, and a few friends. But I've none left to sell. Last year was a bad year, even for wine."

"I don't want to buy wine. We have plenty. But, tomorrow, or the next day, I might have an empty barrel."

"Is that so? An old barrel?"

"No. A new one. A huge one too. A hundred-and-forty gallons. It has the Santo-Nobile arms on it." There were possibilities here he did not wish to think about. "Would that be any use to you?"

Wenzu considered the matter. "I suppose I could take it off your hands."

"It's worth a bit more than that. Indeed, I'm told they're scarce since people have taken to burning them for firewood."

"Maybe, maybe, but a barrel like yours takes up a lot of room." He backed away towards the bamboo blind, motioning with his head for the priest to follow him. "Come inside, Dun Salv. It's too hot out here. And I've just thought of something."

Inside, there was the deep gloom of a windowless room, and a smell of musty sacks. Then shelves, mostly bare, could be made out, and two tables for coffee-drinking customers, and grubby cases of empty bottles, and buzzing flies, and a counter with a pair of battered scales.

"I've just thought of something," he said again. "It's only just been made. That's why I forgot it." He pointed towards something on the counter, hidden by a muslin cloth. "What would you say to a nice veal loaf?"

There were a lot of things Father Salvatore could have said to such an unheard-of luxury, but he contented himself with: "It sounds wonderful."

"It is wonderful." Wenzu removed the cover gently, almost reverently. Even in the murky light the glazed surface shone with richness. At least two feet long, the loaf looked succulent beyond the dreams of hungry man.

Father Salvatore sighed, and swallowed. "It's just what we

186

want." He peered again, more carefully. "But what's in it? You can't get veal these days."

"You can't get anything these days. That's the best goat in Malta. As good as veal any day. As good as lamb."

"Then what's the dark meat? Would it be horse, Wenzu?"

The other man shrugged his shoulders. "Perhaps. Just for colouring. These are difficult times. But taken as a whole—"

"Oh, I agree." He watched while Wenzu put back the muslin cloth, as carefully as if he were covering the face of the dear departed. "Well, thank you very much. It will make a wonderful wedding feast. God will bless you, Wenzu."

But God was not quite ready to bless either of them.

"I'm glad it suits you, Dun Salv." Wenzu rubbed his hands. "What shall we say? Sixteen pounds?"

"*What?*" Father Salvatore was genuinely taken aback. He had thought that this was to be a straight exchange, the veal loaf for the barrel. But before he could speak Wenzu forestalled him, very adroitly.

"Oh, I know it sounds a lot, Dun Salv. But if I sold it by the slice, I could make twenty pounds. People would be round like vultures!"

"That's not what I meant," Father Salvatore answered sharply. "What about the barrel? It is worth a great deal of money."

"Is it?" Wenzu's eyes widened. "I thought you wanted it carted away."

The real bargaining began. There was a certain price, Father Salvatore now knew, which Wenzu would take; it might not be quite as high as sixteen pounds, but it would be very close to it. The Maltese did not bargain like Arabs, not for them the inflated demand, and then the acceptance of half what they asked. They set a good price; and from that, if they chose to retreat, it would be but a single step.

This feeling, this understanding, was in Father Salvatore's blood as well as Wenzu's. Thus not more than three minutes later, "For you, and for the wedding, fourteen pounds," Wenzu said, and they shook hands, "For that, I'll have it delivered. And thank you for the barrel."

The barrel was worth at least another ten pounds, but not to Father Salvatore. He only wanted the veal loaf, and he had got it. Not for the first time, he wondered, that, in the midst of war, the blind-worm of commerce could still bore its way onward with such greedy devotion. It was not only Wenzu: it was himself, it was Malta in both of them. . . . The prizes were an empty barrel, and some money, and a veal loaf made of chopped goat and horsemeat. But they were as real, and precious, as victory.

He went on his way to Sliema rejoicing. A veal loaf. . . . It would be the wedding of the year. . . . Fourteen pounds was a terrible price to pay, even for such a rarity, but no man who had secured exactly what he wanted need feel that he had been duped.

AT THE DEBRINCAT house he found the maid Carmelina once again in tears; long ago, it had been for the war itself, then for her father, now it was for the master of the house. Her pretty eyes beseeched him as she said: "Oh, Dun Salv, isn't it awful? Is it true that the master will be hanged?"

"Carmelina! Of course not! He did something very stupid, I'm afraid. But to talk of hanging is silly. When I saw him this morning—"

"Do you mean one can still *see* him?"

"Of course—" But before Father Salvatore had time to explain further, there was a step behind him, and when he turned it was his sister Giovanna, crossing the hall from the patio. The moment he had been dreading was at hand.

She seemed composed, though pale, and dressed in black, which gave her a sad air of bereavement. She said, in a normal tone: "I thought I heard your voice, Salvu," and kissed him in welcome. But as soon as Carmelina withdrew, her face and manner altered. She became, indeed, more like Carmelina: bewildered, barely able to cope. She asked immediately: "Have you seen Gigi?"

"Yes. I went there early this morning." It was difficult to avoid the terrible word "prison", but he was determined to do so. "He had a good night, and he is quite comfortable."

"You are so wonderful, Salvu. . . . Did he send any message?"

A priest could not lie. "No."

"Does he want anything?"

"No."

Her control showed signs of failing. "Will he stay in prison?"

"Yes, I'm sure of that."

"Well, that's one good thing." And as he looked at her, sad and surprised, she burst out uncontrollably: "He was making our lives hateful! You must know that. Why should I pretend? Why should the children pretend? He *destroyed* everything, long ago."

"But he's your husband."

"Not any more. . . . It's no good looking at me like that, Salvu. I don't care what the Church says. Let him stay in his prison. We are free! And we are going to stay free. I will never live with him again."

Her high voice ceased, choked with feeling, and he could not answer. What could a priest, a stranger to marriage, really contribute to such a moment. All he knew was that, this morning, in this house, he could no longer be a priest. He could only be a brother.

"Giovanna?"

"Yes?"

"Where are the children? What are they doing?"

"Crying, I expect." But already she was calmer, because he had allowed her so much, because he was not going to lecture. "I don't know where they are, Salvu. We're all separate today. . . ."

MARIJA DEBRINCAT was sitting dry-eyed in her bedroom; indeed she had shed no tears for her father: only for her mother, the worst sufferer from all the humiliation. Even to watch her father crossing the hall, flanked by two plain-clothes policemen, had not really been moving. But to have to cling to her mother after the front door shut, because her mother was clinging to her: to feel a dear body racked with sobs, to dry someone else's tears before she dried her own—that was the part that mattered.

Waking next morning, she had been at first appalled, then rebellious at the destruction wrought by love, then strong once more. The new alliance was herself and Michael, with all spare support given to her mother. Thank God that Michael, the rock of her new life, would soon come back from that perilous sky-world, and they would be hand-in-hand again. How wonderful that he was coming to lunch that very day.

But to Pietru Pawl Michael's coming to lunch was an agonizing embarrassment and shame. He had come racing home from school, tears on his face, rage and fear in his heart. He had brushed past his mother in the hall, wild for solitude. "Everyone knows!" he called out, and ran upstairs.

His father was in prison, and everyone knew it, and it was the end of the world. Now he had stationed himself on the roof, because if there was an air raid, and a bomb fell on the house, as he prayed would happen, he wanted it to kill him first.

What would Michael think?

The sun was hot, the sky clear and blue, the water in Sliema Creek sparkling. There was a drone of aircraft overhead. . . . Perhaps it was Michael winging back from some terrific dog-fight, shooting down Italians, the Italians whom his father wanted to win.

Michael would land, and someone would say: "Did you hear about the Debrincats? They've been found out! The father's been put in prison! Better not waste your time with that lot."

He heard his mother call from below, and for a moment refused to answer. But that wasn't fair. . . . There was even the thought that he was now the only man in the house. . . . He walked to the head of the staircase, and called out: "Coming!"

Then he went down to his bedroom, washed his face and hands without prompting, and—sick and hungry at the same time—prepared to join his family downstairs. But he *wouldn't* go back to school. Not that afternoon. Uncle Salvu would understand, and make everyone else understand as well.

Out on the patio, that traditional family rendezvous, they waited a long time for Michael. Their conversation grew so trivial and awkward that Father Salvatore knew he must speak of what was in the forefront of his mind, and in theirs. The evidence of sorrow and guilt sat in all their faces. To ignore it was cowardice.

"Before Michael comes," he said, "I want to say something about your father." It was strange how such an innocent and honoured word could shock, but it was so. "I went to see him early this morning. You must accept that he will be there for a long time."

No one said anything. Their startled faces only grew wary. It was something they had already accepted, in their different ways.

"I don't want to say anything, *anything*, about what he has done. What we have to deal with is *now*. . . . There will be a lot of gossip. But after that has settled down, you will go on as before. People will not think of you as different. There will just be three of you—three Debrincats—instead of four." He prayed that all this would be true. "That doesn't mean that you should forget your father. That would be wrong. But you should remember him, and pray for him, in private. If you are careful about that, then everyone else will be careful, and things will come back to normal again."

He was cutting several corners, he knew. With the Debrincats, things would never be quite normal again: socially it might become true, but as a matter of interior self-repute, never.

He wondered who would speak first, and it was the talkative Pietru, too long silent on a day cursed with more new topics than he could cope with. "Uncle Salvu, you said it would be a long time." He did not want to use particular phrases of shame. "But how long?"

Marija said, with gentleness: "None of us knows, Pietru. Don't make it worse for yourself. It's the same for all of us."

"It's *not*! You don't have to go to school."

His mother said: "But you have so many friends there."

"It's not fair to make them—to expect them to be on my side."

"I think you might be surprised—" Father Salvatore began, and then broke off. Bold words were all very well for adults who did not have to sweat them out. It was cruel to involve a boy of fifteen in such a miserable conflict when it could be avoided. "Do you want to stay away for a few days?"

Pietru looked at his mother, and then back again. "I don't want to go back *ever*!"

"Well, we'll see about that. One thing at a time. I said 'We have to deal with *now*'. This is what I meant." He leaned towards Pietru. "I can ring up the principal, and say it would be better if you didn't come back till next week. Would you like that?"

Pietru nodded, wordless. He was so near to tears that no one could look at him. It was a moment when each one of them could feel, sharp as a thorn, the exact meaning of disgrace. But at least a single step into the future had been taken, one painful corner turned. Giovanna, sitting next to her brother, put her hand over his.

"Thank you, Salvu," she said. Then she glanced down at her watch, and became a hostess again. "Good gracious, it's nearly half-past one! We really should be sensible, and go in to lunch."

Marija came to the alert. "We *must* wait for Michael. I'm sure he hasn't forgotten or—or anything."

Father Salvatore took charge again. "I don't think he'd mind, Marija. Perhaps he tried to send a message. You know—extra duty or something." He rubbed his hands together. "Well—who's hungry?"

"I am," said Pietru. He had things under control again.

"I'm hungry too," his mother joined in, "and poor Uncle Salvu must be starving. Ring the bell, will you, Pietru?"

"I'm *not* hungry," Marija persisted, and in truth she was not. Suddenly she was feeling mortally sick and afraid. Michael *would* have got a message through if he couldn't come.

"Three to one," Pietru said cheerfully. "Democracy wins." His hand, hovering over the bell, plunged firmly down in a triple ring: "Three-to-*one-means-lunch*!"

THEY HAD PROGRESSED past the soup—"It's just soup, I'm afraid," Giovanna told them. "The little grey things ought to be barley, but they're Government lentils"—when Pietru cocked his head on one side. "I thought I heard the front door," he said.

They listened. Footsteps could be heard, and a man's voice—and then the closing of a solid door. The omens seemed very good.

"Better late than never," Father Salvatore declared.

"He's only missed the soup," Giovanna said, "and it wasn't the best soup in the world, was it?" She smiled at her daughter. "Will you go, Marija? Just explain that we had to start?"

Marija stood up, slim and beautiful as a girl could be. But her face was troubled. "I don't think that was Michael," she said, and left the dining-room.

It was not Michael. The man in the hall was Captain Ian Ross.

"Hello, Ian," she said uncertainly. She liked the aide-de-camp much better than in the old days. But she could not guess why he should be there. Was it something to do with her father?—he would have telephoned her mother. Was it just a chance call?— no, he would never call in the middle of lunch. Some news?

"Marija," he said, and touched her shoulder as a brother might. "I'm not sure how to say this, so I'll bash straight ahead. Michael's missing. He was shot down over Sicily last night."

Her hand went up to her mouth. "Did anyone see—"

"No. It was pitch dark, and there was a hell of an uproar going on." He touched her shoulder again. "But darling, for all anyone knows he bailed out, and he may be perfectly all right."

"Oh God."

He looked away. "Oh God, indeed. . . . They rang me up, because they know the—the situation, and I said I'd tell you."

She nodded her thanks, totally unable to speak.

"Well, that's all so far. Just 'missing'. Don't forget it happens all the time, and then the chaps turn up safe and sound, and you get a nice postcard from the Red Cross to prove it."

She found her voice again, though it was no more than a whisper. "Was it over the sea?"

"No. Somewhere inland. I tell you, there are all sorts of chances. . . . Is there anything I can do, at the moment?"

"I don't think so. No, thank you."

"Then I'll move on. But as soon as they hear anything, I'll let you know straight away. All right?"

"Thank you, Ian."

"Oh yes—His Ex asked me to say, he's terribly sorry."

Marija nodded, wordless again.

"About everything."

FATHER SALVATORE left the house in unbearable sadness. He secured a lift to the Auberge de Castile, and then began to walk down through the wreckage of the city. It suited his forlorn mood, to pick his way laboriously past the ruins of its flailing punishment.

The real reason for the award of that George Cross lay before him, to be mourned at every turn. What Valletta had suffered during the last five months of the war was already past belief.

In so far as anything so horrible came from the mind of one man, their ordeal was the brain-child of Field-Marshal Kesselring, the German Commander in Sicily, who had decreed that Malta was now too great a nuisance to be allowed to live. The idea had been thought of before, and even tried before, but now it would be done.

As the raids multiplied, a terrible exhaustion began to grip the island; it was impossible to rest, to move about, to work, to live anything which could be called a life, under the thunder of the bombs and the desperate answer of the guns. There were never less than four raids a day, which might last two hours each; an "alert" could continue for thirteen hours, disrupting all normal behaviour.

Bombs fell by the ton: by the hundred tons: by the thousand. In April, bombers dropped 6,730 tons of bombs (the city of Coventry itself, that tortured monument to the Battle of Britain, only had to endure 500 tons). Bombs came in sizes big and small: bombs weighing 500 lbs., bombs weighing 1,000: huge land-mines which floated down by parachute, like spectral bats against the moon: delayed-action bombs, whistling bombs, butterfly bombs, plain bombs for a plain death.

Sometimes they arrived as strings of bombs chained together, which fell, and bounced, and tumbled over each other like little dogs at play. Sometimes they were "anti-personnel" bombs, shaped like Thermos flasks, that lay, innocent and silent, until they were touched. Then they killed the inquisitive.

With such raw pleasantries did the days and nights pass.

While the people crouched and bled and suffered, the professionals did what they could to ward off the blows, but guns had to be rationed to ten rounds a day—scarcely enough to find a range. Then forty-six Spitfires were brought in by the American aircraft-carrier *Wasp*, and within seventy-two hours every single one of them had been destroyed on the ground by German bombers which pounced on them within a few minutes of touchdown. There was no cure for so baleful a vigilance.

Yet, at a time of such impotence, it was moving to see how the Maltese still trusted and admired their defenders. The flying men, especially, were regarded as heroes. But there were other heroes, too, the ground-crews and the maintenance men, Maltese and imported, whose job it was to protect the planes, to keep them flying, and to patch up the ruined airfields. They lived in caves and concrete holes, like the people they were shielding; and each time the storm passed, they sallied out manfully to repair the damage before the next one broke. Even so, there was a time when, for eleven days on end, not a single fighter aircraft could leave the ground. Exhausted men could do no more than dump a few tons of rubble into a bomb-crater, and then run for cover as the enemy returned to gouge it all out again.

With the defenders thus occupied, countless other iron fists beat at the places where people lived, steadily tearing out the heart of Malta. Father Salvatore, plodding downtown, was now descending with a sick heart into this sprawling hell of destruction, a once-thriving town brought to a standstill, its population reduced from 21,000 to 6,000, most of them cave-dwellers or dispossessed migrants.

Whole streets had now been permanently closed off, choked by heaps of fallen masonry impossible to tackle, deserts of rubbish which must be left to moulder till a brighter day, if such a day ever dawned.

Father Salvatore sometimes stood on a street-corner which he could not recognize, lost in his own city which had become a hopeless maze. Even the Strada Reale, to which he kept returning as his best-known point of reference, was a vista of desolation. Great gaps in its line of shops now offered only a crazy façade of doors and lintels: in front, on the pavement, were placed a few tables where hopeful men, undefeated, set out their wares.

Even in this last-ditch endeavour, such a man had to maintain a watchful eye. Flies and huge rats abounded, feeding on human desperation and disorder. Even *humans* fed on such foul fare. And, while a man mourned his own dead, and his eyes were blurred, his wrecked house might be stripped of everything movable; mirrors, clothing, bathroom taps; the food from the kitchen, the blankets from the bereaved bed. This cannibal lust, which should have been the greatest shame of all, was now a commonplace evil. It did not call for public censure, only for troops.

Still trudging through rubble, Father Salvatore reached the

mined harbour, and found a place in a navy store-boat returning to French Creek. He knew a lot of these sailors by now, and never ceased to rejoice in their cheerful readiness to help anyone, whether it was a pretty girl or a battered old *kappillan*.

Grand Harbour had become, in the last few months, the watery twin of ruined Valletta—the graveyard of broken, burnt-out ships. But there was something different about their passage today. Luminous smoke, pungent to the nostrils, put a uniform blanket of nothingness above their heads, and beneath this smokescreen the dead harbour at last seemed to come alive again. For in French Creek, that boneyard of wood and concrete, there was a new ship, hale and hearty, a thriving centre of activity. It was a grey navy ship with manned guns pointing at the sky, and signal flags drying off after a wet voyage; a ship on which something was happening, the mainspring of the most heartening, bustling diligence which had been seen in Grand Harbour for many a weary day and night.

H.M.S. *Welshman* signalled a romantic revival of an ancient tradition—the lone blockade-runner. Since it was now a harsh fact of life that convoys, or any small clutch of supply ships, however well escorted, could no longer get through to Malta, and that the island was starving, something else must take their place.

The something else was the *Welshman*, which, following a bitter series of defeats and fiascos, *had* to plug the perilous gap in supplies, or see the island lost.

For the blockade run, *Welshman* was romantically disguised. A 2,600-ton minelayer with a speed—35 knots—which made her one of the fastest ships in the navy, she happened to look rather like a French destroyer of the *Leopard* class. All she needed was a little more bulk on the bridge and the quarterdeck, an enlarged third funnel, and a good big tricolor ensign, and she could pass for a Vichy-French warship on her lawful Axis business.

All that the crew needed were some blue-and-white striped singlets, and a cap with a red pompon on the top, and they were in business. The theatrical deeds were done. *Welshman* loaded certain essential stores and people, perfected her disguise with plywood at Gibraltar, and then ran hell-bent for Malta.

A combination of iron-nerved bluff and superb navigation brought her through. First she closed the Algerian coast, and weaved in and out of the territorial limits as she sped eastward. Challenged by shore stations, she fooled around with bad signalling and ambiguous answers until she got out of range. Twice she was visited by a patrolling German aircraft, which made low-level passes overhead. Sweating under this scrutiny, she did not even man her guns. All that the fancy-dress crew did was to wave. The bomber finally waggled its wings in salute, and went off home again. By the time a report could be filed, and checked, night had fallen and *Welshman* was well into her last full-speed dash. After eight hours of pitch-black, truly remarkable navigation at over thirty knots, in and out of the minefields and shoals of the Tunisian Channel, she got into Grand Harbour at 6 a.m.

As soon as Father Salvatore clambered up onto the dock that afternoon, he was caught up in the thrusting activity of which she was the centre. With hardly a pause, he found himself one of a line of men who were passing crates from hand to hand: a human chain connecting the ship's side with a big army truck thirty feet away. By his very presence on the dock, it seemed that he was a volunteer for whatever had to be done next.

There were many like him. One could recognize a stevedore easily enough; but the meagre dock gangs were outnumbered by all sorts of other people: men in business suits, children who should have been in school, soldiers, Capuchin friars, people whom he knew to be farmers, stallholders, loafers: all banded together in an effort to empty the *Welshman* and get her on her way again.

When he asked the man next in line to him how this had happened, the reply was a shrug. "They say there was something on the wireless, but I didn't hear it. I was sitting on the edge of the dock when that man—" he pointed across the quay—"said: 'Come on, you. Give a hand.' So I did."

Father Salvatore looked at "that man". He was a soldier, in khaki trousers and a shirt with the sleeves rolled up: a man of middle age, energetic and straight-shouldered, with a ruddy face and a clipped military moustache, unloading cardboard cartons from a cargo-sling as it descended. There was something about

197

him which was familiar. The air of authority was unmistakable. People round him were doing what he told them to.

They worked for half an hour, and then the pace slackened and died. The loaded trucks were gone; the cranes fell silent: the cargo-hoists on board the *Welshman* produced nothing more. There was nothing but the stretching of weary arms and aching backs, and, for Father Salvatore, an astonishing encounter.

He was sitting on a bollard, staring at the ship, when a shadow fell between him and the pale sun. He turned, to find the commanding military man at his side.

"Thank you for helping us, Father. Jolly fine show all round. Set a good example. What? What?"

Father Salvatore got to his feet. "I was glad to help."

"We need every scrap of help we can find. This ship has been through all sorts of nonsense to get to Malta. Now it's our turn to see that the trip isn't wasted. What would the Navy think if a few Jerry bombers destroyed all their hard work before she was unloaded. What? What?"

Perhaps he always said "What? What?" and never expected a reply. But it still seemed necessary to make a contribution. "It's so good to see a ship at last. Do you know what she's brought?"

"Certainly! I can tell you exactly!" But he was interrupted. Another, much younger soldier approached, carrying a uniform tunic which was, astoundingly, neatly balanced on a coat-hanger. The great man took it and put it on. And he *was* a great man: the tunic had scarlet facings, gleaming emblems on the epaulettes, and such an array of medal ribbons that they seemed about to overflow the breast-pocket. It was now impossible not to recognize him. It was the man with all those names—the new Governor of Malta.

Lord Gort pulled his glittering tunic down, and straightened his shoulders. Father Salvatore, in his shabby black cassock, was almost childishly elated. How could they lose the war now?

"Now what was I saying?" the Governor went on. "Yes, the cargo . . . I can tell you *exactly*! What? What?" The silliness of "What? What?" could not cloak an astute intelligence, and a rat-trap memory as well. "Over a hundred R.A.F. ground-crew. Ninety-six spare Spitfire engines. Torpedoes. Anti-aircraft ammo.

Then, three hundred tons of flour. Powdered milk. Tinned milk.
Olive oil. Canned meat. Seed potatoes. A balance, you understand—something to eat, and something to fight with. I know it
doesn't sound a lot, but the important thing was to get it here, and
get it off the ship. And it was done! All ticketty-boo! Tell your
people that, will you, Father?"

"Yes, I will." But tell them what, exactly?

Lord Gort knew the answer to a puzzled subordinate face.
"Tell them, A—" he ticked the items off, with a stubby forefinger on the palm of his hand, "that fresh supplies have arrived.
Enough to keep us going till next time. Tell them, B, that there *will*
be a next time. Tell them, C, that when ships do get in, they have
to be unloaded. *Forthwith!* Self help! Don't you agree?"

"Yes," said Father Salvatore.

"Then tell your people."

WHEN FATHER SALVATORE reached the catacombs Nero was the
first to greet him, as a sacristan should. But tonight he was also
Nero the bridegroom, dressed in a tiny suit of evening tails, white
tie and waistcoat, glittering patent-leather pumps, and a top hat.

Where had such finery come from? From a circus? Surely there
could be no wedding outfitters who had a pair of tails to fit a body
three feet and nine inches high.

The strange figure capered towards him through the gloom of the
catacombs. "Dun Salv! Dun Salv! Welcome to the wedding! Thank
God you've arrived! We can't do without you tonight!"

"I'm late, I'm afraid," Father Salvatore answered. But he made
his voice sound reproving. Nero had obviously drunk more than
a glass or two already. Granted that this was his wedding day, it
was still impossible not to wish that he had kept himself in hand.

There were worse things to be regretted. Father Salvatore,
looking beyond his sacristan to the depths of the catacomb, was
forced to ask: "But Nero! What on earth is happening?"

He might well wonder. In the flickering yellow light which gave
shape to the great concourse of their cavern, there was nothing but
disorder: an uproar which could only be drunken, a constant
movement which seemed as mindless and destructive as sin itself.

Nero shrugged. "I know it's getting a bit rough, Dun Salv. But what can I do? They opened the wine cask, about an hour ago."

"They shouldn't have done that. It was for the feast afterwards. Why did you allow it?"

"I couldn't stop them. And you know how it is these days. Everyone's so miserable. Then they heard about the ship coming in, and they wanted to celebrate. You can't blame them. I even had a glass myself. Just for the nerves . . ." He straightened his back, and squared his shoulders. "How do you like my suit, Dun Salv?"

It was better to leave things as they were, until he could move about and establish control again. "It's very smart indeed, Nero. It looks just right. Where is Teresa? Has she arrived?"

"Hours ago. But she's still getting dressed." Nero giggled. "I wish I could watch."

"Now, Nero. . . . Was the veal loaf delivered?"

"Yes!" The dwarf's eyes shone afresh. "It's *beautiful*! You have been so good, Dun Salv. And so clever!"

"I hope no one has started eating *that*."

"Over my dead body! I hid it in your room, anyway. Behind the best cassock. Who would dare?" Nero stretched his small muscular arms. "What a day! To think that it has come at last!"

It had not come true without great trouble, and a ferocious tug of wills, and perhaps gross deceit.

The parents of Teresa Grima had been obstructive to the last. Pleading abject poverty, they had steadfastly refused their daughter a dowry. Even when the Baroness offered a handsome sum of money to solve the problem, they still would not give their consent. All the other difficulties remained.

Then, amazingly, the girl herself took a hand. For the first time she showed herself not only a spirited human being but a cunning strategist as well. Perhaps, at last, she had come to accept the fact that she was over thirty-two (instead of the official twenty-seven), ill-favoured, and by now firmly installed on a shelf from which no ordinary suitor would ever rescue her. Without preamble, Teresa told her mother that she had missed her last period. Mrs. Grima screamed her wrath, denounced Nero as a lascivious monster who should be locked up, and fainted dead away. But the shameful facts were far beyond what could be resisted, by any Maltese mother or father.

Father Salvatore, alerted to this terrible crisis, did not believe the story. It had been tried before, as, within the confessional, he knew at first hand. Indeed, when taxed with the crime, Nero denied it absolutely.

Mr. and Mrs. Grima duly gave their permission, but would not tolerate such a wedding in their own village. It would be ridiculous, as well as shameful. *If* Father Salvatore wanted to arrange it himself, and *if* the bishop gave a licence for a wedding in the catacombs, then that was the end of it. But the family would not attend, wherever it was held.

The noise and the rough behaviour abated slowly as Father Salvatore's presence was observed. He found, as usual, that it was enough for him to move about, to talk to some people, to frown at others, in order to restore harmony. Soon the catacombs would be worthy of the sacred hour.

When he returned from his long, slow circuit, it was to find Nero still elated, but less with wine than with a very strange piece of news. "Dun Salv! Your great friend, Monsignor Scholti! He's sitting over there with two other priests." Nero seemed ready to jump up and down with excitement. "It's quite a society wedding!"

There indeed, in a small upper gallery sat Bruno Scholti, flanked by two younger priests whom he knew by sight as assistants on the bishop's staff. The whole watchful trio was staring at him, across a space which, though quieter, was still confused and restless. Against his better judgment—for the visit was inexplicable— Father Salvatore waved and smiled. Scholti inclined his head in the smallest possible acknowledgment; then he looked away towards a corner behind the altar where some of the faithful were still rowdy. It could not have been a more studied rebuke if he had stood up and turned his back on the whole scene.

Very well. . . . If that was the way he wanted it. . . . Father Salvatore found himself first angry, then rebellious. This was his own catacomb. Guests were welcome. But this was a special occasion. It was not to be spoiled by sour faces, by a small inquisition sitting in judgment up there in the gallery. He had

done nothing wrong, and as for his people—well, they had behaved badly, for a short season, and now they would behave well again.

Then Teresa Grima made her entrance, a bulging figure advancing like a veritable tent of white satin, topped by an impenetrable gauzy veil. The accordion band struck up; people craned their necks; some even clapped. Nero, who had been calm, began to shake. The nuptial Mass began.

AN HOUR LATER the wedding feast was in full swing. The wine barrel gurgled incessantly; the food, to which all had contributed something, even if it was only a spoon or two of tomato paste, was being handed round and wolfed down throughout the catacombs; the noise had again grown overwhelming.

At the high table, Nero Cassar and his chosen wife, with Father Salvatore on his other side, sat perched above the company. Unveiled, Teresa Grima's face was as they all remembered it: heavy-featured, black-browed, sullen. To this the summer heat and foetid air had added a flaming colour and a light sweat. There were comments about this from round about. Father Salvatore could not help overhearing a nearby exchange: "She should have kept her veil on." "Never mind—he can put the pillow over it." Teresa must have heard it also. But nothing changed in her face or manner. She knows she is ugly, he thought. She lives with it. She knows that this marriage is a kind of joke. She lives with that also. Blessed are the meek—or better still, blessed are the humble brave.

Raucous cheers greeted the arrival of the golden-cased veal loaf, the most elegant item of food seen in the catacombs for many a long month. People crowded round as it was ceremonially cut: a slice to the bride, a slice to the groom, a slice to the *kappillan*: smaller helpings for the rest of the wedding party. The loaf disappeared, and the guests went back to the wine barrel.

Even this monster was growing hollow, as its legacy of merriment and unbuttoned licence multiplied. Father Salvatore knew that even he had drunk too much; the wine, strong, subtle and delicious, had wooed him from continence, and his exhaustion had welcomed it as an ally. The thought, by natural transfer, made him look up to the galleries again, towards Monsignor Scholti and his friends.

Since they had shown no wish to come down and join the feast, Father Salvatore had done nothing about inviting them. It would only have needed a sign from Scholti, and none had come. A glance upward made it crystal clear that none would come now.

On an impulse, he took up a bottle of wine, perhaps the last to be poured from the failing barrel, and went upstairs to meet them.

Though he came in good heart, bearing gifts, he had a glacial reception. Monsignor Scholti barely acknowledged his arrival, while the young priests stared at him as if *he* were the intruder, not they. But he did his best. "Bruno! How nice of you to come to our wedding! But why didn't you let me know? You could have joined us at the top table."

"We are perfectly comfortable here." Monsignor Scholti's cold glance rested on Father Salvatore for a moment, taking in all he wished to see, and then turned aside.

"Well, have some wine to drink to the happy pair. I think you'll like this. It's very good."

"Thank you, no. I will leave it for you."

"But I've had my share."

"Evidently. And so, I must say, has everyone else here."

"But it's a wedding!"

No answer was made. It had been a mistake to come, but Father Salvatore did not regret it. He said: "What a pity."

As he turned to leave, he heard Scholti's voice behind him. "It is indeed a pity. This has all been *most* irregular."

Downstairs once more, he found that it was time for the bridal pair to leave. There was a truck outside the main entrance, waiting to bear them away to a cousin's house. He went with them to the doorway. Under a starry sky, in the cool of a May night, he blessed them, and said farewell. . . . Nero hung back after Teresa had climbed up. He seemed suddenly depressed. Father Salvatore sought for words of comfort, and unexpectedly found them. "There's one thing I want to say, Nero. As a friend. Treat Teresa gently. Remember how strong you are."

I'm glad I said that, he thought, as he groped his way back into the catacombs. The look of sudden pride, sudden confidence, on Nero's face had been a joy to see. . . .

Standing within the close-packed concourse again, his head slightly muzzy, he was assailed by something most surprising—an almost complete silence. The people had been waiting for him; for some reason they were watching to see what he would do next.

He walked up to the high table, and found it deserted. As he faced the main body of the room, a voice called out: "Tell us a story, Dun Salv! The wine's finished, and we can't all take the bride to bed!"

An impulse made him look up to the side gallery again; to meet the disapproving eyes of Monsignor Scholti. As their glances locked Scholti began to shake his head from side to side.

It was enough. Not all his rebellious thoughts returned, but sufficient to clinch a resolve. Scholti was only there to spy on him. Was this the act of a man of God?

Very well . . . He would show them what *real* priests had done, and *real* people, in days just as fearful as these. . . . He took up the last glass of wine, drained it defiantly and began to speak.

HEXAMERON V

A.D. 1798 Tyrant, Priest, and Frigate Captain

"I have not spoken to you for two hundred and thirty years," he began. It was an extraordinary start, and it caught their attention instantly; not least the attention of Monsignor Scholti, who exchanged glances with his companion priests before bending forward to listen. "During those two hundred and thirty years, from the time of La Valette to the time of Napoleon, Malta grew and prospered. However, the Grand Masters, and their Knights with them, had decayed fatally. They had nothing to do, except bicker about fancied insults and quarrel over minuscule points of precedence." Here he looked up at Monsignor Scholti, in a manner direct and certainly imprudent, so that many other eyes followed his. "It was a life of white-gloved ceremonial, of soft living, of the worst of murders—the killing of time. The Knighthood of Malta had run its course, and was ripe for the scrapyard of history. The

villain of the tragedy was to be Napoleon Bonaparte who, at the age of twenty-nine, had already made himself the master of most of Europe, and whose dream was now that of Alexander the Great: the mastership of half the world. For a start, he must conquer Egypt and then India. But at the moment the island of Malta, in the narrows of the Middle Sea, stood in his way. . . .

IN COMMAND OF THE ISLAND was Grand Master Ferdinand von Hompesch, a man ready-made for Napoleon to topple. The last, and feeblest of the line, flabby, irresolute, and unpopular, plagued by his idle quarrelsome Knights, he dithered while others acted.

But there was a worse infection among his Knights than unemployment. There was treason.

The French Revolution, eight years earlier, had turned Europe upside down; and the Order of the Knights, who looked to Europe for money, moral and political support, had been up-ended with it. The French *langue*, those privileged aristocrats, woke up one morning to find their titles and rights abolished, and all the property of the Order, in France and Italy, confiscated.

This bad news was brought by a flood of refugees who now found their way to Malta, followed by other visitors: certain odious agents of despair, intriguers, spies; within months these had formed inside the citadel a fifth column of collaborators who penetrated to the very heart of the Order. Their message, slipped into every conversation, hammered home in every argument, was simple, persuasive, and disabling: "Make a deal with Napoleon. He is coming to take your island away. Resist him, and you will lose all, including your lives."

Among the Knights, the talk grew free. The more they talked, the less they wished to withstand the great fraternity of progress, and Napoleon presently judged, from the reports of his professionals, that he had enough friends within Malta to weaken its defences and poison its courage. He sailed from Toulon with over four hundred ships.

Another voyager, more seamanlike than Napoleon or any man in the world, stood in his way: Nelson, the admiral with "one eye, one arm, and one ambition". At forty he was older, physically more battered; but his string of victories and brave endeavours stretched from Corsica to Cape St. Vincent, from Toulon to Santa Cruz; and they could be etched as big upon the blue sea as were Napoleon's campaigns on the brown earth of Europe. Now, with his flag hoisted on the *Vanguard*, Nelson was scouring the Mediterranean, looking for the French armada.

In this endeavour he made one bad guess, relying on false news that Napoleon had by-passed Malta and was making for Alexandria. He chased a phantom fleet, carried on too long, and then doubled back too late. Napoleon was not in the eastern Mediterranean. He was anchored in Grand Harbour, his troops already ashore.

Even given the cunning preparation, it had been shamefully easy. On the afternoon of 9 June, look-out men, posted on the eastern heights of the island, reported a total of 472 sails, led by Napoleon's flagship, *L'Orient*, spread out just north of Valletta.

A French pinnace sped ashore, carrying a request from Napoleon to the Grand Master, couched in peremptory terms, for permission to enter the harbour and take on water. Hompesch chose the only course of valour; he called a committee meeting.

With one eye on the enemy fleet and the other on their own unmanned defences, the Knights laboured to produce the soft answer which the Grand Master insisted was all that could be sent. "With the greatest sorrow", the French request was refused. They ventured to remind Napoleon that the Treaty of Utrecht had declared Malta a neutral port, and that the statutes of their Order did not allow them to admit more than four belligerent ships at any one time.

In reply, Napoleon exercised the tyrant's traditional gambit of flying into a rage when frustrated. "They refused me water!" he shouted, as if he were some pitiful parched child in the middle of the Sahara. "Such barbarians! This means war!"

The same night, his troops landed simultaneously at four different, well-calculated points. There was hardly any opposition. By 8 a.m. the whole coastline was occupied; by noon the old capital, Mdina, was in enemy hands. Gozo took a little longer, until Fort Chambray succumbed to bombardment by battleship. There was also some stalwart resistance from the Cottonera Lines.

But within twenty-four hours the Grand Master had sent a deputation to the flagship *L'Orient*, asking for the French attacks to cease, and at midday on 11 June Napoleon's senior aide-de-camp rode up the road to Valletta to dictate the terms of surrender.

The Knights signed away every vestige of their sovereignty. They might retain only their religion, and their private possessions. Grand Master Hompesch, however, could enjoy his "military honours", together with a notably golden handshake: an annual pension of 300,000 francs.

The next day, with French troops lining the whole of Valletta, Napoleon walked up Merchants Street to the Parisio Palace. It was the morning of 12 June, 1798: one of his shorter campaigns—fifty hours.

Napoleon set up his headquarters in the Palace. From there he set to work, in the six days he was to be on the island, to turn Malta into an orderly department of the French Republic.

French was declared the official language. The population must sport red-white-and-blue cockades. The Palace Square became the *Place de la Liberté*. All armorial bearings were torn down, and all Maltese declared "equal in rights". Malta and Gozo were to be administered under a brand-new constitution.

Grand Master Hompesch, and such of his Knights as might be dangerous, were given three days to leave. Every town and village was garrisoned. Taxes were laid on every common commodity, from bread to candles, to meet the cost of this occupation.

Maltese sailors were press-ganged into the French fleet, and their families left to starve. Religious marriages were declared illegal; and when this was protested, further stern rules were laid on all ecclesiastics. The bishop was ordered to call a meeting of Maltese clergy, and Napoleon himself addressed them, with a nice blend of ironic courtesy and blatant threat: "Reverend gentlemen, preach the gospel, respect the constituted authorities, and recommend submission and obedience to your people. If you are good priests, I shall protect you; if you are bad priests, I shall punish you."

Napoleon hardly gave them time to digest this homily before he began a systematic plundering of all church and civic property in

Malta. Gold, silver, and precious stones were all poured piecemeal into a huge "Army chest". The most exquisite silver plate, two hundred years old, was melted down. Pictures and tapestries were rolled up, and packed like stage properties. The whole of the plunder, which included the gates of Valletta Cathedral, was then loaded on board the giant three-decker flagship, in time for Napoleon to keep his next appointment, which was with Egypt.

At the head of his enormous fleet he sailed before Nelson could catch him. As a final calculated blasphemy, he allowed the church to keep its most revered relic, the right hand of St. John the Baptist, brought from Rhodes nearly three hundred years earlier. But before returning it he pulled off its precious ring, crowning his brief tyranny with an atrocious tyrant's joke: "The hand is yours. But the ring suits mine much better!"

THE FRENCH FLEET reached Egypt undetected, and there it disembarked Napoleon and his army, who marched away to attack and take Alexandria. Then his warships—thirteen battleships and four frigates—sailed further east up the coast and anchored in Aboukir Bay, near the Rosetta mouth of the Nile.

There they thought themselves protected by the rocks and shoals guarding the entrance. They were thus relaxed, half their crews ashore filling water barrels, when Nelson came upon them. It was the evening of the first day of August.

He led his squadron of twelve ships, without charts and near nightfall, straight into the bay. In the course of the night action, fought with the greatest courage on both sides, the British fleet sank, crippled, or captured thirteen out of the seventeen French, without a single loss to themselves.

The last ship to go down was *L'Orient*, the 120-gun pride of the fleet. She had spent the day painting ship; thus she was readily set on fire, and served as a torch for the whole battlefield. Towards midnight, under an August moon, she blew up, with a shattering roar heard twenty miles away in Alexandria, taking to the bottom every scrap of her Maltese loot. Though the loss to Malta had been terrible, the swift punishment had matched it.

At the end of August, the survivors of this Battle of the Nile limped back into Grand Harbour: one battleship and two frigates (the fourth French ship to escape had sailed elsewhere). The Maltese watched them in amazement, and then in mutinous speculation. Was this all that was left of the invincible armada?

During the ten weeks since the tyrant had left the island, General Vaubois, installed as Commander-in-Chief of Malta, had continued his master's rule. Malta was under his yoke, and was made to feel it every day. Yet Vaubois was "affable", and a diplomatic phrase-maker of some note; so when the three French ships returned to harbour, he announced that Napoleon had scored a tremendous series of triumphs in Egypt, "only marred by a slight mishap to the fleet". But the smooth tongue could not mask the repressive acts. And, on the very day that the bruised rump of the French fleet returned, there was a further proclamation. All remaining church property was to be auctioned off. The process would start with a sale of tapestry and valuables in the Carmelite convent church of Mdina, on 2 September—a Sunday.

Something must be done. But who could act, who could lead? The Knights were scattered. Hompesch had retired to Trieste. The answer was no one—no one but themselves.

On the morning of the auction, huge crowds began to converge upon Mdina and the Carmelite church. They could not all be buyers. . . . Those of them who were able to push their way into the church found it transformed into a disgraceful circus: a cheap market place of stolen goods.

In charge were two auctioneers, men of some position, known to the crowd: Notary Allessandro Spiteri and Giuseppe Farrugia. Notary Spiteri, knowing the contempt he aroused, stepped forward and put upon this charade the best face he could. "By order of General Vaubois, Commander-in-Chief of the occupation forces. . . ." He read the French proclamation, in a matter-of-fact voice. Then he said: "Now. . . . A number of red curtains . . . what am I offered?"

A priest standing in the forefront of the crowd called out loudly: "No!"

Notary Spiteri, doing his duty as he saw it, persisted: "I am asking for bids for these curtains."

210

The priest repeated, in the same voice of shock and disgust: "No! It is sacrilege! Let no one offer money."

The crowd moved forward menacingly. Spiteri was a comfortable family man with a good heart. In the face of bitter resentment which he could understand, he fell silent. His companion Farrugia tried to intervene. "Keep silence. . . . Let us have order. . . . This is an official sale—"

He was interrupted by the sheer pressure of bodies, forcing their way up to the altar which had become a common auctioneer's rostrum, a place of no account. The noise of the crowd, which had been a low-pitched growl, rose to a howl of anger. Notary Spiteri gave up. "The auction is postponed," he shouted, and dived for the side door.

Though both he and Farrugia were roughed up by the crowd, they managed to escape to the headquarters of Citizen-Colonel Masson, commandant of the Mdina garrison, and told him their story. When, next morning, Colonel Masson rode out, he rode headlong into disaster.

It was thought that he planned to summon reinforcements from the Valletta garrison, to disperse the crowds and force the auction through. He and his escort were followed downhill from Mdina by a crowd, howling insults and pressing in on the soldiers. But it was a small boy who triggered the final explosion—a small boy with a well-aimed pebble.

Sailing through the air from behind a wall, it hit Colonel Masson on the bridge of his prominent nose. While the crowd roared their delight, Masson drew his sword, and made as if to jump the wall and ride the boy down.

As the spectators screamed in anger, Masson lost his nerve, whipped his horse round, and galloped back to the citadel. But he had made too many enemies. Chased through the narrow streets by a howling mob, he took refuge in the house of Notary Bezzina. The doors were battered down, and the mob surged in; within minutes, a balcony window above was flung open, and Colonel Masson's body, sailing through the air like the pebble, landed with a crash on the cobbled street. The priest who ran forward and knelt beside him was too late to catch his soul.

In the next twenty-four hours the entire garrison of Mdina was hunted down and slaughtered, and their corpses burned in public. There could be no turning back now. The bells began to ring all over the island, from St. Paul's Bay to the Three Cities. The priests called, the people answered; and their courage flowered like a blood-red clover-field under the surge of spring.

The rebellion spread, and a ring closed round Valletta, as the French were driven into the city, or pushed out into the sea, or killed in flight. Presently, the ring was tight, and the invaders penned up in the capital with the Maltese patriots screaming for their blood before the bastions.

By now the sea approaches to Malta were blockaded by a particular friend of Nelson's, one of the gifted and daring "band of brothers" who so brilliantly commanded the ships of his fleet.

Captain Alexander Ball of the 74-gun *Alexander*, with two frigates, a sloop, and a fire-ship, had arrived to support from seawards what the Maltese were doing on land: strangling the French.

It took a long time. Vaubois was brave and determined. He refused two demands for surrender, one from Captain Ball, one from Nelson himself. He was always polite; once, even at the last extreme, he replied: "You would no more expect me to dishonour my country by surrender, than I would expect you to fail in your own duty. . . ."

Ball now gave the land-fighters such encouragement, and made so many friends, that the Maltese civil government sent constant appeals to have him named as their "protector" under the British flag. It was something for the hopeful future. But there was always Valletta the fortress, and Vaubois the valiant defender, standing in the way. Five British ships could not maintain a cast-iron blockade. Four thousand British and Maltese soldiers—Maltese by nearly three to one—could not storm the bastions nor tempt the enemy to a pitched battle.

Presently another Maltese patriot, another priest, tried something else: a plot.

It was a daring plot: certain Maltese within the citadel should, at an agreed moment, ring the church bells, open the gates, and let the attackers into Valletta. Three men were involved as leaders: outside the city, Canon Caruana of the Provisional Civil Government; inside Valletta, the man who had conceived this valiant stroke, Father Michael Xerri, whom his faithful friends knew as Dun Mikiel; and the third, Guglielmo Lorenzi, who was to trigger the attack and unlock the city gates.

There was a gala performance at the Manoel Theatre that night. A gala performance during a cruel siege? Why not? No Frenchman worth the name would tolerate a life which was *all* starvation and disease and despair. The bright lights beckoned, and death could take at least an evening's holiday.

But there had been too much plot-talk. Not every man-at-arms was at the Manoel Theatre that night; important commanders remained on the alert. Movements inside and outside the city were noted. Certain curfew-breakers on their way to a mysterious rendezvous were detained. At the appointed hour, the bells did not ring, the guards were not overcome, the gates were not opened, and the enterprise collapsed before a single blow could be struck.

In the cold dawn, a terrible *post mortem* began. Lorenzi refused to betray his accomplices, and died in that defiance. But mute courage was no shield for men whose names had been whispered for weeks in cellars, behind doors thought to be closed. Forty-five conspirators were rounded up, among them Dun Mikiel, and after a brief court martial they were condemned to be shot.

A moment of glory lightened a desolate scene. Dun Mikiel, who felt the guilt of a leader whose followers now had to pay the supreme penalty, did not beg for mercy. Instead, he spoke calmly to the commander of the execution squad.

"Shoot me last of all," he said. His only wish was to comfort his companions. "Grant us a few moments of prayer. I will give you the order to fire."

The French officer agreed. On such a bleak morning, who could have a stomach for this task? Dun Mikiel moved among his friends, confessing, absolving, loving. When his fortitude had become theirs, he walked forward, and gave his silver watch to the French commander. "In memory of today," he said. "You may fire now."

When the echo of the volley ceased, Dun Mikiel walked back, and stood among the ring of forty-four bloody corpses. Then he nodded, and embraced his own death with courage, bright as flame.

THOUGH THE BRAVE PLOT failed, Vaubois was also failing. There was a limit to endurance, even for such a resolute commander. No food, no men, could now come to the aid of the citadel, following two great sea engagements which removed from the scene the last two French battleships in the Mediterranean, with Alexander Ball and Horatio Nelson sharing the honours.

The Maltese and British troops closed in. Broken at last after more than two years, reduced to bread and water, refusing to eat rats even for the honour of French arms, Vaubois marched out of his citadel, and Captain Alexander Ball marched in.

The cry of the Maltese was still: "Give us British rule! Give us Captain Ball!", and he was confirmed as Civil Commissioner

of Malta, in 1802. He set up house in San Anton Palace, and there
he worked for eight devoted years; and there he died.

He would have been the first to say that he had only built on
what the Maltese themselves began.

In Limbo

In his borrowed cell, Father Salvatore lay back, and stared at
the ceiling, or where the ceiling would be when the dawn light
gained a little. Shuffling sandalled feet outside told him that the
brothers were assembling for Mass. He was excused from this. He
was excused from everything. He was a guest, and the world—even
the monastery world—let him go by without comment.

The world might stare at him a little, and speculate, and perhaps
even condemn. But it did not say anything out loud. He was a guest
of the Capuchins. He was important. He was nothing. He was two
weeks old, or dead for a thousand years. He was Father Salvatore,
the famed *kappillan* of the catacombs.

THE INTERVIEW with the bishop had been short and, for so gentle
an old man, sharp. He was to leave the catacombs, and go into
retreat in Gozo. He would be notified when he might return.

Father Salvatore, sitting upright on what must be the hardest
chair in the palace, a chair of true penitence, might pretend to
be surprised, but he was not. When he asked "Why?" with due
respect, he knew the answer—all the answers.

"I spoke to you before about this, Salvu." They were still
father and son, but the son had erred, and the father was telling
him so. "Quite apart from the bad behaviour on the night in
question, which was perhaps understandable, there is your own
role. I warned you that this should not enlarge *you*, rather than
the faith. A priest is not to be applauded when he speaks to his
people. . . . He is not to make himself a popular hero, poking fun
at authority. . . . Above all, he is not to take pride in war, in the

215

military activities of other priests, however brave. Our faith is the faith of the Prince of Peace. . . ." The old man's face was grave; there would be no appeal from what was to come. "When we last met, I said: 'Search your conscience.' I do not believe you have done so."

Father Salvatore said nothing. It was all too true to be denied: biased in a certain measure, as the Church itself was biased towards strict observance of the faith, but true.

"I have come to the conclusion," said the kind, stern old man, "that you are tired, overstrained. I may say that your mother feels the same. . . . Please understand that we are your friends. One might even say, admirers, in a certain sense. But there comes a time when friends must speak out, and admirers must examine what they are admiring. After that, the Church which we both love and serve demands one thing more—obedience."

He agreed, and kissed the ring, and withdrew from audience. Monsignor Scholti did not make an appearance.

Father Salvatore had kissed the ring in true humility, but he could have wept, he could have raged. What happened to him was nothing; what happened to his people, everything. Was it pride which made him think: How can they survive without me? Or was it plain fact? He could not stay to find out.

What made it unbearable was that he knew in his heart that the bishop was right. He had used the words "tired" and "overstrained"; they were both true. Lately Father Salvatore had caught himself in a fit of giddiness as he clambered up the steep steps of the catacombs. Furthermore, nowadays he never felt like eating. Fanciful and sweating dreams robbed many of his nights of their healing promise. The war had become a grinding, monstrous, *personal* yoke clamped across his shoulders, and not even faith could make it lighter.

Someone else had noticed his ordeal; someone sharp-eyed, and dear to him, and traitorous. In farewell, his small despairing mother said: "I am sorry, Salvatore. Don't blame me. Don't be bitter. You *are* tired, exhausted. You *do* need rest. . . . If you go on like this, you will kill yourself! . . . What could I do but agree?" He left her wordless, as he had left the bishop.

He dressed, and waited for the knock on his cell door; and the knock came at six o'clock, as punctual as the sun, as predictable as the bell for the first Mass. It was Brother Ninu, the friar who served him, and seemed to love him; a man whose simple heart would have put any rebellious priest to shame.

Brother Ninu was small, and rather fat—all the brothers seemed fat, on a diet of bread and *pasta* which never varied. He was also earnest and enthusiastic, gullible and kind, ready to laugh at the joys of the world, apt to weep for its cruelty. Now he put his head round the door, smiled his good-morning, and brought in breakfast.

Breakfast was coffee—of a sort—and bread which the brothers baked for themselves, a dab of precious jam, and a peach from Brother Ninu's own small orchard. While Father Salvatore ate, Brother Ninu tidied the cell, and talked, and seemed to enjoy the answers as if they were pearls of revelation.

"Are you rested, Dun Salv? Did you have a good sleep?"

"A very good sleep, thank you."

"That's wonderful! When you first came here, I said to myself: 'There is a man who is *really* tired.' Isn't that true?"

"I was tired, yes."

"But a few more days or weeks, and you will be better than ever!" Brother Ninu was looking at something on the shelf at the head of the bed, just below the crucifix. He reached out his hand, then thought better of it. "Dun Salv? Can I ask a favour?"

"You want to see the relics, Ninu?"

"*Yes!*" The friar's eyes brightened wonderfully: he looked just as ready to laugh as to cry, and both for joy. "You did say you would show me one day. Is this a good time?"

"I think so. . . . Will you take them down for me?"

"Can I *really*?" And, with the most reverent hands Father Salvatore could ever remember watching, Ninu lifted the shabby old case from the shelf, and put it gently down on the cot. Then he laced his fingers together as if in prayer, and waited.

The case lay between them on the blanket. With a whisper of devotion which he must have uttered a thousand times, Father Salvatore raised the polished mahogany lid, to show the garnering, the prizes, of a lifetime's faith, belief, and adoration. They were under a glass cover, and he could point to each one, as it rested in its small compartment, and explain it to Brother Ninu, and tell where he had bought it or been given it—in Rome, in Rhodes, in Crete, one on the never-to-be-forgotten pilgrimage to Jerusalem. Brother Ninu listened, and stared, as if miracles were unfolding under his very eyes.

There was a tiny fragment of cloth labelled "*Ex Velo S. Veronicae*"—the very veil of Saint Veronica, with which she had wiped the sweat from Christ's face on the road to Calvary. There was a sliver of grey-black wood, *Ex Vero Ligno*—from the True Cross. There was a faded grey speck upon a piece of parchment, on which was written *Latte della Beatissima Vergine*—the Milk of the Blessed Virgin. There was the greatest prize, the holiest of all: another splinter of wood, with the awesome title: *Cunis Dom. Nost. Jesu Christi*—the Cradle of our Lord Jesus Christ.

Father Salvatore sat back, while Brother Ninu continued his rapturous examination of these treasures. He sat back, and suddenly, in an awful avalanche of doubt and shame, he found that he did not believe a word of what he had said and shown. Cynical thoughts flooded in like a sewage tide. A veil that had wiped off the sweat of Christ? Who could possibly believe that? A piece of the True Cross? There must be enough of those for all the standing timber on the Mount of Olives. The Virgin's milk—what rude member of the family had collected *that*? A piece of the cradle of Christ? There had once been a manger in a cowshed in Bethlehem. Had it had a preservation order slapped on it by the Jewish Office of Works, in A.D.1?

He felt sick unto death. He had believed in all these things for so long. Now they could only be lies, tourist trash, a brisk line of goods for the hucksters who waylaid the faithful. He felt a sweat breaking out on his own brow. My turn, Veronica . . . The cell was now stifling, the odour of sanctity worse than a cesspit's.

Brother Ninu, looking up from his adoration, noticed the change. "Dun Salv! Are you all right?"

"I feel a little faint, Ninu. I think it's the heat. Will you ask the *Gwardjan* if I can see him?"

"Immediately!"

But when Father Salvatore saw the head of the monastery, it was not to seek his help. It was to say that he was going to interrupt his retreat.

For the *Gwardjan*, an old monk with sad brown eyes, this was his first real dilemma for many years. It had never proved difficult to control a flock which was not high on the church's tables of precedence, but Father Salvatore was not only a famous man, but technically his superior, and Father Salvatore seemed very determined, even desperate, for private reasons which the *Gwardjan* hesitated to probe. Conversely, the bishop had hinted— no, it was Monsignor Scholti who had hinted—that his retreat was in some sense a disciplinary matter. Yet it was a great honour to have him here, and he must certainly be humoured. And then there was always his mother. The Most Noble Baroness had long been a generous benefactor of the church.

The *Gwardjan* temporized. "Believe me, I do understand. Life here must seem very confined. Perhaps a daily walk in the gardens?"

It was not an acceptable answer. Father Salvatore wanted to leave his retreat for some days. How many, he could not say. He felt that he *must* have freedom, a space for the soul to breathe. He feared—he truly feared—that unless he left his cell, and wandered at will, he would choke, or be poisoned by his own evil thoughts. Lord, I do believe. Help Thou my unbelief.

"Brother, I *must* go. Today."

"Very well. I will see if I can telephone the bishop. I will have to ask his permission. I'm sure you will appreciate that."

While this was being done, Father Salvatore collected his small store of money, and made a parcel of some spare socks, an undershirt, a razor and his breviary. Before the *Gwardjan* could relay the bishop's answer, Father Salvatore had walked past a dozing gatekeeper, and gone on down the hill to Marsalforn—and into blessed liberty.

Gozo was different. He had forgotten how different; he had forgotten its simplicity and peace. This was his haven, his new-found paradise.

A half-day's walk to Marsalforn was to become a walk round the whole island. It was a time between seasons. The last of the onions had been picked; the purple grapes were fattening; pumpkins lay large and yellowing, while the clover ricks were turning black in a valley burnt dry and bleached as old bones. But already hopeful men were attacking the soil again, forcing it towards its next harvest.

Father Salvatore's aching tiredness, his self-disgust, gently vanished. He refused to think, only to feel. He found a beach with a tiny patch of sand. On an impulse, he bent down and took off his boots. Then he stepped barefoot into the water, and began to paddle like a boy. The touch of the warm seawater on his liberated feet was delicious. He hitched up his cassock and waded out till the water reached his knees. What bliss! What heavenly happiness! Within an hour of loosing the monastery's grip, and retreating from his shameful thoughts, he had become free.

HE SLEPT THAT NIGHT at the priest's house in Gharb: a priest surprised to see him, but glad of the news he brought of the world outside. Then he moved on, walking the rim of the island. The days passed: sometimes he slept rough, sometimes he found a friend, once he bedded down in a police cell, which had not been used since 1931.

No one followed him; no one seemed to care who he was. They might stare; perhaps they talked afterwards; but here his cassock was enough. He was a priest. Perhaps he was looking for somebody.

He was looking for nothing; for no one, not even himself. The briny smell of the sea, the scorched smell of the earth, were all he wanted from Gozo. It was still, blessedly, a time to feel, and not to think at all.

There came a day when he had to buy bread, and he walked into San Lawrenz. The main street was quiet, and shuttered against the sun; but on the shady side a few women sat at their front doors, facing inward according to custom, and hooked lace on worn wooden bobbins which had been old in their grandmothers' day.

Lace-making was a hallowed trade, in Malta and Gozo both. He remembered reading that Queen Victoria, to encourage the industry, had once ordered sixteen dozen pairs of mittens, and a scarf. . . . One-hundred-and-ninety-two mittens, and *one* scarf? He would never understand kings and queens.

The people seemed glum. Of course, it was hot, and there was the war and the poor food, and a dusty priest plodding up the street was not very interesting. Only once did he have a proper smile, from a girl who turned from her front door and her lace-making, and greeted him. She was perhaps thirty, but still lively and pretty, a young boy on the doorstep beside her, a baby in a wooden box at her feet. Clearly she was busy, but not too busy for a stranger, even a stranger in a cassock.

He bought a loaf—priests didn't seem to need bread-coupons in San Lawrenz—and a little wicker basket of sheep's cheese, at a shop in the shadow of the church. Then, walking back up the road, he was attracted by sound and movement in a nearby field.

The sound was the chuff-and-chug of an old steam threshing-machine, and the movement the teamwork of a gang of twenty harvesters, old men and boys. Dust was everywhere, surrounding the thresher with a choking yellow cloud, floating away across the valley. Every man, every boy, though stripped to the waist, was pouring with sweat. But the work went on without a pause. After this field there would be the next one, and threshing time was short.

There was one figure who stood out from the working team. The sheaves were being carried up a ladder to the top of the machine. But one man, one huge man, disdained to use it. He, and only he, could hoist and toss a sheaf up with a single heave. Waiting his chance, this giant turned away to spit the dust from his throat, and then stretched his stiff neck.

It was Rafel Vella.

Father Salvatore and Rafel caught sight of each other at the same moment. The *kappillan* stood with a smile as the giant let out a great shout, and ran forward, and dropped onto his knees to kiss his hand, and then rose to embrace him.

"Dun Salv!" Rafel could not believe it. "*Bongu, bongu!* Bless me, for the love of God!"

"*Tkun imbierck.*" Father Salvatore loosed himself from the huge embrace, and stood back. "Rafel. . . . How well you are looking."

221

After the emotion of the first greeting, Rafel was suddenly embarrassed, as if he remembered more of the past than he wanted to. "Have you come to find me, Dun Salv?"

"No, it was just by chance."

"Have you come for the *festa*, then?"

"No. Is it your *festa* today?"

"This evening. But *why* are you in San Lawrenz, Dun Salv?"

"Just a little holiday."

"Ah . . . good, good. If anybody in the world deserves one. . . . Are you still angry with me?"

"I was never angry, Rafel. I was very sad you had to go."

"And I was so ashamed. . . . But please understand. I had to get away."

"I know."

They talked a little more, and then some grumbling in the background recalled Rafel to his duty.

"Dun Salv, I must get back to the machine, or they won't pay me. But please come to the *festa*. Five o'clock. I'll tell my mother, and you can have something to eat with us afterwards."

IT WAS A POOR, sad little *festa*, and no one could pretend otherwise. There were no fireworks, no bells, no flickering torches: no band playing on the *pjazza*, hardly any drinking—wine was hard to come by—and no *pasti* to be wolfed at the end of a long happy day. The statue of Saint Lawrence was lifted from his pedestal, and borne through the village streets, and carried up the steps and into the church. That was all—a bare hour of devotion, and no fun.

Once again, the only smiling and generous face seemed to belong to the lace-making girl in black. She stood alone as she watched the saint's progress, but seemed ready to share her enjoyment with anyone who would catch her eye.

Walking back from a *pjazza* now sinking into gloomy shadow, reassuring Rafel about the *festa* ("But it *was* good. I would not have missed it for the world!") Father Salvatore asked him who she was.

The giant was not at all complimentary. "Oh, *that* one. Maddelena something—I can't remember the name. If she *has* a name, which we doubt." The "we" was especially telling. Rafel now spoke as a pillar of the San Lawrenz establishment. "She came into a bit of money from an uncle—if he *was* an uncle—so there she lives, within fifty yards of the church, and there's nothing to be done about it. Two children."

"But where is her husband?"

"What husband? You should hear mother talking about her!"

Father Salvatore heard plenty from mother during the course of the evening. She had no good word for anyone or anything, and when Rafel mentioned Maddelena, she pounced like a harpy, and the Great Whore of Babylon seemed to enter the room, lie down, and spread her loathsome wares for all to see.

Much as he loved Rafel, Father Salvatore found that he could not stay long. He took his leave, embraced and blessed his friend on the doorstep, and went off down the street.

As the door closed, and the bolt slammed, he heard old Mrs. Vella begin, once more, a long and bitter monologue on the sins and omissions of every other person in the world.

HE AWOKE AT DAWN, stiff and cold, on a clover rick on a little slip of land perched above the sea. Bad dreams had assailed him: the noise of the sea was restless, unceasing; but his exhausted body prevailed. By the time he was fully awake, it was halfway to sunrise, and he had slept for seven hours.

The sun came up, putting a sparkle on the sea and deep shadows on the cliffs all round him; and with the sun came the wind. Soon he was finding it difficult to breathe. This was a *sirocco* wind, a hot wind howling out of Africa, bringing with it a dust storm, a myriad tiny particles of sand ripped up from the desert and blown two hundred miles across the sea to plague Malta.

It was in his eyes, his nose and mouth, everywhere. He got up, and groped his way towards some sort of cover, anything which would give him relief and a chance to fill his lungs. The wind howled, and tore at his cassock, as he crept among the rocks, blindly seeking shelter in the whirling gloom. Presently he found a crack in the cliffs near the seashore, and clambered inside.

There had been a hymn which his father used sometimes to sing

at home. It had a noble tune, with words to match. "*Rock of ages, cleft for me*", Commander Westgate-Saul was wont to sing when he was shaving, or when he stopped reading the newspaper, or when he was happy: "*Let me hide myself in thee*". The idea of his father needing to hide himself anywhere was ridiculous. But now his son was hiding in a rock, cleft by God for him.

The choking feeling which had assailed him at the monastery, and again in Rafel's house, returned in full strength. Now at last, at this foul moment of his life, in a hot roaring sandstorm, he was being forced to think instead of to feel.

He clung to the side of the cave in terror. All his terrible thoughts, his jeering relic thoughts, flooded in again. Moment by moment, he seemed to be growing unfit to be a priest.

He doubted all things, silly things, sacred things, scraps of the faith by which he had lived for forty years. He suddenly thought, for no reason at all, of the Last Supper. Had it really been such a solemn festival, with wine which turned to blood for the next two thousand years?

It wasn't like that at all. It was a marvellous Man who knew that he must die, taking leave of his friends and raising his goblet at the end of a cheerful evening, and telling them: "Don't forget— when I'm gone, have a drink on me."

It was not Jesus, but his Church that was in love with death. Birth, life, and hope on earth were made to sound unimportant. Why? It was all wrong. *Jesus was not like that.*

Christ loved life. He came to teach *living* hope and love on earth: not the ceremonial worship of death. Would he have loved a rich church? Gorgeous vestments? Bishops in solemn sanctimonious procession, graciously allowing a jewelled ring to be kissed? Never! He would have called out: "Here come the rascals! Watch your purses!" He would have given the prelates as rough a time as he gave the Pharisees.

This was awful, rebellious, blasphemous, degrading. . . . But Father Salvatore could not stop the impious tide of thought. Perhaps he was already mad. . . .

The wind and the sandstorm blew very hard for most of that day, while Father Salvatore crouched in his cave, sometimes close to the mercy of unconsciousness, sometimes waking to the abject terror of his degradation.

Then, towards evening, as so often happened in this turbulent sea, the wind dropped and with the passing of the storm, some of Father Salvatore's own peace returned, and his thoughts, like the waves trapped in the bay below, retreated from their curling spite to mere tumbled confusion.

At sunset he rose and went to the cave's entrance, kicking aside the drifting sand, and stood looking down at the bay. This was peace at last: peace for the world, if not for him. Drained of everything except fear and self-disgust, hungry but not deserving to eat, he waited for the sun to quench itself in the sea, and then went inside the cave again, and dropped on his knees.

But prayer would not come, and he knew why: words without heart could never reach heaven. For the second night, exhausted sleep—the coward's relief—came to his rescue.

THE BOY WHO ARRIVED at sunrise was a cheerful whistling boy, and his passage across the rocks to the mouth of the cave was not at all silent. Father Salvatore waited in the half-darkness of his refuge until the hesitant summons came. "Dun Salv? Are you there?"

He called back, and came out. They met at the mouth of the cave. It was Maddelena's son. The boy, who carried a fishing-rod and a little sack on his shoulder, was smiling up at him, with a touch of wonder in his face. Father Salvatore smiled back.

"*Bongornu*. How do you know my name?"

"I asked Rafel," the boy answered. "I am Ganni."

"How did you know I was here, Ganni?"

"I was fishing last night, and I saw you. I told mother when I got home." He unshouldered his sack, and held it out. "She sent some food for you."

The generous thought was enough to make him weep. "How very kind of her! I *was* getting a bit hungry."

Inside the sack there was a bottle of wine, a loaf of bread, a cheese wrapped in vine leaves, and two rock melons, warm from the sun. The sight made him absolutely ravenous. He broke off a piece of the crust, and crammed it into his mouth.

Ganni peered past him. "What are you doing in the cave?"

Father Salvatore swallowed a big chunk of the cheese before answering: "Just resting. I'm having a holiday."

"I wish I could live in a cave. . . . Mother says, if you get hungry again, come and eat with us. Or if you want to stay at the house, that's fine too." With a generous swig of wine, Father Salvatore had returned to his meal, and the boy, after watching him, said: "You *are* hungry." But boys had better things to do than look at priests eating. He began to fidget. "Well, the fish won't wait, Dun Salv . . . Shall I say you're coming?"

"I don't know. I don't think so. But please thank your mother very much for the food."

"She's a good cook too. *Sahha*, Dun Salv." Then he shouldered his rod, and the empty sack, and ran off towards the beckoning water. Though the whistling faded away down the rocks, it lifted the heart on its journey.

So did the food. The crusty bread and soft wet cheese were delicious: the melon honey-sweet, and the strong Gozo wine, deep yellow and smoky on the tongue, was a blessing. He drank half the bottle, sitting at ease in the mouth of the cave, watching a tiny figure at the margin of the bay cast and re-cast his line.

Then, feeling stronger and happier than for many a day, Father Salvatore decided that it was time for another walk. He shaved as best he could, with a dry blade and no mirror; then he packed the wine and the rest of the bread and cheese, and set off up the hill. The noise of bombing from the distant south only proved how wise he was to be so far away.

He spent the day in the valley west of San Lawrenz: a fair day, full of sunshine, unclouded, benign. In this paradise, the fall of man—the fall of this man—started when he noticed a farmer coming towards him across the valley, leading a breeding ram to its day's engagements.

It was done with a delicacy which delighted him. Their approach was at first silent: the farmer plodding along the top of a dividing wall, the ram at the end of a rope, picking its way from stone to stone with the sure-footed ease of a rustic celebrity.

But halfway across, there was a subtle enlargement of policy.

227

The man stopped, and drew from his pocket a bell, and tied it round the ram's neck. When they took up their progress again, it was to the sound of a continuous tinkling melody which told all who might wish to be involved, that action was on the way.

The man and his profitable friend drew near to where Father Salvatore was sitting. Greetings were exchanged. The farmer stood patting and fondling his prize; the ram – whose endowments were manifest—waited and munched and looked up the road. Then the linked pair passed on up the road, to the sound of music.

Father Salvatore should have been instantly on his guard, but he was not. The wine which he now drank, and the drowsy peace of the day, and the pastoral sensuality of this encounter, all lulled him into acceptance. Instead of praying, or reading his neglected Office of the Day, he relaxed, and slept in the shadow of the wall. When he awoke, it was to see the ram being led back, its duties done. It walked with lowered head; it was not even very steady on its feet. O happy ram! Contented sheep! O ram of God. . . .

The frightful thoughts which now descended took Father Salvatore straight to hell. They were thoughts not only blasphemous, but grossly sexual. A sensual daydream grew to a nightmare of the lustful: Father Salvatore found that he could not stop thinking such thoughts. Presently he did not try. The devil was in his loins after all the years of chastity, and would not be exorcized.

It was now near sunset. He rose, and with willing feet, to the far-off sound of gunfire and the turmoil of some murderous attack, he went through the village towards Maddelena's house.

In the tiny cottage, neat and clean, he found Maddelena drying the baby after its bath. She did not seem surprised by his sudden appearance. Perhaps she was never surprised by anything.

Close to, she was a handsome woman with a fine generous figure: whatever the extravagance of her life, she had kept her looks to a degree unusual in rural Malta, where girls, often quite ravishing at sixteen, grew harassed after long five-year engagements, were often plain and lifeless by the time they became brides, and were then pregnant for the next twenty years.

She welcomed him with a glass of wine. Then Ganni burst into the house, full of his fishing though bereft of fish. There had been

228

one as big as this—the small arms stretched to their very limit—which had *just* got away! But he had other news for Dun Salv.

"I saw Rafel on the way home. He just met a man from Malta. They say there's a huge convoy coming in at last. That's what all the bombing means. He said a friend of yours had been hurt. Little Nero, Rafel said. He was hit by a bomb, and his wife was killed."

Such was the corruption of this day that even now Father Salvatore could not treat the awful news as it deserved. Though he said, "What a terrible thing," he might have been speaking of a train-accident in some far-off country. He did not *want* to think otherwise. He wanted everything in his life to be here and now.

Presently Maddelena produced a succulent rabbit pie, and they ate in warm family companionship. Darkness fell; an oil lamp glowed in the shadowy room; the atmosphere, which had been domestic, grew charged with frank desire. Ganni went unwillingly to bed. Across the room the girl's bright eyes met his. She stood up, insolent, melting, signalling unmistakably. He stood up also, and she was so close that her body brushed his.

It was for Father Salvatore a moment of terrible confusion, then with a groan, in agony, in a violent tempest of shame, he fled from the house.

On a dark street corner, at the far limits of the village, God appeared in shadowy form and said, with great compassion: "Thou fool."

He began to walk, almost to run, towards the harbour.

The Dawning Day of Father Salvatore
15 August 1942

Father Salvatore sat in a corner of a small waterfront bar, and waited for word that the *luzzu* was ready to take him across to Malta. At midnight, the bar should not have been open, but it was and would remain so on this particular night, until certain transactions had taken place. If a policeman chose to poke his nose in, so much the worse for him, he would get a flea in his ear.

Certainly the priest stuck out like a sore thumb, and had at first been looked at with suspicion. But presently the word went round that he was clear. He was not a spy, and not on holy duty. He just wanted to cross to Malta, which was forbidden during the hours of darkness. Since he must have his reasons, good luck to him—as long as he paid the fare, and forgot the faces.

He sat alone in a corner, drinking his coffee with trembling lips, and tried desperately to fix his mind on something better than bar-room customers and the fearful trail of sin he had left behind him.

His self-loathing was absolute. Though the worst sin of all, the breaking of his sacred vow, could not be charged to him, yet the intention had been there, and thus the guilt. He had resolved, that only by returning home could he begin to make amends.

No matter what the scale of disobedience, or the guilt which he would carry with him, he must go back to his flock, and to poor wounded and bereaved Nero. His earlier reaction to the news had been so contemptible, so obscene, that it was past thinking about. Robbed of honour, a cripple of the faith, he *must* return to his sole service, even if only for a short hour. "They that wait upon the Lord shall renew their strength." He prayed with all his might that it would prove so.

The tattered piece of fishnet which served as a door to the bar was pushed aside, and a man came in. Father Salvatore looked up. It was the man he was waiting for. The *kappillan* knew him only as Twanny, the man who had been fetched when he asked about a boat. Twanny looked like a pirate, and possibly was—a real rogue in fact, and the very man Father Salvatore needed tonight.

Twanny crossed to Father Salvatore's corner, and sat down. The bar owner, unasked, brought a tumbler of wine, and Twanny swallowed half of it before he spoke. Then he leaned across the table. "Ten minutes more." He had a voice to match his looks, as rough as barnacles. "It took a bit longer to load than I thought."

"What are you taking across?"

"Oh, bits and pieces." No good to ask why bits and pieces went across by night instead of by day. Sudden gunfire across the straits changed the subject for them. "They say a big convoy got in today. Five ships . . . God knows we need them." Twanny looked at Father Salvatore's shaking hands. ". . . Are you feeling all right, Father?"

"Yes, yes. I'm a little tired, that's all."

"Ten minutes, then. Just walk to the end of the beach. You'll see the *luzzu* there." He got up. "There's someone else coming with us. But don't let it bother you. We're all friends."

Father Salvatore waited an exact ten minutes, then paid his bill and left the bar. A little way from the shore, he saw the outline of the promised *luzzu*, and the immense figure of Twanny standing thigh deep, holding its prow. The other passenger was waiting on dry land: a tall man with his back to the shore.

When his footsteps drew near, the tall stranger turned.

"Uncle Salvu!"

"Michael!"

Michael Ainslie clasped him in strong arms, and almost lifted him off his feet by the warmth of his welcome. Then they stood back, and looked at each other.

"Michael! Thank God! Thank God!"

There was enough light to see that Michael was tonight not so much a Fleet Air Arm pilot as a walking derelict. He was burned dark by the sun, thin as a rail, dressed in filthy rags, which might have started life as some kind of boiler-suit. He smelled of all sorts of things: garlic, tar, sweat, diesel oil, and one extra ingredient which Father Salvatore could not place. Amazingly the spirit was still there. "Have you come to meet me? That's what I call service!"

"Well, no. I'm here by chance. But where have *you* come from?"

"Sicily," Michael answered. "Delightful country, and I mean that. And a marvellous place to say good-bye to. I sailed across, and now we're on the second leg of the cruise. . . . But fancy you going over in Twanny's *luzzu*! Surely you're not in this racket too?" He did not wait for an answer. "How's Marija, Uncle Salvu? I've been thinking of nothing else but her, and a *really* good steak, since the tenth of May. That's ninety-seven days. But how is she?"

"She's very well. Sad, of course, but she won't be sad in a few hours. I've been in Gozo quite a time, but when I last saw her she was—" what did lovers want to hear? "as beautiful as ever."

231

Michael gave a great sigh. "After all this, we've *got* to get married."

"I think that's a very good idea. But how did you escape?"

There was a warning whistle, and Twanny called out: "Come on! You'll wake the dead!"

"I'll tell you on the way over," Michael said. "Let's get started. . . ."

He led the way out to the *luzzu*, and Father Salvatore followed close behind. Soon the *luzzu* was gently sliding away from the shore, the painted eye of Osiris gleaming steadfastly on its bow.

Twanny whispered: "You know each other?"

"Certainly," Father Salvatore answered. "He's going to marry my niece."

"Better feed him up. . . ."

While Michael steered, Twanny rowed clear of the bay. Then they hoisted the lateen sail and it filled to the southwest wind. After they cleared Comino it would be safe to start the engine.

Father Salvatore sat in utter peace, loving his surroundings: the great arc of the night sky, the noise of the water, the creak of sail on its yard. The *luzzu* was loaded deep, with mysterious bales that seemed to smell like—well, like Michael Ainslie.

Twanny came aft to take the tiller, and Michael was now free to tell his story. "I was lucky," he said. "There was a colossal bang, and half the plane fell off, the rest caught fire, and I was swinging on the end of a parachute."

He had parachuted down on the first wild slopes of Mount Etna, and into utter silence. He might, he said, have landed in the middle of the Sahara. He went through certain prescribed drills: burying his parachute, stripping off most of his uniform but leaving enough for identification, to avoid being shot as a spy; and hiding in a ditch, till dawn.

First came some soldiers, but they missed him. Then some children, who saw him and ran away. Then lots more soldiers, but by that time he had left the ditch and hidden in a barn. Then a different child: a little girl with large eyes, who did not run away, but put her fingers to her lips and disappeared at a pace curiously sedate, as ordinary as doing nothing.

232

Then came a man on a bicycle, pedalling very slowly—who stopped by the barn, carefully turned his back on it, and called out: "Hallo. Hallo. Englishman!" After that, it was easy.

"*Partigiani*," Michael explained. "Some fool called them the spaghetti underground. . . . The most gorgeous bunch of cut-throats I've ever seen. And a couple of professors, and a pianist, and some crazy girls, and a priest. They all had one thing—they loathed Mussolini. They hid me, and fed me, and passed me from hand to hand, right down to the beach. Then they gave me a pair of water-wings—water-wings!—and pushed me out towards a fishing-boat in the middle of a hurricane. They all kissed me good-bye—you know, I *love* the Italians! That was—let's see—eight days ago. Eight days for sixty miles—plus a little help from our friend."

Michael nodded towards Twanny, now steering a steady course with the aid of a faithfully chugging engine. Ahead of them, on Malta, violent things were going on which happily drowned a small *luzzu's* engine: the crack of anti-aircraft shells, the *whoomph!* of the bombs, the bark of naval guns.

"Here we go again," said Michael. "I should have stayed in Sicily. . . . It was so peaceful there, even though it was run-and-hide, all the time. But I met some marvellous people. . . . There was a man who played the guitar—no, it was the mandolin, and he always said 'Puccini—*pfui!* Verdi—*bellissimo!* Have some more Chianti. You want a girl?' That's about all he knew. . . ."

He fell silent, looking up at the stars. Perhaps he had done so for hours every night, in hope or in fear. Then, absurdly, it had been an enemy sky; now those same bright candles were the stars of freedom. Father Salvatore gently prompted him. "What happened after you got on board?"

"Well, it was slow. We pretended to fish for a couple of days, edging south all the time, and then we had to stop and wait for Twanny to find us; and *he* had to be careful not to go too far north, or the Italian navy would have picked him up. Talk about cloak-and dagger stuff! I really felt quite important, till I realized what it was all about. It wasn't me at all. You know what? These chaps were smuggling cheese! I was just shovelled in with all the Gorgonzola."

"That's it!" Father Salvatore exclaimed. "I smelt it. Gorgonzola. But I couldn't quite place it."

"You can place it firmly over the side, as far as I'm concerned. I've been sleeping on Gorgonzola for a week. . . . Well, that's about all, Uncle Salvu. Twanny found us and collected his cargo, and swanned down to Gozo again, fishing all the way. Gozo is where he keeps the main cache. Then he takes it across to Malta in small doses, like tonight. The price is better that way. He's a real character, that one: all bad. But he got me home, bless him."

"Michael—I couldn't be more happy to see you, and listen to you, if I was Marija herself."

"Well, what a sweet thing to say. . . . Do you think there'll be any trouble about marrying her?"

"There'll be trouble if you don't."

When, in a deserted corner of St. Paul's Bay, the time came to say good-bye, Twanny's voice became conspiratorial. "If you want to buy any of this cheese, Father, try a lad called Wenzu on St. Nicholas Street. Tell him I sent you."

"But I know Wenzu!"

"*Do* you? I'm surprised at you, Father. *Sahha.*"

Then they walked along the edge of the beach, keeping in the moon-shadows, and began to climb the steps of St. Paul.

IT HAD BEEN after three o'clock when they landed from the *luzzu*: now it was after four. Already there were signs of the dawn, though no bird had yet been hopeful enough to hail it. The faint light from the east had to contend with the massive fireworks of the battle below the southern horizon.

In an hour, they had stumbled two bone-weary miles: past closed shutters and barking dogs which snarled their way back to sleep, and ghostly fields which smelled of burned crops and tired soil. Though they had expected to be stopped, no soldier had challenged them. Nor had anyone else. The world was sunk in sleep, or was holding its breath in fear of what might happen next, or else it did not want to know.

Breasting the last slope to the summit of the Victoria Lines, Michael said: "What's happened to security tonight? These brown

jobs are jolly slack. There must be some way of getting arrested."
He began to shout. "Come on! Hasn't anybody seen me? I've just
parachuted down. You could all be murdered in your beds!"

It recalled to Father Salvatore, struggling between laughter
and the tears of exhaustion, that Michael as yet knew nothing of
Lewis Debrincat's disgrace. But when he told the story, Michael
only said: "Poor Mrs. Debrincat. But isn't it silly? Some darling
Italians helped me to escape, at the risk of their lives, and I love
them for it. My prospective father-in-law does *exactly* the same
thing, in reverse, and now he's some kind of polecat. That's why
war is such a joke. The only thing to remember is, you've got to win."

They were coming up to the crest of the hill when a pebble,
dislodged from the small bastion above them, rattled down into
the roadway. Then a head popped up against the pale skyline, and
a soldier with a gun said: "Halt! Who goes there?"

Michael had become slightly light-headed. "About time too!
Come, come, my man! Asleep on sentry-duty? Penalty, *death!*"

The soldier now revealed himself as a stocky red-faced corporal
who did indeed look as if he had just woken up. He slithered down
the hill, and confronted them with a rifle at the ready and a broad
North Country accent. "Who goes there, I said. Identify yourselves."

"Lancashire Fusiliers."

"Eh? What the hell! *We're* the Lancashire Fusiliers."

"Now, now—careless talk. Take me to your leader."

"Don't get cheeky with me, or I'll clump you." The corporal
noticed Father Salvatore. "Are you an *actual* Father?"

It was time to intervene. "It's all right. I'm a Maltese parish
priest, and this is a Fleet Air Arm lieutenant. We've just landed
from Gozo. The lieutenant has come from Sicily."

Another, more authoritative voice from above them called out:
"What's going on down there?"

"Gawd knows, sir," the corporal shouted back. "A couple of
loonies from Sicily."

"*Sicily?*" An extraordinary roar of military alarm took precedence over all other sounds. "Turn out the guard! Watch them,
corporal! *Where's my helmet?*"

Their troubles were over.

THE RISING SUN was staring them straight in the eye as they were driven, like gentlemen of leisure, towards Valletta. On the outskirts they said good-bye, and Michael Ainslie prepared to continue on to the people waiting for him at the airfield.

"Would you like me to ring Marija?" Father Salvatore asked.

"No, thank you." Then, as he stood by the army truck with its engine still roaring, Michael changed his mind. "Come to think of it, you *would* do it much better than I can. I don't want the dear girl to die of shock. Can you prepare the ground?"

"Yes, of course. What shall I say?"

"Just that I'm alive, and I love her . . . Tell her I'll meet her at ten o'clock. On the bastions—all the best things have happened on the bastions, and they're going to happen again." Michael held out his hand. "*Arrividerci, padre mio*. . . . I must go and comb my hair. . . . If you'd like to come along, we won't mind at all."

HE HAD A MUCH BETTER idea than ringing up Marija, which was to go direct to the Sliema house and break the joyful news in person. But he could hardly walk another step, so he waited on the street corner, sitting on an upturned biscuit box. Finally he attracted the attention of a *karrozzin* driver.

When they reached the Casa Debrincat it was barely six o'clock: much too early to wake the household, even on such an errand. But as Father Salvatore hesitated, a gruff voice somewhere above gave him an eerie greeting: "Halt! Who goes there?"

He looked up, and saw the head of Pietru Pawl Debrincat, three storeys up, peeping over the edge of the roof-parapet. He waved, and got an instant response. "Uncle Salvu! You've come back!"

He put his fingers to his lips. "Sh'h. Not too loud. It's so early. Come down and let me in."

The light patter of feet on the tiled floor within was the prelude to slamming bolts and a door flung wide open. Pietru, in pyjamas, stood ready to welcome him. "I've been watching the convoy come in." Then, "Is anything the matter? Why are you limping, Uncle Salvu? Have you been wounded?"

"No." They were still whispering to each other. "I've been walking a long way, that's all." He paused. "With Michael."

"*What?*" This was no whisper, but a squeal of delight. "Has he come back? But where is he? Why didn't he come with you?"

"He had to report first."

Pietru, steeped in the traditions of the Fleet Air Arm, accepted this. "Oh yes. Of course. Shall I tell Marija?"

"Not yet. I want to speak to your mother first."

"She's at Mass." Then Pietru looked beyond Father Salvatore, and down the front steps. "No, she isn't. . . . Mother! Michael's come back!"

Giovanna Debrincat, formally dressed in grey, stopped dead on the second step. Her face, which had been blank and preoccupied, changed on the instant to a rapturous happiness. She said: "No! It's not possible!" and almost ran up the steps into the house. "Oh, Salvu! If you only knew how I've prayed!"

"Well, your prayers have been answered." He embraced her.

"Have you really seen him?" Giovanna asked as he closed the door behind her. "Or has there been a message?"

"I've seen him, touched him, spoken to him, walked all the way from St. Paul's Bay with—" Father Salvatore stopped. At the head of the stairs, Marija appeared in a silk dressing-gown. Fresh from sleep, she looked beautiful, and young, and not yet with the waking world. When she saw him she called out: "Uncle Salvu! Is it some news?" and her voice showed that she hardly dared put the question. After ninety-seven days of hopeless nothing, what else could be expected?

He held out his arms. "Come down, Marija. I have something wonderful to tell you."

IT WAS HARDLY POSSIBLE to see anything from the bastions. Soon after dawn, tremendous crowds had begun to stream out to welcome the four ships, now lying under the shore guns. A convoy at last! Big ships, deep laden, after all the miserable months of starvation! It was no wonder that the crowd was singing and cheering, praying and weeping, as they gazed at the evidence of a siege raised, a blessing bestowed on this happiest of days.

Father Salvatore, leading a bewildered, wildly elated Marija by the hand round and round the outskirts of the crowd, wondered if

their search was going to fail. What a place to meet one man, even a man in uniform. Suddenly she released his guiding hand, and darted forward. Michael had appeared on the high ground at the back of the bastions, and was walking swiftly towards them. He looked nothing at all like the ragged wreck with whom Father Salvatore had passed the night. With the vitality of youth, he was now simply a tall slim naval officer, deeply tanned, immaculately dressed, on whose face was the pride and urgency of love.

Father Salvatore took plenty of time before he joined them. He had never seen two people more closely wrapped in each other's arms. The few watchers nearby at the back of the bastions were all smiling. Ah, the brave sailor and his beautiful Maltese girl. . . .

It was Michael, being taller, who first took note of his approach. "Uncle Salvu! *Padre mio*. . . . How are the feet?"

"Terrible," Father Salvatore answered. "But the heart makes up for them."

"Spoken for both of us. . . ." He kissed Marija again, and by chance a sudden burst of cheering erupted along the bastions, at the same moment. "Well, isn't that nice? Are they cheering us?"

"No," said Father Salvatore, who had turned away to look towards the harbour. "They could be, but believe it or not, there's something else happening. Look there."

He pointed downward, to the smoky focus of Grand Harbour. There, they saw what the crowd had been cheering: a ghastly ruin of a ship, nursed like a dying man, about to come alongside.

After the cheering there came a hush, as people gradually took in the details. The wreck was a very large tanker, wire-strapped between two destroyers for support. She had a cavernous torpedo-hole under a mass of twisted plating at the bows, and another further aft. Her decks were ploughed up from end to end, as if the world's biggest can-opener had been at work. On the fire-charred upper deck, amid a tangle of piping, two separate scrapheaps of metal which were crashed aircraft, still smouldered, adding a freak element to disaster. She was so low in the water that a man could be seen sitting on deck and trailing his fingers in Grand Harbour.

Michael Ainslie was moved to sum it up: "Even poor old *Illustrious* wasn't as bad as that."

But on the other side of the account the four ships, and now this last fugitive from the convoy, had all brought their cargoes safely in. The tremendous cheering which now broke out again as the ship was nudged towards her berth hailed the miracle.

Ohio, launched in America only two years earlier, had been lent to Britain for wartime purposes. She looked what she was—a big new modern tanker—and she had thus, in this convoy, been a ship marked out for special attention. She carried thousands of tons of highly inflammable aviation spirit; barring a few anti-aircraft guns, she was not a fighting ship at all, but a big oil drum ready to explode if a single match were put in the right place.

She was the first ship to be hit: by a torpedo from an Italian E-boat. It was almost enough to take her out of the fight at one stroke. It knocked out her steering gear, and set her on fire. But the torpedo-hole was a monstrous 25-foot square cavern, and this helped to dowse the flames. Hand-steering from aft, she worked up to seven knots again and began a hazardous night journey.

At dawn she was already a lone straggler, and the first flight of bombers found her easily enough. She was shaken and holed by six near-misses; and then a plane, shot down by an escort, landed on a big wave, bounced fifty feet in the air, and crashed onto her foredeck. The captain had barely started to clean up this mess and plug a few of the wounds when a second plane did exactly the same thing, this time landing on the stern and restarting the fires. Down below, meanwhile, worse things were happening: the engines were beginning to surrender. Towards dusk, after a few labouring miles amid near-misses which lifted her bodily out of the water, she took a direct hit. The fuel pumps died: her boilers blew up. She came to a dead stop, one hundred and fifty miles from home. There would be no more steaming on that day, nor on any other.

She was taken in tow, but with the great gulf in her side, and her rudder jammed, she was almost impossible to manage. The tow-lines kept breaking. She would move forward a hundred yards, and then the tow would part, and she would drift to a standstill again.

At dawn on the third day, as she was still making her agonized way towards safety through air attacks which never slackened, a near-miss from a huge bomb blew a hole in her stern. Tons more seawater poured into the dead hull. The towlines parted. *Ohio* stopped and settled once more.

But Malta, was now only seventy miles away, with air-cover at last available; and to Malta she presently came, strapped between two destroyers, sagging like a corpse, but still bearing her cargo.

The watchers on the bastions could not know the dark side of the story; they could only see the good news, which was the four solid ships already unloading, and the fifth, now secured alongside an oiler and preparing to deliver her cargo.

On the bastions, Michael Ainslie looked down at his girl: "Marija! You're crying! Just like me."

"It's so *marvellous*!" She clung to him, as if for her life. "I didn't know I had any tears left. I'm sorry, Michael."

"Don't worry. Use them up now. We won't be needing any more."

It was time for Father Salvatore to take his leave.

When he said so, they pressed him to stay, to come back with them for lunch. But the answer could only be No. Today, these two did not need anyone else, and the moment had come for him to go to the catacombs, as he had resolved in the black depths of yesterday. He blessed them, and watched them go, hand in hand, smiling at all the world as if it had been invented for their delight. Let it last, he prayed. Let it last for ever.

He sat down on a fallen stone of the bastion wall. The sound of cheering receded as he dropped his head in his hands. The children had taken happiness with them. He felt drained of everything, yet he must somehow summon strength for the next step.

From this high point of the bastions, his way could only lie downhill. He must go to the catacombs, find Nero and comfort him, greet his people and perhaps speak to them. It might be the last time for all these things. Tomorrow, at the latest, he would have to see the bishop, and confess his disobedience, to accept any verdict. He would not resist. There was nothing the old man might say to him he had not said to himself already. He would submit. If it was his priesthood, he would submit that also.

The thud of an explosion, not too far off, made him raise his head and look about him, as did almost everyone else on the bastions. The cheering and singing died away as they searched anxiously for the cause. There had been no warning. It could not be an air raid—the sky was clear and innocent. Then a man, shouting "Look there!" pointed, and heads turned, and Father Salvatore's head turned also. Foreboding gripped his heart.

A cloud of smoke and dust was billowing up, half a mile away near the crown of Valletta. It must be the Auberge de Castile. . . . No, it was nearer to the Palazzo Santo-Nobile . . . He rose, forgetting his aching legs, and began to walk towards the city: and then to run.

THE POSTERN DOOR hung drunkenly from a single hinge. Father Salvatore, panting after his swift journey, stepped past it and inside, and was confronted by everything he had trembled to think of since that first moment of panic on the bastions.

Some awful force had ripped through the Palazzo, with a searing breath not even this ancient fortress could withstand. At the head of the courtyard, the main doors, thick as a strong man's thigh, lay splintered on the ground. The balustrade which Manwel had repaired was sagging like some tawdry fire-escape, the bougainvillea torn from it. Windows were broken everywhere, leaking their tapestried curtains down like flags of surrender. Part of the portico had collapsed into rubble. Father Salvatore had hardly taken in half of this horror when he became aware that there were other people in the courtyard including a police-inspector whom he knew, from many another bloody "incident" of the past.

"What happened, Leli? There was no air raid, was there?"

The policeman, who was dusty and haggard, shook his head. "Delayed-action job, they say. It was just up the street. Some men were digging, and they must have touched off a bomb. I'm afraid a lot of people were killed. But here—" he gestured round the ruins of the great house, "it must have caught the main blast. I'm sorry, Dun Salv. It was so beautiful."

But where, amid this wrecked splendour, was the human being most precious of all to him? Trembling, he asked.

"Over there." The policeman pointed across the courtyard

towards the armoury, and then looked aside. "The doctor is with her."

There were ambulance men whom he recognized, who also avoided his eyes. Outside the armoury door, two frightened girls turned as he approached. They were weeping. "Thank God you've come, Dun Salv," one of them said. It was the girl who had dropped the sauce-boat at the terrible Christmas lunch, and had exclaimed "*Gesu, Marija!*" to the consternation of the faithful. Let her say it again now, in true pleading humility. . . .

As he made to step past them, and enter, one more friendly face swam into his blurred view. This time it was a hospital doctor, Anton Farrugia; they had been partners many times, often at that desolate moment when a doctor shook his head and yielded to a priest. Beyond Farrugia he caught a glimpse of a shattered room, with a ceiling from which torn plaster hung like bleached seaweed. The armoury, which he had always told his mother to trust, had not proved strong enough.

Farrugia's face was grave. He put out his arm, and touched the *kappillan* on the shoulder. "Salvu! What a day to meet!"

"What's happened, Anton?" The touch of the hand on his shoulder was deeply ominous: he had made the gesture himself a thousand times before: "How is my mother?"

Doctor and priest met each other's eyes. After an appalling moment, Farrugia answered: "At her age. . . . The explosion was a terrible shock. A lot of plaster from the ceiling fell on her too. There has been some internal bleeding. I've decided not to move her." Again the touch on the shoulder, the message of No.

"I don't think I can do anything, Salvu."

"And I can?"

"My dear friend—yes."

He trod his way forward, through crumbling stone dust and strips of wood from the ceiling, towards the bed. Under a shroud of white plaster, the Most Noble Celeste Emilia Santo-Nobile lay like a grey corpse. The beautiful face, thank God, was unmarked, but it was as if the fullness of life had already ebbed away. In this bed where she had been born, where she had lain as a bride, as a mother, as a widow, his beloved mother now lay near death.

He took out the little golden phial containing the holy oil, exquisitely shaped under the hand of a Roman master two centuries ago, which his mother had given him when he first became a priest. So it returned to her. . . . He began to pray, and then to anoint, with the gentle hands of a lifetime of ministry.

His voice was as strong as he could make it, at such a moment. "Through this holy anointing and His tender mercy, may the Lord forgive whatever sins you may have committed through the eyes—" his hands were shaking, but he forced himself to touch her, to brush with oil the dying features, "through the ears—through the nostrils—through the mouth—through the hands—through the feet. . . . Amen. Amen."

When he turned back towards her pillow, uncertain whether life still lingered, he found that her eyes were open. They were full of shadows, but they were fixed on him.

Her lips opened also. He moved swiftly, and bent to catch her words. "Salvatore. . . ." It was the merest rustle of dry breath. "You did that very well—for a young fellow. . . ."

He had forgotten that he had ever told her that long-ago story. While he was still remembering, she smiled, as if pleased with this last surprise for a dear son, and closed her eyes, and was gone from life.

After a long moment he bent to kiss her, and thanked God for a soul at peace. Then he was on his knees, and weeping bitterly, as a son was entitled to do. He would remember this till the day of his own death. . . . But he *must* believe what he had told countless others, at the same moment of anguish. . . . Since underneath were the everlasting arms, no grief need be insupportable. . . . If one believed, if one believed.

EVERYTHING SEEMED TO BE happening for the last time. Even crossing Grand Harbour had something of a farewell feeling about it; whatever happened on the morrow, it was unlikely that he would pass this way again for months or years which could not even be guessed at. The harbour itself, despite the activity on board the big tanker, was the same graveyard, overgrown with all the weeds of war. When he came to the Three Cities, and began his accustomed journey through the outskirts of Cospicua, the picture of ruin was complete. He had often spoken of hope. Where, in this desert of destruction, was hope to be found?

But then—then it all changed. The nearer he got to the catacombs, the more his spirit revived. He felt that he was at last moving towards something real: something which lived, and had always refused to die. In the Cottonera Lines, which he had grown to love, there was still a living faith to be found.

The welcome he received on his return was enough to warm the heart of any man, no matter what his mood was. He had forgotten the enormous vitality of this tomb. He went from group to group among the smoky caverns of his domain, shaking hands, embracing, blessing. There was only one thing they were ready to be sad about, but as soon as he reassured them, cheerfulness overflowed again. It was the matter of the Palazzo Santo-Nobile.

They had heard that it had been bombed. Was it true? Well, there had been a little damage. And his blessed mother, who had been so generous? Had anything—

"She is resting peacefully," he told them.

"Thanks be to God!"

Now he had his own questions. How was Nero?

"He's here in your very own cell, Dun Salv," an old streethawker answered. "It was the best place to put him."

"But how is he?"

"Oh, full of life. Try to keep that one down! You know he lost his leg?"

Even in the summer heat of the catacombs, Father Salvatore felt a cold chill at the appalling news. "No, I didn't know. I was told he had been hurt, that's all."

But here at home, there had been more time to get used to it. "These things happen. Sliced off, clean as a chicken's head. And the girl was killed, too. But you know about that, surely?"

"Yes. I *must* go and see him."

"Soon, soon. But first—come and look at the new cookingstoves. You know who gave them to us? The bishop himself! Ah, what it is to have influence! Who needs a saint in heaven?"

It was not quite within the pure doctrine of the Church's

teaching, but Father Salvatore let it go. He was moved at the bishop's generosity, yet not at all surprised. The old man had an exact sense of who should be punished, and who should not.

Even the reunion with Nero, which a moment before he had been dreading, turned out to be a joyful one. Once again, he had forgotten the spirit of the catacombs.

The dwarf lay in his stone cot, a rug over the lower part of his body. There was pain in his face. But as soon as he caught sight of the *kappillan*, he was transformed. "Dun Salv! You've come back!" He made as if to rise, and then remembered, as they both remembered. "Ah, this stupid leg. . . . I've so many things to ask you. I don't know where to begin. Give me a blessing, first."

"God bless you, Nero."

"Now I'm better. . . . But I must get out of here. It's your room, after all. Why didn't you send a message that you were coming back?"

"I didn't know, Nero. It all happened so quickly. But you mustn't think of moving. There's plenty of time."

"But where will you live?"

"We'll see . . . Please tell me what happened. You know how sorry I am."

"You can't be more sorry than me. . . ." Yet it was a joke, not a complaint. The dwarf was not in mourning for himself, whatever else he might find pitiful or wretched. "It was all so stupid. I took Teresa out for the evening. We were so happy, Dun Salv, you wouldn't believe. We went to that bar on St. Ursula Street. It might have been any other bar in Valletta, but it had to be that one. And then—" he made a great sweep with a little arm, "down came the bomb. We actually heard it coming. It makes a noise like—like a mad woman screaming at you. When I woke up, I was in hospital, with a funny feeling in my leg—only there was no leg there—and they told me she was dead."

Father Salvatore did his best, in the desperate urge to comfort. "Nero, there's hardly anything I can say. I needn't tell you to be brave. You *are* brave. Try to remember, she has gone to God."

"I need her more than God!" It was a sudden bitter protest from the depths of a resentful heart. "Was God jealous of me?"

247

"Nero, Nero."

"I'm sorry, Dun Salv. Give me a little time."

Then it was quiet in the tiny stone cell, while outside the voices rose and fell as people started gathering for the night. Presently a subdued Nero asked: "When did you hear about it?"

"Only yesterday. I was in Gozo. When did it happen, Nero?"

"Eight days ago. . . . Who told you?"

"Well—it was Rafel. Someone brought a message from him. I'd met him earlier."

"Rafel! You really saw that old mountain man?"

"Oh yes. He sent all sorts of remembrances. I think he misses the catacombs."

Nero looked wary. "Well, he had his chance, didn't he? We don't need him back, Dun Salv. In a couple of weeks, I'll be hopping about like a flea. A flea on crutches—think of that." Suddenly Nero clapped his hands together. "I was forgetting! All my own troubles! We heard the Palazzo had a bomb. Is it true? Is your mother all right?"

"She is resting peacefully," he answered, as before.

"That's good. And isn't it wonderful about the convoy? At this rate we can hold out for ever. I *knew* it would turn out like this. So did you. You always told us to trust God, and to hope."

"It has *never* failed." Looking at the dwarf, Father Salvatore knew that he was growing exhausted. He got up from the bed. "It's time I left you, Nero. Why don't you have a little nap?"

"I'll have a think, anyway . . ." Nero lay back on the pillow, and closed his eyes. His voice came sleepily. "I've had a lot of thoughts, lying here, Dun Salv. I *still* don't see why we had to have a war. Why God allows it. Malta never did any harm to anyone. Yet it always seems to happen, like you've been telling us. And so many people get killed and hurt, or their lives are spoiled. . . ."

"It is one of the greatest mysteries, Nero."

"Then you won't expect the answer from me." Nero's eyes were still closed, but now he was smiling. "Oh, we've missed you so much, Dun Salv! . . . Will you talk to us tonight?"

"I think so. But not for long. I'm rather tired myself."

A man came hesitantly to the cell door, to ask about Mass, and Father Salvatore touched the dwarf gently on the forehead, and left him. He did not really feel equal to speaking tonight, but it would come. At a moment of private grief and public joy, he was privileged to be joined with his people. What else could he do, but tell them once more of peace and strength, life and hope?

HEXAMERON!

A.D. 1917 Pax Britannica et Melitensis

The kappillan *could always surprise them.*

"When I was a young man of twenty-two," he began, "I sailed into Grand Harbour on the bridge of a destroyer, just like the ones that came in today, holding up the big tanker. No, I was not in the navy, though I certainly wanted to be. I was a seminarian, already, dedicated to God, but at that moment I wanted to be the ship's captain! I tell you this tonight, because tonight I feel very close to you again, and we are all happy, and people who are close and happy should have no secrets."

He waited for them to quieten down. The idea of Dun Salv wanting to be a naval officer must have seemed very odd to them. He hoped, somehow, to show them why it had been so.

"That was in the first world war, in 1917," he went on, "and I was coming back from Rome to Malta. You must remember that Italy was an ally in that war. I was only a passenger, and on a sad errand: returning for the Requiem Mass for my father, who had been killed at a big naval battle called Jutland. But the sad journey turned into a glorious one. In fact it was a great day when we came into Grand Harbour, a day like today, when we can at last see an end of war. In 1917, the war had not yet been won, but it had been won here—because of what I saw when we arrived. . . ."

THEY MADE THEIR LANDFALL, in misty morning sunshine, at Tal-Gordan lighthouse on the northern point of Gozo, and then ran on down the coast towards Malta. The ship's crew was cheerful.

Scorpion had been away for more than a month: she was due for a boiler-clean, which involved a rest and a spell of leave, which was all that mattered.

Salvatore was on deck, engrossed in the peerless view of home, when he felt the chief steward touch his elbow. "Captain's compliments, sir, and would you like to come up on the bridge?"

Salvatore knew enough about the navy to realize that this was indeed a compliment. He dusted himself carefully before ascending. As he came to the top of the bridge ladder, Commander A. B. Cunningham turned from the wing of the bridge to greet him. "Up you come, young fellow! I thought you'd like to watch us entering harbour."

The captain was a tall, fair-haired man with a merry face and a very sharp eye. He was dressed in whites, and had a telescope tucked under his arm. Salvatore thanked him for his invitation.

"That's all right," the captain said. "It's a bit dull at the blunt end. . . . I hear you're Westgate-Saul's son. . . . A great chap! We were shipmates in the old *Suffolk*, and he was kind to me. Sorry he's gone. . . . Now—do you know where you are?"

Salvatore did know, exactly. They were gliding past the handsome watchtower on Sliema front; just ahead lay Dragut Point, and beyond it the magnificent bastion of St. Elmo. He was nearly home, and it was a breathless delight.

Commander Cunningham was the calm centre of great activity: signals were being flashed to shore, flags hoisted, and orders relayed down to the fo'c'sle, where a line of immaculate sailors had fallen in. "I think you'd better keep out of sight while we actually go in," the Commander said with much friendliness. "Rig-of-the-day isn't cassocks, even though this *is* Sunday. Duck in at the back of the signal bridge. You won't miss anything, but the Commander-in-Chief will miss you."

They made a slow turn round St. Elmo, and then the whole length of Grand Harbour opened up, and with it the most incredible sight Salvatore had ever seen. It was the Mediterranean Fleet.

There were so many ships that, from where they were entering harbour, one could almost have walked ashore. Line upon line of them came into view: all trim and grey, all at rest, and secure in their strength. Gazing at them, Salvatore could have sung with pride and happiness, or wept that he was not a sailor.

There was a message here: a declaration that peace-keeping had virtue, and virtue did not die in war: that out of death and suffering, endurance and courage, there could come a mighty tranquillity.

His father should have been there, to enjoy this moment. . . . But perhaps his father *was* here, standing back with his hands on his hips and his head up, able to declare: "I have fought a good fight, I have finished my course, I have kept the faith."

Commander Cunningham's voice interrupted. "Stop engines!" he called out suddenly; and then, to his first lieutenant: "We'll wait two minutes, Number One. They're just finishing church."

Across the waters of Grand Harbour, from the nearest big ship, there came the sound of a brass band striking up, and then of men singing in full-throated chorus. Salvatore recognized the tune immediately: it was the Protestant hymn which started "Eternal Father, strong to save, Whose arm hath bound the restless wave".

His father had sung it often, not as worship but as something to accompany shaving, bathing, strolling in the garden. When it came to the part which said: "Oh hear us when we cry to Thee, for those in peril on the sea", he used to give it all the vigour of an unmusical man who could hold a tune with the best of them. . . .

The hymn died away. Bugle-calls sounded all over the harbour. Commander Cunningham said: "Slow ahead both!" and *Scorpion* began to weave through the fleet towards her mooring buoy.

As they passed ship after ship, pipes shrilled, and were answered: men came to attention: salutes were returned, ensigns were lowered and then raised. Once again the message was clear. *Scorpion* was rejoining a fleet which had made of Malta a fortress, and a refuge for the weak, as the old Knights Hospitallers had decreed. Indeed, in the past two years Malta, "the nurse of the Mediterranean" had established twenty-seven hospitals, where all wounded and battle-weary men could come and be cared for. Here they were safe within a framework of the twin elements of life on earth: the valour of man and the glory of the Lord.

Father Salvatore, now pale with fatigue, fell silent, and the silence was not interrupted for a long time. He had told his story, and it had filled their hearts to overflowing. Peace! Peace at last! Peace would come, just as it had done before. What more could a man ask? Miracles?

They were not to know, on that night, that it would be left to Nero to announce what was indeed a sort of miracle, Nero who, only a year and a month later, would tell his hearers: "Do you remember the last story of Dun Salv? About the destroyer, long ago in the first war, and the captain called Cunningham? It's all come true! It's in the paper today!"

He jabbed triumphantly at the newspaper of September 1943, where it said that this was the end of the war for Malta, and how the signal which proved it had just been sent off. He pointed to the name of the man who had sent it, Admiral of the Fleet Sir Andrew Browne Cunningham, Commander-in-Chief, Mediterranean, and

then to what he had said: *"Be pleased to inform their Lordships
that the Italian battle fleet now lies at anchor under the guns of the
fortress of Malta."*

Epilogue

Memoirs of a Day-Tripper 2

The hearse had long disappeared from sight. The procession of
mourners had plodded away down the dusty road. Now the bell
tolled, not only for the dead priest but for us: the dwarf, and the
giant, and the privileged intruder.

They had shed tears. *We* had shed tears—no one who had seen a
black-plumed, black-caparisoned horse go by, hauling the mortal
remnants of someone on whom so much love centred, could be
aloof from feeling. The dwarf wiped his eyes, as did the guardian
giant behind him. Since he was now so composed, I made the most
of it. "Can I ask some more questions?"

"Why not?"

"Tell me then, why is Father Salvatore being buried in Gozo?
Did he come to live here?"

"Father Salvatore lived here in the monastery for the last thirty
years of his life. I cannot tell you why. Some say he was sent here,
as a punishment. *For what?* Some say he went mad, and was put in
a cell. Who can tell? Some say he chose to live here, instead of
Malta, because of something that happened. They say he never
spoke of it. It was a secret between himself and God. And perhaps
the bishop . . . who knows?"

"So Father Salvatore never kept in touch with you?"

The dwarf shook his head. "He was in a closed part of the monastery,
and could not see anyone. It was said that when the gardener died,
he took over all the growing. He was always very strong, like a
farmer. It was said that he grew more beans and onions and melons
than they could ever eat! But that was just a rumour."

Rumour or not, it sounded something like a waste of talent, as
well as a lonely end. "Did he have any relatives?"

"But of course! And his mother was noble! But she was killed by a bomb, and after that, the family seemed to . . ." the dwarf gestured with spread hands—"to melt away. There was an elder brother but he was shot in Paris at the end of the war. Or he was made to kill himself—there were a lot of funny stories. . . . There was also a sister, *Sinjura* Giovanna, and she died last year. Then there was a niece, Marija—a beautiful girl! She married an English sailor, and now he's a sea lord. What does a 'sea lord' mean?"

"An admiral. But at the very top."

"Well, he was too far away to come to the funeral. So there was only the baron, and he too busy also. At the United Nations."

"What baron?"

"The—what do you call the son of the sister?"

"The nephew."

"The nephew Pietru Santo-Nobile." The dwarf smiled. "To think I knew him as a little boy. Clever like a monkey, even then! Now they say he's the greatest man we have."

I had recognized a name. "Do you mean the Santo-Nobile on the Secretary-General's staff?"

"The very same. . . . You know, I can remember him coming down to the catacombs, and playing with a toy aeroplane! He was so proud of it. . . . Now he tells the Arabs and the Jews to stop their fighting. . . . So he could not be here today, either. So, of all the family, there was only one at the funeral, and he was the worst."

"Who was that?"

"The one that married *Sinjura* Giovanna. What a *brikkun*! He was in prison during the war, for helping the Italians. Then they let him out and suddenly he was a rich man with a finger in every pie. They say he bought a million Italian flame-throwers, and sold them to farmers to burn off the weeds. They say he bought up all the black shirts of the Fascists, and turned them into dresses for widows. They say he runs a bank with no money in it. Not a penny! But at least he came to the funeral. . . . Did you not see the fat old man in a smart black suit and the smart white tie, following the hearse? But in a Mercedes, like a big government minister?"

"I don't think so."

"Well, that was him. Of all people! I'll tell you one thing. It would have made Dun Salv laugh!"

I was getting a little lost among all these characters.

"Were you surprised that so many people came to the funeral?" I asked. "It's all such a long time ago. It must be thirty years."

The dwarf grew suddenly animated. "We would have come if it had been a hundred years! We would have risen from the dead without any trumpets! I can tell you, we have never stopped talking about Dun Salv, and thinking about him, and thanking God for him. After the war we started a sort of club in Cospicua. First it was called 'The Children of the Catacombs', and then it was just 'Dun Salv Club.' We have our own band, and a football team as well. Sometimes we even win! I'm the manager." He caught my eye, and smiled one of the more gallant smiles of the day. "Yes, I had to give up playing centre forward. I was too good for them. . . . Then every year there's a big Requiem Mass for his mother the Baroness, in the cathedral. We all go to it, but we really go because of him. Such a man, no one can ever forget."

Suddenly I remembered something else about this much loved *kappillan*. "Do you recall saying that Father Salvatore might come again, if he was needed?"

The dwarf gave me a very close glance, under bushy black eyebrows. He countered with his own question. "Do you believe that he *could* come again?"

"Well—no."

"Ah—a true answer! That's the best kind."

"But why would you need him again?"

He took longer to reply to this. I had the feeling that, though I had not yet become a nuisance, Maltese courtesy would not last indefinitely. Finally the dwarf answered: "Troubles never end, do they? Malta has always had troubles. Why should they stop for us? Dun Salv taught us that it has always been the same. Malta is in the way of people, so they want to take it. We've tried to say No, time after time. Now we want to say No for always."

"On your own?"

255

"If we can."

"So you don't want any outsiders?"

"We want tourists." He grinned: he was in full command of this exchange, and we both knew it, and I did not mind. "Just like rich America, or London. But we don't want soldiers or sailors." He must have caught a wary look in my eye, for he continued swiftly. "I'm sorry. I like sailors. Dun Salv liked sailors. Once he said he really wanted to be a sailor, like his dad. But Malta has been the country of everyone else, for hundreds, thousands of years. Now it is ours, and we must prove it. We must be strong ourselves." He sighed. "Oh, I know it sounds mad. It might make us poor. We *are* poor. But not in spirit."

Under the bright sunshine there was a gang of children coming back up the road, truants from the solemn procession. When they saw the dwarf they gathered round him, as if the little man was the one person they really wanted to see in all the world. A small barefoot girl gave a bunch of ragged wild flowers, pink and yellow, picked for private reasons and now awarded with all the generous impulse of the heart.

While the giant beamed, the dwarf thanked her very formally. But his last word was for me: "You see—it has started already. No one is poor today."

Nicholas Monsarrat

Although Nicholas Monsarrat is now a Maltese resident, living on Gozo, he claims no descent from the gallant Maltese Monserrats, Knights of St. John at the time of the Great Siege. After all, as he himself points out, the Knights were surely pledged to celibacy . . . .

No, Gozo today is Nicholas Monsarrat's well-earned 'place in the sun'. After many years of northern European winters he gratefully moved there four years ago, at the time when he was beginning to work on *The Kappillan*. Metaphorically speaking, of course, Monsarrat has had a place in the sun for a good few years now: ever since, in fact, the publication of his sensationally successful *The Cruel Sea*, back in 1951. In the ten years following that he himself estimates his income from his writing at around half a million pounds.

Not that fame and fortune came to him easily. For six long years before the war he had survived only precariously by his pen, writing humorous articles, an unsuccessful stage play, and three novels for which he was paid less than £30 apiece.

During the war he served with distinction in the Royal Navy, and afterwards he entered the Diplomatic Service. He wrote *The Cruel Sea* entirely in his spare time and indeed it was not until the publication of *The Tribe That Lost Its Head* (Condensed Books, 1958), when he was serving as Director of the British Information Service in Canada, that he finally decided to become a full-time writer. Since then, of course, there has been a steady flow of successful novels, and two brilliant volumes of autobiography.

Monsarrat writes very slowly: *The Kappillan* took one year to research and two years to write. He plans ahead in very great detail, and may rewrite a single sentence as many as ten times. It is this perfectionism, perhaps, that gives his books their special excellence, the rare quality of truth with which he is able to invest the lives of his memorable characters.

LA BALSA
Vital Alsar with Enrique Hank Lopez

LA BALSA

The Longest Raft Voyage in History

A CONDENSATION OF THE BOOK BY

Vital Alsar

WITH ENRIQUE HANK LOPEZ

Published by Hodder and Stoughton, London

As their raft bobbed away from the coast of Ecuador, they were fully aware of the perils they faced. Along their 8600-mile route to Australia lay some of the worst weather in the world and treacherous reefs that could destroy them in a moment. They might succumb to starvation or thirst, or to attack by the sharks that would be with them all the way. And could four men—a Spaniard, a Frenchman, a Canadian and a Chilean—endure six months on a tiny floating prison without bitter, even fatal, quarrels?

Vital Alsar was convinced that the ancient South American Indians had made such voyages, and he was determined to prove it. His story of the epic journey is enlivened by humour—much of it provided by the "fifth crew member", an intrepid kitten named Minet—and by the colourful personalities of the men themselves. *La Balsa* ranks with *Kon-Tiki* as one of the great sea adventures of all time.

Survival depends on the total cooperation
of all men—whether their world is a raft,
a village, a country, or a planet.

—Vital Alsar

1

WE BEGAN our journey on one of those dark moonless nights that my superstitious grandmother would have called a "bad time for starting anything."

Two hours past midnight on May 29, 1970, as the tidal currents of the Río Guayas began to ebb, a small dumpy tugboat edged toward the dock to take *La Balsa* under tow. We had hoped to make the first stage of our voyage from Guayaquil, Ecuador, under sail. But after watching the river's unpredictable currents, we had sought the help of a local tugboat captain to guide us out to sea.

Even so, the 120-mile journey down the river and across the turbulent Gulf of Guayaquil would take almost three days, since we could be towed only at low speed. And from the moment the bowline snapped taut, the raft seemed to hold back, like a fighting bull clinging to its *querencia,* that special area of the bullring where it feels safe.

"The raft must know something we don't," said Gabriel. "It senses danger out there."

"No, it just doesn't like being towed," I replied. "Rafts like to ride with the winds and the currents, and they show how unhappy they are in these conditions. Anyway, we'll reach the ocean safely. That's where the real enemy is."

Actually there were many "enemies" lying in wait for us, some of which we couldn't anticipate. But we knew that the equatorial climate of the Pacific would be both blisteringly hot and chillingly cold, that there were untold numbers of treacherous reefs, that sharks would trail us almost daily, that we might fight among ourselves, be crushed by a ship on a fog-shrouded night, or die of starvation or thirst.

That morning the sun rose behind us, revealing the tropical beauty of the Ecuador coast. The Gulf of Guayaquil was rougher than we had expected. In the excitement of the previous night I had been almost unaware of the raft's motion. My attention was focused on the last-minute stashing away of supplies and equipment. Now I became aware of the jerky, lurching movements of the raft, and the splashing of waves across the bow.

My stomach felt it first, a faint queasiness, like serpents moiling inside me. Then I staggered to the stern and vomited. When I told Marc about the snakes in my gut, he laughed, and told me to go and lie down.

The following day, however, Marc, Gabriel, and Normand were also sick. That evening we tried to take our minds off our discomfort by playing poker. In the pale, quivering light of a lantern hanging from the low cabin ceiling, I studied my three companions.

The oldest was Marc Modena, a weather-beaten man of forty-four with a gentle sense of humor. We sometimes called him *Pépère* (Grandpa). His long angular nose and firm mouth appeared to be carved from granite, and his scraggly beard concealed a strong chin. Marc had sailed with me on the ill-fated raft, *Pacifica*, which sank near the Galápagos Islands in 1966, nearly costing us our lives. He lived with his wife and two daughters in Montreal, where he managed a restaurant: he was thus the ideal principal chef and supply master. He was also an experienced sailor, having been for five years a signalman in the French Navy.

Our youngest crew member was Normand Tetreault, twenty-six years old and a Canadian. Because of his thick, bushy light hair and beard, we called him *L'Homme du Bois* (Man of the Woods). Quiet and shy, although quick to smile, he found most conversation a chore. Frequently he had only one comment: "Oh boy," but he could say it in so many different ways that it became a new two-word language. An industrial designer with a lifelong love of sailing, Normand had built his own oceangoing sloop and was studying celestial navigation when Marc asked him to join us.

The pessimist of our crew was Gabriel Salas, a twenty-seven-year-old Chilean geologist. Full of charm and quick intelligence, he had blue-gray eyes that brimmed with mischief. He had been hitchhiking around South America and happened to arrive in Guayaquil as we began building our raft. He immediately volunteered to help us, working as hard as anyone else. I knew, without his having to tell me, that he wanted to sail with us. But I thought he might be too much of a hippie— too unstable for the long haul. He wrote poetry in his spare time and frequently talked about political revolutions. I had reserved judgment on him,

Normand, Gabriel, and Marc, with Minet the "fifth crew member."

hoping to find out how serious he was, but finally I asked, "Will you come with us, Gabriel?"

He responded with a wild "Yippee!" Then he reached into the pocket of his trousers and took out a gold coin worth fifty dollars. "Take this," he said. "I know the rest of you have contributed a lot more, but it's all I have."

Curiously, all of us were about the same height and weight— around five feet ten or eleven inches, and from 160 to 170 pounds. Consequently we could sleep in equal spaces inside our twelve-by-seven-foot cabin, which was only four and a half feet high at its highest point.

At the end of the second day most of us were still seasick and miserable. Our progress would be smoother when we reached the open sea. As we approached that vast expanse, however, Gabriel was unable to mask his natural skepticism. Could we actually sail

8600 miles, twice as far as Thor Heyerdahl's *Kon-Tiki?* Although Heyerdahl's voyage had proved the seaworthiness of balsa rafts built to ancient Indian designs, there were still many people who thought we would fail. For beyond the Tahitian island where Heyerdahl had finally pulled his waterlogged raft ashore, we would face 4300 additional miles of some of the most treacherous seas in the world. Huge coral reefs, sometimes hundreds of miles long, would block our path like jagged petrified monsters half-submerged in angry waves.

Vice-Admiral Samuel Fernandez of the Mexican Navy had given me charts of the South Seas, but he had warned: "Many reefs, even some large ones, haven't been charted yet. And thousands of small ones are lying just below the surface, unseen traps that never get on a map." The vast stretch of water between Samoa and Australia would be especially hazardous for a craft without radar, and night sailing would be as chancy as Russian roulette. Hundreds of vessels had been torn apart in this region.

"You're crazy, Vital!" exclaimed an old Mexican friend. "How can you possibly avoid those reefs without a motor or radar?"

"That's why I'm going," I said. "To prove that a simple raft can be navigated on the most treacherous seas. All the way across the Pacific."

There was considerable method in our madness. I had spent countless days in the naval archives and libraries of Mexico, Ecuador, and Peru, poring through time-yellowed documents, copying sketches of balsa rafts which the Huancavilca Indians were still sailing when the Spaniards arrived in the New World, and studying the pre-Columbian Indians' amazing navigation techniques. Captain Bartolomé Ruiz, one of Pizarro's most skilled navigators, reported to the king of Spain that the Indians had developed safer and better ways of sailing the coastal waters of South America than anything he had seen in Europe. He particularly mentioned the special keel boards, or *guaras,* which gave the Huancavilcas such control of their balsa rafts that they actually maneuvered more effectively than the Spanish galleons.

The distinguished Argentine anthropologist Juan Moricz offers strong evidence of long voyages across the Pacific on these ancient rafts. The Huancavilcas, he writes, thought of the ocean as "a forest of rivers," with predictable currents to and from the Polynesian islands. They also knew about "friendly and unfriendly" winds and the use of astronomy in navigation.

Unlike our friends, my wife, Denise, never tried to dissuade me from the voyage. Sometimes her mother would try to provoke an objection, asking such questions as: "Why must Vital desert his two children? Has he no concern for them? Doesn't he love you?"

Denise would simply shrug her shoulders. "We'll be all right, Mother. You don't understand Vital. He's got to prove whatever he's got to prove, and he won't rest until he does. Nor will I. So please don't interfere." But I knew that the prospect of becoming a young widow was never far from her mind.

Preoccupied by thoughts of my family, I hardly noticed that the Gulf of Guayaquil had been receding and the water had turned from a murky brown to a clear bright green. The Pacific stretched before us.

"We're here!" yelled Gabriel.

We all cupped handfuls of water and joyously splashed it on our faces. With a ceremonial blast of its foghorn the tugboat cast us adrift on the open sea. We felt a mixture of optimism and awe. We would be alone now on this giant body of water that would feed us, wash us, carry us toward our goal—or perhaps kill us at any moment. In our enthusiasm we almost forgot to thank the captain of the tugboat. He had cast off the heavy manila towline at his end, yelling that he was donating it to *La Balsa*, as he circled around us before heading back to port.

"The captain probably knows something he's not telling us," suggested Gabriel with a mock frown.

"Maybe it's the sharks," said Marc. He pointed to a couple of dorsal fins slicing through the water behind us.

"What monsters!" said Gabriel. "They must be ten feet long."

"You'd better get used to them," I said. "They'll be with us all the way."

Freed of the towline, our raft floated with remarkable ease. I was thankful for the care we had taken in selecting the balsa logs, and the hours we had put into the raft's construction.

OUR LOGGING EXPEDITION had begun weeks before in Quito, the capital of Ecuador, nearly two miles above sea level. Our Indian guides, following the precepts of their ancestors, had advised us never to cut down a balsa tree until there is a crescent moon, when the sap has drained from the trunk. Such sap-drained trees are called female, while the heavier sap-filled ones are male. So we had waited patiently for a waning moon, determined to find seven female trees that would resound with a hollow *thooong* when slapped with the heel of the hand.

It was a bright cool morning when we left Quito, crowded into a Land-Rover. When the dirt roads became too narrow, we left the car in a small village and proceeded on foot, with all our camping and woodcutting gear perched on the backs of three sturdy mules. As we made our way slowly down the mountainside, ultimately descending some ten thousand feet, I was dazzled by the dramatic landscape. Here the western slope of the Andean range dipped abruptly to the jungle far below, with paths that teetered on the edge of deep gorges. Progressing single file along the winding precipices, we hugged the walls for safety.

With each downward loop of the path the air grew warmer and damper. Clouds of rising vapor obscured the way ahead. It was like walking into a hothouse. As we neared the jungle floor, the soft clay banks of streams, lush with moss, yielded a bewildering array of ferns and giant plants with leaves like elephant ears. Lizards and snakes slithered in and out, vibrating the leaves behind them. The birds were highly visible in their brilliant plumage—and incredibly vocal.

"They apparently don't like Spaniards and Frenchmen," said Don Cesar Iglesias, our lumber expert, teasingly. "I've never heard them act like this before."

Our guides, who were native to the region, could locate as if by instinct the best balsa forests in Ecuador. Time and again, as we came upon a cluster of balsas, they would slap a tree trunk and listen. If it hadn't the precise hollowness they expected, one of them would mumble to Don Cesar, and he would translate.

"That trunk is too *macho*."

"*Macho?*" asked Normand.

Don Cesar winked. "Your friend Vital knows all about the *machos* and *hembras*," he said.

The old man was referring to my experimentation with male and female balsa wood after our unsuccessful *Pacifica* voyage. The logs of that raft had rotted away in mid-ocean. To avoid another such disaster, I had decided to learn more about balsa. After reading all the literature I could find, I had gone to the Instituto Nacional de Investigaciones Forestales in Mexico City to talk with experts. I had also spent many hours studying the intricate internal structure of balsa through a high-powered microscope, then floating numbered pieces of the wood in a tub of water to register the degree of buoyancy of each one. Consequently, when I met Don Cesar I was crammed full of information about balsa. Annoyed by my arrogance, he had decided to challenge me one night.

"Okay," he had said, placing seven pieces of balsa wood on a table. "Tell me which are the best ones to use on a raft."

Weighing each one in my hand and examining the exposed ends, I had said, "This one's too *macho* . . . this is in between . . . this is two-thirds female . . . this one *macho* . . . this a good female." Right down the line, with very little hesitation.

Don Cesar was obviously thinking about that incident now as we slogged through the jungle, searching for trees.

Finally we found a cluster of the right gender. Although the females were lighter than the sap-filled *machos*, the log cut from each tree trunk probably weighed a ton. Watching our helpers tug and strain, hauling the huge logs one by one to the riverbank, I felt a certain anxiety as to how well they would float.

My doubts vanished, however, as each log hit the water with a great splash, then quickly bobbed up onto the surface. Most trees will float, but balsas can be maneuvered almost like plastic ducks in a bathtub. With hardly any effort we lashed the logs together with liana vines. Then we loaded this temporary raft with bamboo for later use, and climbed on; it took the additional weight without losing any of its buoyancy.

We shoved off from the riverbank into the swirling current that would carry us some 125 miles downstream to our construction site at Guayaquil. Our woodcutters stood on the shore, waving, and yelling *"Buena suerte!"* (Good luck!)

The next afternoon we reached the port city and began construction immediately. Unlashing our seven logs, we slowly rotated one and then another, to find the closest fit between their contours. Marc was in charge of this operation, and he handled the balsas with infinite care, searching for the best pairings.

Supervised by Don Cesar Iglesias, native workers strip bark from balsa logs in the Ecuadorian jungle (left). At Guayaquil the logs are rotated to find the best pairings (near right) before being taken ashore for shaping and grooving (far right).

"He's a born matchmaker," observed Normand.

"It will be a strange match," I said. "They're all females."

"And how will four *machos* like us sustain a life together for six months?" Marc asked.

The question had been there in the back of my mind, persistent as a toothache. How do four men live together, twenty-four hours a day, for six months, in a cramped floating prison cell? We had all heard of prisoners going stir crazy, sometimes killing each other on the tiniest provocation. Obviously we couldn't expect to have found four perfectly stable individuals. But if we were lucky, our neuroses might prove complementary. We needed introverts and extroverts, optimists and pessimists, romantics and realists, conservatives and liberals—a mixed bag of human strengths and weaknesses. Moreover, we had to establish a modus vivendi that would minimize friction and prevent a fatal blowup.

Consequently, one evening about a week after our arrival at Guayaquil, I leaned back in my chair at the Hosteria Madrid, the neighborhood restaurant where we ate after work, and broached the subject as casually as possible. "I've been thinking we should have some guidelines," I said.

"Like the division of work?" asked Marc.

"Well, that's important. But I mean our relationship to each

other. On a long journey in such close quarters we're bound to get on each other's nerves from time to time." I hesitated, searching for the right words. "First, we should never violate each other's personal space. We should never—under any circumstances—touch each other. No horseplay, no wrestling—"

"But why?" interrupted Gabriel. "If it's only playing . . ."

"That's just the point," I replied. "Once you have violated another man's space, even in fun, it will be easier to touch him in anger. So we have to imagine that each of us is surrounded by an invisible bubble of privacy that must never be shattered. And another thing, we must never criticize each other."

Gabriel softly drummed on the table with his fingers. "You think even a small criticism could blow up into a fight?"

"Precisely. When you start to complain about a man's eating habits or his snoring—it makes no difference that you're only joking—human nature dictates that he will end up hating you."

"You want us to become saints," said Marc.

"For about six months, until we get to Australia. Then we can be humans again."

The following morning I was up early to check the progress on our raft. Marc had indeed performed the best marriage between the seven logs, with the longest, a forty-two-foot trunk, in the middle. Their forward ends were cut on a diagonal to form a pointed bow. We then bound them together with thick hemp ropes, presoaked in water for added pliancy, carefully fitting the ropes into parallel grooves we had carved into the logs. To preserve the logs, Marc coated their undersides with crude oil.

The raft takes shape as heavy crossbeams are lashed across the logs.

Now we were ready to start on the superstructure. Four heavy beams were laid across the base logs and firmly secured with one-inch hemp. Then a deck of split bamboo was placed across the beams, creating narrow storage spaces between the deck and the logs. The deck itself was covered with mats of woven reeds.

It was slow, tedious work: hundreds of knots had to be tied with great precision, for if only a few were carelessly tied, our raft might rip apart in mid-ocean. I found myself rechecking some that Gabriel had tied near the starboard stern. Each one was perfect. When I saw Normand checking my knots, I laughed. "We're all spies," I said. "No one trusts anyone."

Gabriel was no less vigilant when we started to build the cabin, checking everyone's handiwork as if he were a straw boss on a construction gang. "We've got to be careful with the roof," I said. "If it comes loose in a high wind, it'll be like a second sail." Thus we took special pains with the walls of woven bamboo reeds and with the roof made from bamboo slats and tough, pliable banana leaves.

In front of the cabin we erected the 30-foot mast: two poles of hard, durable mangrove wood, tied at the top to form an inverted V. Atop this was a small crow's nest and a flagpole from which, in good weather, we would fly the Spanish colors.

The sail was a rectangle of strong canvas, 18 feet wide and 21 feet high. In a moment of whimsy I decorated it with a huge bright-red sun, in the center of which I painted a sketch of *La Balsa.* There wasn't room for a spare sail, but we had plenty of needles and thread for repairs.

Perhaps the raft's most advantageous feature was its set of *guaras,* vertical keel boards, or centerboards, each two feet wide and six to eight feet long.

Complete but for the mast, *La Balsa* prepares to enter the water.

Situated between the logs, they protruded under the raft like multiple fins—three in a V-shaped formation near the bow, two under the cabin, and four in a straight line at the stern.

Ecuadorian fishermen, who steer their balsa rafts much as their ancestors did, had shown us how the *guaras* were used. To steer the raft from left to right, we would slide the starboard (right) *guaras* deeper into the water while pulling the portside (left) *guaras* out of the water. The most important were the *guaras* at the corners of the stern. These would have to be shifted to compensate for winds blowing from an angle. Although simple, the technique is crucial to keeping a raft on a steady course.

The final addition was a tall dignified "throne" of choice balsa wood, with a large hole in the seat like an old-fashioned privy. And that's exactly what it was—an amphibious toilet, which we perched on a special portside shelf hanging over the water.

273

Several weeks later, our raft completed, we proudly inspected our work. Not a single nail, wire cable, or metal spike had been used. We wanted *La Balsa* to duplicate, as closely as possible, those ancient craft that had been navigated across the Pacific thousands of years before.

2

THE DAY we left port, fifty or sixty friends and skeptics came aboard our little raft at Guayaquil to wish us well—or to shake their heads with dismay. One optimist was Senora Paladines, the wife of a local doctor. Wearing a floppy hat and a flowery dress, she carried in her white-gloved hands a scrawny black and white kitten. "It's a mascot, for good luck!" she exclaimed.

"But it's only a baby," I protested. "This is going to be a rough journey."

"Kittens are always good luck," she said.

One potbellied old sailor said, "Two or three days is all I give this thing before the logs start soaking up water like a sponge."

The doctor's wife cut him short. "Nonsense," she said. "*La Balsa* will go all the way to Australia."

Grateful as I was to her, I was not happy with the mascot she'd given us. We already had four pets: a much older cat, Cocos; a large parrot, Lorita; and two smaller parrots. I would have to give this fragile little creature away before setting sail.

More pressing matters, however, demanded our immediate attention. Our secondhand radio—a patchwork of Japanese tubes, German condensers, an American tuning device, and Ecuadorian adhesive tape—suddenly went dead. Joe Megan, an American who happens to be president of one of Ecuador's largest electronics companies, helped us fix it, warning us that it probably wouldn't transmit anything beyond a few hundred miles.

We hardly listened to such talk as we loaded our storage area with 52 gallons of fresh water, kerosene for our small stove, gasoline to run the radio's generator, extra rope, a few books, medicines, and fishing gear.

Marc's special concern was the food supply. In a wooden box

274

behind the cabin we had 330 pounds of canned fruit; 220 pounds each of potatoes, green bananas, and unripened oranges; and 44 pounds each of flour, rice, and dried beans. We expected to catch fish every day.

It was Marc's duty, which he seemed to enjoy a bit too much, to curb our natural appetites. Nothing extra that anyone wanted to take (pizza for Gabriel, mangoes for me) could meet his rigid specifications. "It will spoil without refrigeration," he would say.

I managed to eat three farewell mangoes as, for the benefit of a cameraman, we lightly stitched Salvador Dali's beautiful painting over the sun I had painted on our sail. Dali had given us an emblematic portrait of our raft as a good-luck token, but we had decided to protect it against the sun and salt winds with a plastic sheath and only to display it when the weather permitted.

Immersed in all these preparations, I completely forgot about the kitten. Not until several hours after we had gotten under way, when I felt it crawling across my bare leg as I lay inside the cabin, did I realize our unwanted mascot was still with us. "What's this damned thing doing here?" I yelled, lunging for it.

Gabriel held the kitten out of my reach. "I'll take care of him," he said. He turned to Marc and Normand for support. "I'll let him sleep with me."

Realizing it would be impossible to change his mind, I finally gave in. Let them learn for themselves, I thought. The cat smells would soon drive them crazy.

Much to my annoyance this little creature, whom they christened Minet, was the only one that showed no signs of seasickness during those first few days at sea. Skittering around the deck on his tiny white paws, he looked almost perversely healthy.

"I hate healthy cats," I groaned. Still, I couldn't resist the kitten's outrageous charm or his refusal to be disliked, which is typical of so many rascals. Consequently, when a huge wave gushed over the bow and caught Minet in its backwash, I jumped to the rescue, colliding with Gabriel and Marc. When the wave receded, there was Minet clinging to the edge of the raft, with his small, sharp claws buried in the log, shaking his water-soaked head and mewing like fury. Stumbling back to the cabin with the kitten in his hand, Gabriel grabbed a towel and dried him off. "Don't cry, Minet," he mumbled.

Shortly after his narrow escape, Minet was back, frisking about the deck, playing with the crabs swept aboard by the waves, hovering around Normand as he pulled in a fiercely flapping tuna. As Normand began cutting it up, Minet lapped the blood off the deck as if it were milk.

Having been unable to consume anything but hot bouillon since we set sail, I was momentarily sickened by the kitten's appetite. Yet I couldn't help envying its lust for life.

Unfortunately neither Minet nor Cocos was housebroken. They laid claim to one corner of the cabin, and the smell became intolerable. "Gabriel," I said, "you promised to train those cats. Now look what we have—a real mess."

He shrugged. "I'll try harder, now that I'm not so seasick."

"You'll never housebreak them," I said. "We'll simply have to keep them outside. That goes for the birds, too."

"Outside!" he protested. "But they'll get washed away."

There was a long, painful silence, but I was determined not to give in, knowing that my low tolerance for odors would eventually result in anger.

"I guess you're right," he said in a barely audible voice. "It's silly to fight about cats." He took Minet and Cocos outside.

On the third or fourth day we were escorted by several large dolphins, scores of tuna and bonito, plus other species we couldn't identify. And toward sunset—an incredible burst of flame across the entire horizon—some flying fish came whizzing past our sail and plopped on deck, flapping toward the cabin as Cocos scrambled for cover. Minet, on the other hand, started circling one of the fish and pawing at it.

"*Cuidado* (Look out), Minet!" said Gabriel, holding him back by the tail. "He'll swat you."

The smaller flying fish we used as bait for the more edible thirty-pound dolphins; the larger ones were fried in a skillet. Useful as they were, they often proved a nuisance. At night they would come winging through the air unseen, often crashing into our faces. One gave me a black eye that bothered me for a week.

Other small fish, such as sardines, were tossed on deck by the waves, and one of the night watch's final chores was to collect them for the day's meal. Occasionally Minet would participate in the roundup, and sometimes he would carry a sardine into the cabin as an offering to one of the sleeping crew. I was not amused when he tried to feed me one in the middle of a prolonged snore.

By now our seasickness had subsided, though mine had left me with a fever. We had all developed hearty appetites, especially when Marc prepared fillets of shark stuffed with crab meat. But most of the time our seafood meals were plainer fare. I was a mediocre cook; Normand and Gabriel left much to be desired. Since cooking chores were evenly divided, we ate well every fourth day.

Shortly after dawn of our sixth day at sea the wind shifted suddenly, blowing from astern with increased force. We struggled to pull in the sail and were nearly swept overboard before we managed to haul it down. The waves grew higher, pushing us forward at a breakneck pace, and our main worry was the danger of broaching—twisting around broadside so that a breaker could roll us over. Finally, by maneuvering the *guaras,* we were able to keep *La Balsa* moving with the waves, which resembled rows of foam-capped mountains marching behind, then under and past us.

Time and again the peaks would curl forward and splash down into the trough we had just vacated. And once in a while a huge rogue wave would break the rhythm, dropping tons of water against us broadside. Had any of these hit us a few seconds sooner, the thundering avalanche would have smashed our cabin like a straw hat. Fearing that possibility, we stayed outside, clinging to the crossbeams, while the raft pitched, yawed, reeled, and spun around like a matchstick in a whirlpool. Fortunately we had left the *guaras* in the proper positions and our steering worked by itself, for the waves blinded us and incapacitated us completely.

Then gradually the gale shifted away from us, and the watery Alps became a rippling prairie.

TOWARD the end of our first week we reached the Humboldt Current, that broad cold mass of water that sweeps north from the Antarctic, runs along the coasts of Chile and Peru, then veers northwest across the Pacific just below the equator. I checked the sea temperature and found it much colder than I had expected. The water was also a deeper, richer green, indicating an abundance of plankton, the drifting forms of marine life, ranging in size from microorganisms to jellyfish, which move along with the sea currents and provide food for fish and other larger marine bodies. Since we would be riding the Humboldt well past the Galápagos

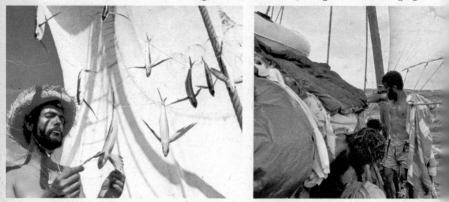

Left: Vital, with a few minutes' catch of flying fish.
Right: After a storm bedding is spread on the cabin roof to dry.

Islands, we would be assured of a steady supply of fresh fish.

Halfway to the Galápagos we began shedding our clothes for two reasons. With waves and spray constantly washing over us, and frequently rain, too, we soon realized we wouldn't be completely dry again until journey's end. We spent hours wringing out our clothes and blankets, and hanging them up, until the next barrage of waves soaked everything again.

The second reason was the blisteringly hot sun. Soon after dawn each day we abandoned our sweaters, shoes, and shirts, until finally we were wearing only skimpy loincloths. The 115-degree heat would make the cabin feel like the inside of a boiling teakettle. "I could poach a fish in there," Marc observed one afternoon as clouds of steam drifted through the doorway.

Thus, unable to shelter ourselves against the noonday sun, we would lie or sit helplessly on the deck, getting darker than the natives who had helped us cut down the balsa trees. We also got blisters, and our hair became so dry it felt like needle-sharp wire filled with electricity. Worse yet, Normand and I broke out in saltwater boils that itched worse than poison ivy.

But when the sun disappeared and the night winds blew, the temperature would drop fifty or sixty degrees in a few hours. We'd be shivering in the sudden chill, and all we could do was wrap ourselves in damp clothes and blankets, and huddle inside the cabin. "I can't believe that you can freeze and catch pneumonia right on the equator," Gabriel said one night.

"Don't worry, Gabriel," Marc said comfortingly. "After sunrise you'll long for the cold again."

Now, favored by a steady wind out of the southeast, we sailed a course that would take us well south of the Galápagos Islands. On clear days I would check our course on the sextant. I generally took at least three sightings of the sun, then plotted our location on a chart. We were moving at a slow, even pace, which we could gauge by tossing slivers of banana leaves into the water and then counting the seconds it took for the raft to pass them. If it took us ten seconds to pass the marker, our 42-foot raft would be moving 84 yards per minute, thus covering approximately three miles per hour, or 72 miles a day. This yard-by-yard progress might have been disheartening, but we did not dare let it depress us.

As we moved into the swiftest part of the Humboldt, the waves got bigger. Standing watch one morning Normand failed to notice a large wave breaking toward the stern. It washed him overboard before he could yell for help. Fortunately he was able to scramble back on board after a frantic few seconds.

"What were you doing—chasing sharks?" I asked him.

"Oh boooy," he said in an expiring whisper.

"Well, you can't chase sharks without a rope around your waist," I said, thereby establishing a rule that all watchmen must be attached to the mast by a long rope. Even as I spoke I noticed two sharks cruising about twenty feet astern. They could have chewed Normand to mincemeat.

Since there were four of us, each had two three-hour turns at the helm every twenty-four hours. Those first days, when we were

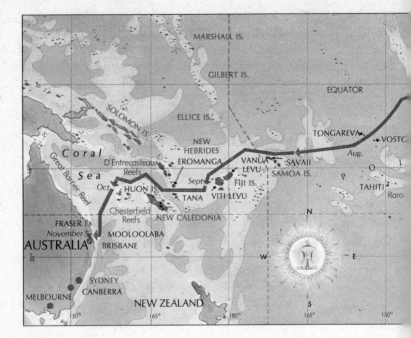

still relatively soft landlubbers, were especially hard. Fatigued and muscle-sore I would crawl into my sleeping bag, but inevitably, just as I fell asleep, someone would awaken me for some emergency. Thus I was finding it impossible to shake off the high fevers that persisted long after my seasickness had gone.

"You'd better lay off for a couple of days," Marc finally warned.

But having seldom been ill I foolishly believed that the best way to fight sickness was to ignore it. So I took aspirin and continued with my share of work, drenched in cold sweat and suffering an occasional dizzy spell.

As it turned out I had no time to rest. On the ninth day a huge storm assaulted us close to sundown, gradually forcing us north. In an effort to avoid the treacherous currents just south of the Galápagos, we pulled in the sail and lashed down our *guaras,* hoping they would hold us to a westerly path. Then, having seen how well the cabin weathered the first storm, we took refuge in it.

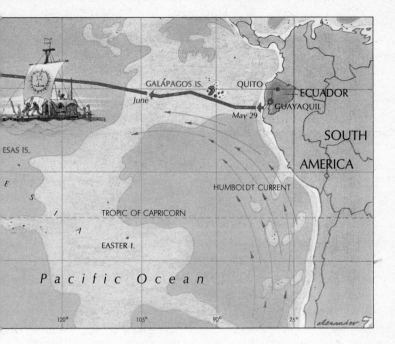

The waves grew to ten or fifteen feet high. "Tie your waists!" I yelled, securing my own and tying the loose end of the rope to a post. "It's going to be rough!"

"What about the animals?" asked Gabriel, already holding Minet in his arms.

"I'll take Cocos," Marc volunteered. "Vital can take Lori, and Normand the smaller parrots."

Then it came. A huge mass of water loomed over us for several agonizing seconds, then crashed into the cabin, spinning the raft around. Cawing madly, Lori tried to flutter out of my grasp. Minet let out a frightened but angry meow, then another, as the next wave gushed through the doorway and tilted the cabin crazily.

But the bamboo cabin held firm throughout the two-hour storm, the knots of the ropes pulling even tighter with the additional strain. When the sea finally subsided, however, the interior was chaos, our bedding strewn about like limp dishrags.

Gabriel, with Minet now perched cockily on his shoulder, was the first to leave the cabin, quickly surveying the damage with a flashlight. The rest of us followed.

"Not too bad," Gabriel said. "We came off pretty well."

"I'm a little worried about our course," I said, feeling slightly dizzy again. "Damned storm probably carried us too far north."

I dragged myself back to the cabin, hot flushes of renewed fever rising through my chest and head. We were approaching the Galápagos, where my first raft expedition had come to a sorry end, and I kept thinking about that voyage.

The winds and ocean currents had pushed the *Pacifica* into the treacherous eddies north of the Galápagos. Round and round we had gone, imprisoned in a huge loop of contrary currents and erratic winds, unable to get back to the westward swing of the Humboldt Current. Days, weeks, finally months had passed with no ships coming near us. Our only contact with land had been our often malfunctioning radio. Finally, after 143 days at sea, the raft had begun to absorb water, the balsas rotting from the core out as the sap fermented.

I remembered the frantic messages to and from the radio hams who had followed our progress, the bizarre upward tilt of the raft as the stern began to settle. We had scrambled onto the roof of the cabin as several sharks slithered across the sinking logs. Then, as the cabin itself began to founder, we had been miraculously rescued by a German ship—just two hours before the raft submerged completely.

I had relived that nightmare adventure many times, and so had Marc. But both of us had been determined to try again.

The next morning the sea was still running high, but with the sun beating down on the matted deck, everything looked clean and bright. Gradually, the sea grew calmer.

"You're looking much better, Vital," Marc said.

"I think so," I said. "I'm ready to read my maps again."

With Normand's help I laid out the navigation map Admiral Fernandez had given me, and located our whereabouts with the aid of a compass and my sextant.

My calculations indicated that the southeast trade winds and the Humboldt Current had been sending us northwest at about fifty to sixty sea miles per day. Once again we were faced with the possibility of drifting into the trap where the *Pacifica* finally sank. With great caution I swung the sail a few degrees to the west, shifting our path from northwest to northwest by west. With luck we would swing west with the main part of the Humboldt, ten or twenty miles south of the Galápagos.

"I wish we were going closer," said Gabriel. "I've been told that the islands are beautiful."

"They are," I said, and described for him the jagged black lava rocks rising out of the sea, polished for centuries by Pacific waters and gleaming in the equatorial sun like black diamonds. I also told him about the multicolored lizards, flightless cormorants waddling along the coasts, marine iguanas that looked like miniature prehistoric monsters, and playful sea lions body surfing and drying themselves to a light beige on the hot sand.

"There are also enormous turtles in this region," I said.

"I know," said Gabriel. "Normand caught one this morning." He pointed over his shoulder. "We've got him tied to the stern."

"I've got an idea," said Marc. "We'll tow him behind us to attract fish. The dorados are always chasing turtles."

Gabriel made a hole in the back end of the shell and secured a strong line through it. Then we lowered the huge turtle into the water. Soon a procession of dorados, tuna, and sardines was trailing after us. That evening we had Dorado L'Modena, since it was, fortunately, Marc's day to cook.

After supper we all sat on deck, playing Parcheesi and speculating about the weather. During a lapse in conversation I became aware of a continuous creaking and groaning in the raft under us—the deck, the crossbeams, the mast, the cabin, the *guaras*, were constantly straining against the ropes. No raft built with inflexible nails and screws could have lasted very long on these waters. Would our ropes withstand the ceaseless friction?

The next morning I examined a few, and was relieved to find they were in excellent shape. The balsa wood showed no signs of excessive wear, and I detected no shredding of the sail—though the sun I had painted in the center was somewhat faded.

Aware of my scrutiny, Marc touched the lower margins of the painting. "I'm glad we've got the Salvador Dali painting encased in plastic. The salt winds would ruin it."

"How did you get him to paint it?" Gabriel asked me.

I had been convinced from the outset that we needed a fine painting for our sail, something that would inspire us all the way to Australia. Being a Spaniard, I naturally wanted to have it

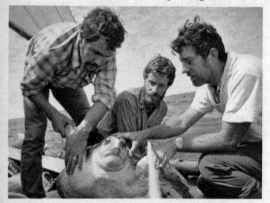

painted by one of my countrymen—either Picasso or Dali. It would have to be a gift, however, as we could not afford even a pencil sketch by one of these artistic giants. I soon found out that Picasso would be impossible to reach, but I managed to get Dali's phone number in Madrid and called him. Not until later did I realize that it was three in the morning when his phone rang.

Vital, Gabriel, and Marc inspect the giant turtle.

"Aalooo," said a raspy voice at the other end.

"Is this Salvador Dali?" I asked.

"I think so," he said sleepily.

"This is Vital Alsar," I said. "The man who is sailing a raft from Ecuador to Australia. I want you to do a painting for my sail."

A long silence on his end of the line.

"Maestro? Are you still there?"

"Yes, I'm here."

So I proceeded with a breathless spiel about my need for a talisman, stressing that I couldn't pay for it. Finally, I asked, "Will you give me the painting?"

Another agonizing silence.

"*Olé!*" he said, his voice coming to life. "*Olé! Olé! Como tienes macho, hombre. Sí, te lo doy.*" He meant that I had a lot of nerve and that he would give me a painting.

Several months later, in the presence of numerous reporters and TV newscasters, with klieg lights and cameras, Dali spread out a canvas on the floor of a hotel banquet room, and painted an "instant masterpiece" for *La Balsa*. It was a rather abstract painting of a raft, a heart, and a huge sun against a background that symbolized courage and daring.

Later that afternoon, when I crawled into the cabin, I saw Minet sitting there facing Dali's painting, which we had taken down and stored against the rear wall. He whirled around like a burglar caught red-handed. In his paw was a loose end of the string we had used to hemstitch the canvas. He bolted between my legs and escaped.

There goes a cool kitten, I thought. And a born delinquent. It was hard to believe he was less than five weeks old.

During dinner I was about to tell the others about Minet's latest stunt when I was interrupted by a raspy sound. It was Gabriel. With every bite, he would crunch his teeth into the base of the spoon—*craack!*—then scrape the food off with his upper front teeth, producing a *rassp* like a shovel on bare cement. *Craack rassp craack rassp*—all through every meal. It was beginning to annoy me almost beyond endurance. But, according to my own rule, I couldn't complain to him about it.

Worse yet was the way Marc ate on the days when Gabriel or Normand did the cooking. He would show his disdain for their food by dropping his lower jaw after every chew, letting it sag for three or four seconds, and then swallowing with a painful effort.

Occasionally, when my nerves reached the breaking point, I would sneak off to my favorite retreat behind the cabin and brood until my pent-up emotions gradually subsided.

We each had such a retreat, where no one would bother us. Normand's was the starboard corner of the bow; Marc's was on the portside edge of the stern; and Gabriel would always sit inside the cabin. The time we spent there would vary from a half hour to several hours, and the only one who dared to intrude was Minet. But he himself had a retreat—the forward tip of the cabin roof, where he would sit on his haunches, immobile as a gargoyle.

3

By the grace of God and strong southeastern winds, we managed to skirt the Galápagos without being snared in the treacherous crosscurrents. But our luck soon came to an end.

Our pets began to die. One by one they succumbed to a strange viral infection that I later learned was akin to psittacosis, the deadly and highly contagious fever carried by certain birds and readily transmitted to other animals—as well as to humans.

One of the little parrots, Fernando, was the first to go. He had shrieked a few swearwords on our first day at sea, but after a while he could barely manage a weak phlegmy *aaark*. Finally, on June 16, he fell dead. We slowly lowered his cage into the sea, then watched it gently sinking as a hundred sardines converged upon it.

Cocos, the older cat, was the next to die. He had been sick, off and on, from the very beginning, feebly resisting Minet's devilish pranks. How he must have resented the kitten's good health.

"You can't kill a kitten that drinks blood," Marc had observed one morning when Minet was skittering around the sleepy prone body of the larger cat, vainly trying to start a game of tag. "There you have the perfect symbols of life and death."

A few hours later Cocos crawled into a corner of the cabin and quietly lay down to die. Minet was nuzzling his face, apparently trying to awaken him, when I discovered the body. We wrapped him in a bag and lowered him into the water.

The other little parrot, Isabel, was the next victim. After she died, Gabriel assumed the role of ship's doctor, turning his attention to the last remaining parrot, who was also very ill. But Gabriel's practices were somewhat unorthodox. He tried to cure Lorita by crooning a lullaby as he poured wine into her beak. Two hours later she was madly flapping around her cage, but then she let out a loud, raspy squawk and flopped to the floor, dead.

We were all visibly shaken. Marc quietly wrapped her in an old blue shirt and tossed her overboard, as far out as he could. Instantly an eight-foot shark grabbed the unexpected feast.

It was a grim reminder of what might happen to all of us. My own fever had refused to respond to large doses of aspirin, and I had what I assumed to be severe bronchitis. (Later I learned that I was probably suffering from the same disease that had killed our pets, but fortunately I didn't know it.) Weak and depressed, I saw everything in shades of gray. When I tried to play Parcheesi, the dice felt like hunks of lead in my palm. Trying to sleep at night, I could hear the beating of my heart above the noise of shifting logs and creaking ropes. I was to suffer this way for forty-five days, and for fifteen of them I was hardly able to leave the cabin. But eventually my fever subsided. I could see the relief in my crewmates' faces as they noted my improvement.

Perhaps to celebrate my return to the living, Gabriel, who knew my mania for cleanliness, set up an experimental washing machine. By hanging his pants and shirts under the raft, where the onrushing waves produced a natural agitation, he got a fairly effective saltwater wash. "I'm going to patent this and start a new business in Chile," he said. But by the fourth or fifth washing his pants were torn to shreds, and he gave up the idea. "It's all capitalist nonsense anyway," he said. He then launched into a long lecture on the glories of socialism. Inevitably he started to criticize the United States Government, which provoked counterarguments from Marc and me.

"There's more freedom in the U.S. than any other place in the world," I told him. "Even for the poor."

"How can you say that, Vital?" he protested, smacking the steering oar for emphasis. "Look how the black man is treated."

We would go on like that for hours, our voices rising, our fists pounding.

Such an argument was cut short one night by the sudden appearance of a huge pair of gaping jaws, with a double row of sharp teeth, moving toward the raft as if to bite off a chunk six feet wide. Then the jaws slowly closed and seemed to back away. Rushing to the edge of the raft, we saw an enormous "sea monster" with a broad flat head like a toad, two ridiculously small eyes on the sides, and on the immense back a fin five or six feet tall. His entire body was covered with phosphorescent plankton, so that he was clearly visible in the moonlit night. And in front of him swam a mass of striped pilot fish, reminding me of armed henchmen preceding a powerful underworld figure.

"*Mira*, Minet," Gabriel whispered to the fascinated kitten on his shoulder. "There you have the ugliest thing in the world."

"Are the fish running interference for him?" asked Marc. "Or is he simply following them because he's too dumb to know where to go by himself?"

The answer came almost immediately. Diving suddenly, the creature lost his escort, but the striped fish quickly dived after him and regained their up-front position, like a bunch of yes-men frantically trying to second-guess the boss.

I was later told that he was probably a whale shark, a species said to reach seventy feet in length, and often weighing as much as twenty tons. Ours was only half that large, but we all felt it could be terribly dangerous if aroused.

"One swat with that tail could tear this raft apart," said Marc.

The giant shark hesitated beneath us, nuzzling the barnacles under the starboard logs and tilting us slightly to port.

"The sonofabitch is teasing us," I said.

Then, as the huge body rolled and heaved under the bow, the entire raft swayed back and forth with a loud creaking and rasping. For twenty minutes the monster remained under *La Balsa*, rocking it, all of us waiting for the sudden heave that would surely capsize us. Finally Marc reached for a thirty-pound dorado he'd begun to slice for dinner and flung it as far as he could to starboard. Immediately the striped escort fish trailed after it, and the monster followed them.

"You're a genius!" I said to Marc.

"I was a fool not to do it sooner," he growled. "But now we won't have Dorado L'Modena for supper. Just plain ordinary tuna."

Marc's tuna dishes were never ordinary, but Gabriel's were something else again. The next evening, after toiling over our little stove for more than two hours, Gabriel served us fillets of tuna floating in a goo of highly spiced grease, accompanied by a huge mound of black beans. I had swallowed two mouthfuls of the beans before I detected the odor of kerosene.

"Gabriel, you've poisoned us!" I yelled.

"What's wrong?" he said, calmly chewing a mouthful.

"The beans! They have kerosene in them."

"They do taste a little different," he finally said. "I'd better check." Though it is difficult to believe, Gabriel had actually cooked the beans in kerosene instead of water, mistaking the gasoline can for the water jug. How he had managed to avoid causing an explosion or a fire is something only his angels can explain.

Normand's manner that evening disturbed me. He had noticed nothing unusual about the beans and would probably have eaten them all if we hadn't told him. When Gabriel and I laughed about the mistake, Normand simply stared beyond us at the darkening waters, his eyes blank.

"Something's wrong with our friend," said Gabriel when we were back in the cabin.

Inside the cabin Gabriel relaxes on a sleeping mat.

"I'm afraid so," I said. "He's been that way all day." His problem, whatever it was, plagued him for the next few days. His response to any order was mechanical, like a bearded robot.

Somehow, we had to break into his withdrawal before it was too late. It would be disastrous to have him break down on the raft. I had visions of him succumbing to a serious state of immobility, or perhaps going to the other extreme, suddenly bursting into a raving anger and violence that none of us could deal with.

On the third day of his strange mood, I saw him standing near the stern with his eyes fixed on the far horizon. "The Eiffel Tower is to your left, monsieur," I said in my best Parisian French. "Or perhaps it's of no interest to you people from Marseille."

There was a faint hint of a smile, but not a word.

An hour later—once again relying on my amateur theories of psychological problems—I walked up to him with ramrod severity.

"I must collect your passenger ticket," I said. "We can't allow any stowaways on this ship."

No response this time, not even a twitch.

Clearly we must try something more dramatic, something that would force his involvement. Perhaps a bit of psychodrama would help. Taking a flying fish from the kitchen basket, I started to slice it with a knife, knowing that Minet would soon come around to lick up the blood. Sure enough, within a few seconds he was squirming between my legs to get at the red puddles.

Cursing Minet loudly, I grabbed him and threw him across the deck, straight toward Normand. By reflex action he caught him. Still feigning rage I rushed toward him, yelling, "Give me that damned cat—I'm going to drown him!"

"Like hell you will," snarled Normand. "He's my cat."

It worked; I had broken through to him. Normand grinned. "Oooooh boy," was all he said, but it was music to our ears.

The incident reminded us again of our limitations. What, for example, would we do in case of serious illness or a traumatic injury such as a shark bite? Anticipating these contingencies, I had gotten some practical training from a group of Mexican doctors who were personal friends and patrons of our voyage. They had made me keenly aware of both the strength and the vulnerability of the human body, and had impressed upon me the frightening possibility that I might be called upon to perform a primitive operation. I kept our butcher knife sharpened to a keen edge at all times. What worried me greatly about the prospect of performing surgery was the continuous motion of the raft, even on the calmest seas.

I was most concerned about shark bites, because of the sharks' constant presence. Toss an empty can from the raft, and one was there to snatch it. A piece of wood or paper—another shark. They were more menacing either very early or late in the day, when their bellies were empty. During the voyage we harpooned about one hundred sharks to keep them from scaring away the fish that followed us. Those fish were our natural larder.

One afternoon, about mid-June, Gabriel was cleaning a tuna near the stern when suddenly a huge wave carrying a six-foot shark washed over the raft. The shark's nose bumped against Gabriel's hip, knocking him against the rear wall of the cabin. Assuming someone was playing a joke on him, he shouted in mock anger, "What kind of game is this?"

Then he noticed the shark floundering on the deck. *"Mira, el monstruo!"* he said. Marc finally killed it with a harpoon.

It was always dangerous to kill one on board because you could never be sure it was really dead. You might bend over an inert fish, only to be clobbered suddenly by its tail. Once we cut one open and took out its pulsating heart, holding it in our hands and feeling it throb for several minutes. Sometimes a shark's heart will stay alive that way for more than a half hour.

Their will to live was incredible. I remember a seven-foot shark that trailed us for several miles, west of the Galápagos. We had just caught a fairly large dolphin when the shark zipped in and chewed off its tail. Marc rammed his harpoon into the shark's back again and again, but, although blood spurted from the wounds, the shark kept snapping at the dolphin, until he had almost devoured it. Then, after a last desperate lunge, he died.

Minet is introduced to his archenemy, the shark.

That night, as I lay half asleep with the high fever that still plagued me from time to time, I was aware of a strange gnawing noise. I crept through the cabin doorway and saw thousands of fish nibbling at the edges of our raft; in the bright moonlight their eyes, unblinking and neon green, stared at me from all angles. Then, as someone behind me shouted my name, they all disappeared. It was Marc.

"There were thousands of fish," I said, shaking my head.

"There's nothing there. You must have had a nightmare."

IT WAS, INDEED, nothing more than a fever-induced hallucination. I've been told that sailors often have such hallucinations. The American sea captain Joshua Slocum, on his solo voyage around the world aboard the *Spray*, had visits from a ghostly figure who claimed to be a pilot for Christopher Columbus. I like to think that it was the ghost of Juan de la Cosa, the man who drew the famous world map and who sailed with Columbus to the new world. He was from my home city, the port of Santander.

In my childhood I was forever reminded that America might never have been discovered without the help of Juan de la Cosa, "the pride of Santander." He was always on my mind as I sat by the harbor, watching the fishing trawlers go off into the treacherous Bay of Biscay. I remember the women wailing for the men who did not come back. The harshness of the sea was etched into the character of these people—pessimistic, brooding, rugged. I loved the fishermen; they were brave, good-hearted men. Yet they feared the sea; they allowed it to dominate them.

I spent many happy days fishing or sailing on the coastal waters. "That boy will be eaten by sharks someday," my father prophesied. "He's always fooling around on the ocean. All sailors are crazy."

"What about Columbus?" my mother asked, a hint of defiance in her usually soft voice.

"He was crazy, too," my father answered. "No one else was foolhardy enough to try to reach the east by sailing west."

My childhood was interrupted by the Spanish civil war. Night after night the city of Santander, controlled by the Republican Loyalist forces, was bombed by German airplanes. Our family survived, though we had some narrow escapes.

In 1954, anxious to see the world, I dropped out of school and signed up with the Spanish foreign legion, where I became a full lieutenant at the age of twenty-two. Assigned to Morocco, my battalion had to guard some munition dumps along the Moroccan-Algerian border, fighting off attacks from Algerian rebels. While there, I came across a Spanish edition of *Kon-Tiki*, which so impressed me that I began mulling over the possibility of sailing my own balsa raft someday.

Before I could consider any such project, however, I had to

complete my education and find a way to earn my living. With the thought of becoming a language professor, I enrolled at the Alliance Française in Paris for a course of study in French. To pay my tuition, room, and board, I worked as a longshoreman, waiter, and furniture mover, attending classes after work.

After three and a half years there, and a similar period in Germany, where I learned the language while earning my keep as a construction worker, I found that the idea of an ocean adventure had become an obsession. Of course, such an expedition would cost money (even with all my bumming and scrounging of supplies, the first voyage would run about eight thousand dollars). So when someone at the construction company told me there were good, high-paying jobs in Labrador, I decided my language professorship could wait, and boarded a plane for Canada.

I worked four months at the iron mines at Wabush Lake, and managed to save almost all of the four thousand dollars I earned. I was still considerably short of my goal, so I went to Montreal and got a job teaching Spanish at a local language school. By the time I had enough money I had met Marc Modena, and we had agreed to undertake a raft voyage across the Pacific.

4

IN JUNE, as we were breezing along on a westerly current far beyond the Galápagos, we had several nights of intense fog that worried us. My charts indicated that we were crossing through shipping lanes, and we all realized the danger of a nighttime collision with a vessel that might not see our feeble lamps. Fog, particularly at night, was to be one of our worst enemies.

One night we were sailing through a thick patchy fog—the visibility ranging from five feet to two hundred—when Marc noticed some lights directly ahead of us. A large ship was moving toward us fast. Grabbing a flashlight, Marc tried to signal the approaching vessel, but the ship kept coming straight at us. Finally he managed to light two flares and shoot them upward. By then the ship loomed ahead of us like a rhinoceros bent on destruction.

"Get ready to jump," I yelled. But it wasn't necessary. The ship angled to the right, charging past us at full speed, creating a chaos of waves that hit us broadside. "That was a real miracle," I said to Marc.

When the waves had subsided, we could see, through a break in the fog, that the ship had stopped about two miles away. "We'd better let them know who we are," I said.

The ship slowly steamed back toward *La Balsa,* its crew exchanging signals with us. Marc and I hopped into our rubber dinghy and rowed toward the vessel, beaming our flashlight so they could tell we were coming. I was hoping to ascertain our latitude (the day before, skies had been too cloudy to get a sextant reading) and perhaps get a bit of kerosene to replace the two quarts Gabriel had wasted on the beans.

Once on board we were taken directly to the captain's cabin. He was a slender, militarily erect Chinese with the coldest eyes I've ever seen. "What do you want?" he snapped, in clipped, faintly accented English.

"I want to thank you for not killing us," I said. "And to apologize for causing you to stop. I know how expensive it is."

"It certainly is," he said, in the same hostile tone.

"But now that we're here," I continued, "could you tell us the latitude?"

Consulting his chart, he read us the latitude, then added without looking up, "All right, that's all."

"Could you spare us some water?" asked Marc. "And perhaps a little rice?"

Staring at us with cool disdain, the captain turned to an officer and snapped, "All right—and give them a kilo of sugar and two kilos of rice. No more!"

When we were getting ready to leave, I approached the captain again and said, "Our raft is about three miles from here, and with all this darkness—I wonder if you could take us part of the way."

He nodded, unsmiling. But when the ship started toward the raft, which was a barely visible point of light on the dark horizon, one of the sailors noticed that our dinghy was missing.

Rushing to the portside rail, I stared into the night, but could see nothing. "The rope must have slipped loose," I said.

"Do you really need that rubber boat?" asked the captain, as if it were a useless trifle.

"It's the only one we have," I answered.

The ship circled round and round, its two huge spotlights sweeping the dark water, and the dinghy was finally located about two hundred yards away. By then the captain was furious. "If you want your dinghy," he said, "you can swim for it!"

Knowing the ship's lights might have attracted sharks, I thought he must be joking. But he was dead serious. "All right," I said. "I'll swim for it, and you'll have a good show, Captain."

I climbed down the rope ladder seething with anger and sick with fright. Halfway down, I dived. Expecting a shark at any moment, I swam those two hundred yards as if the devil himself were chasing me, and finally scrambled into the dinghy.

Numb with fatigue, I started rowing back to the ship, but when I started up the ladder, my aching muscles couldn't sustain me. I lost my grip and fell back into the dinghy. As I was about to try again, I saw Marc starting down. The captain had ordered him into the dinghy with the few supplies the crew had given us. He was abandoning us at least two miles away from *La Balsa*.

"That dirty swine," said Marc, shaking his fist toward the deck.

Water kept splashing into the dinghy, and I had to bail it out while Marc rowed. The waves were so high we kept losing sight of the raft's lantern. Worse yet, the fog was back again.

"We're going to lose them," said Marc. "We've got too much cargo on this thing."

So we dumped the rice, sugar, and water, leaving us only two bottles of rice wine, which one of the sailors had given us. Finally, after more than an hour and a half, we reached *La Balsa* and flopped on the deck in exhaustion. It was a hard night's work for two bottles of rice wine.

THE FOG finally lifted. The next few days were calm, giving us an opportunity to study the amazing variety of marine life around us. We were especially fascinated by the bright phosphorescence of the plankton, which at night turned the sea into a vast bed of glowing embers and streaks of fire.

The "embers" were actually tiny shrimp and barnacles, and the "streaks of fire" were tuna diving under the raft. But the most spectacular mirages were the strange whirling coils of flame we saw skimming the surface two or three hundred yards away.

"Those are dorados chasing each other in circles," said Marc.

"You're crazy," said Gabriel. "They're flying saucers."

The daylight hours were equally absorbing, though less dramatic. All kinds of fish and mollusks constantly swam or floated around us, washing on board with the high waves. One afternoon a baby octopus was swept onto the deck, and Minet tried to trap one of the wiggly tentacles with his paw. But the octopus suddenly wrapped its tentacle around the cat's leg. Surprised and frightened, Minet scooted around the deck, trying to knock it off, until I finally pulled it loose. In the commotion we almost knocked over the pan of rice that Marc was preparing for dinner.

"Damn it," he growled, "you'll spoil my experiment!" He was making a casserole of rice and barnacles, with oregano, thyme, and other spices. Only a French chef would know how to make such good use of barnacles. The casserole was delicious.

In spite of our high-protein seafood diet none of us seemed to lose weight. We probably weren't exercising enough. At the beginning we did push-ups, knee bends, and other calisthenics, but we eased off after a while, convinced that our regular chores would keep us in shape. Our legs stayed firm and muscular because of the constant movement of the raft. Our stomach and shoulder muscles would have benefited from daily swimming in the ocean, but the sharks and swordfish ruled out that possibility.

"All this water," Gabriel said, "and we can't even swim in it."

Gabriel's desire to swim was satisfied sooner than he expected. That night he was sitting near the stern, on his regular three-hour watch, when a large wave heaved the raft to portside and hurtled him overboard. Totally surprised, he thrashed about for a few moments, then started swimming back toward *La Balsa*, only to be thwarted by a large and playful dolphin that started nibbling his toe. By now the raft had surged ahead fifteen or twenty feet, and he had to swim furiously to catch it. "I thought it was a shark," he later told us, "and it boosted my adrenalin."

Relieved that he hadn't drowned or been eaten by sharks, I neglected to ask why he hadn't tied a rope around his waist. I thought of it next day but decided not to broach the subject.

Usually his noisy eating habits annoyed me intensely. But to my surprise he didn't scrape his spoon at breakfast. Nor did he at lunch or dinner.

"Have you noticed how quietly Gabriel has been eating today?" I asked Marc that evening.

"It's that swim he took last night," said Marc. "I think it relieved some of his tensions. He never made noises like that in Guayaquil. It isn't bad manners; it's just pent-up tensions."

Forever analyzing our personal quirks, Marc often sounded like a professor of psychology. He was, in fact, a self-educated man. Born in France, he had been captured by Nazi storm troopers at the age of fourteen and interned in a concentration camp. Finally escaping, he joined the French underground and served as a gun-runner for two years. Then, at seventeen, he got a job on a merchant ship and visited nearly every major port in the world, learning a thing or two about women and diverse cultures, and reading a vast number of paperbacks on an even greater variety of subjects. Still yearning for adventure, he joined the French Navy on his twenty-first birthday and was soon involved in the French Indochina war. Having seen so many people at their best and worst, Marc had become a wise man at an early age. His soft-spoken observations always commanded attention.

Unfortunately the therapeutic value of Gabriel's swim soon wore off, and within a few days, he was back to his *craack* and *rassp*. Had we been able to get regular music on our radio, I would have played it at top volume to drown out that noisy spoon, but we were limited to periodic messages on shortwave.

Our only communication was with a few radio hams who kept in touch with us. About two weeks after we left Ecuador, we had started hearing from a woman named Liliana, who operated a ham radio from Guayaquil. She had a soothing voice, full of warmth and subtle enthusiasm.

"I forget my husband, my children, everything for you men on *La Balsa*," she once told us. Calculating the time differentials as we got farther west, I realized that she often tuned in way after midnight. How could one resist such loyalty?

"When we get to Australia," I promised her one night, "we'll get you a big a koala bear."

Listening to Liliana's soft, beautiful voice, we inevitably started to speculate about her. How old was she? What did she look like? Marc was sure she was past thirty but under forty.

"She's also slender, tall, and brunette," he added.

"Nonsense!" protested Gabriel. "She's a blonde with gray-green eyes and full heavy lips."

"She's fat, fifty, and funny," I said, to tease them. "Only a homely woman can be that charming." Actually I envisioned her as gracefully slender, thirty-two years old, dark-haired, olive-skinned, and enormously sensual.

The other radio hams evoked less passionate responses. My good friend Admiral Samuel Fernandez was always in close contact with *La Balsa* through a ham station in Mexico City. From Guadalajara, Mexico, we had continuous messages of concern and support from a man named Rafael Corcuera. There were others who kept track of our progress by asking our position and charting it on maps. Occasionally the hams would arrange direct communication between one of us and a member of our family. Two or three times I talked to my wife, Denise, who was always cheerful and full of good news about our two little daughters.

On July 10 a radio ham in Santiago, Chile, managed to arrange a conversation between Gabriel and his mother. "How are you, my son?" she said in Spanish, a quaver in her voice.

"I'm fine, Mama," he answered. "We're nearly halfway, and all goes well."

There was a brief pause, and then her anxious voice again: "Is there anything you need? I'll send it right away."

Luckily the circuit was cut just then, and she could not hear our laughter at her wonderfully naïve offer.

A couple of days later we hit a dead spot in the Pacific. There was not even a breeze; our sail hung limp, and the raft drifted at a snail's pace, while the sun beat down relentlessly. Drugged and drained by the fierce heat, unable to tolerate the fetid cat smells and body odors inside the cabin, we slouched around on deck, scarcely talking to one another.

"This could drive you crazy," said Marc when the sun had gone down on the second day. "It's like living in a vacuum."

"I think I feel a breeze," I said, with more hope than conviction. "Should be better tomorrow."

Fortunately next morning a stiff breeze puffed out our sail like a pigeon's breast. Our revived spirits were reflected in my log:

July 14:

We covered 132 miles yesterday, 5½ miles per hour for a 24-hour stretch. The current is very strong and the wind from the east. My sickness has almost gone. Marc has just checked the food supply, and we have very little left—maybe not enough to reach Samoa. We shall have to live on nothing but fish or perhaps soups made from plankton.

July 17:

Good fishing. Hundreds of flying fish, with dolphins chasing them. Also lots of tuna and sharks. Everyone smells of fish, especially Minet.

The playful dolphins were around us almost constantly. They seemed extremely social and gregarious, usually traveling in groups of seven or eight, swimming side by side in perfect harmony. They communicated in a language of squeaks and whistles, which we often heard as they circled our raft, leaping over the waves in unison like chorus girls. Often called "the littlest whale," the dolphin is perhaps the most approachable of all sea animals, but for that very reason he is also the most vulnerable. They were so trusting that we were almost reluctant to catch them.

July 19:

On a raft you really get the feel of the sea—a feeling you can never have on a ship—because you are actually *on* the sea itself, in close physical contact with it. You can feel the currents, the changes in temperature. Sometimes you can actually see the fingers of a new current rippling toward you, often at speeds of 10 knots or more. The water temperature sometimes changes abruptly—particularly near the equator—from 25 to 35 degrees in seconds.

I'm convinced that you must become a part of nature to feel nature. You must become one with the sea, one with the fish. The sea is like a woman—soft, wild, sweet, moody. You can never understand these changes of mood. It is like your first love, pure and virgin, stormy and turbulent—always testing you and confounding you. If you want to conquer the sea, you must first prove that you are really strong. She will push you to the limit, but if you come through, she will open her arms and protect you.

July 30:
Today we pass 142° 05′ W, the longitude of the *Kon-Tiki's* final landing on Raroia Reef after its 4300-mile voyage from Peru. *La Balsa* has taken 62 days compared with *Kon-Tiki's* 101 days, and we are passing Raroia 1000 miles to the north.

IT WOULD be false modesty to minimize the pride we felt in having duplicated Thor Heyerdahl's historic voyage on the *Kon-Tiki*. But now we faced the most difficult part of our journey, the treacherous expanse of the South Seas.

Almost every sailor who has traveled the Pacific has his own story to tell of the passage through the Samoa Islands, the Fijis, the New Hebrides, and the Saumarez Reefs. There are hundreds of reef barriers, most of them uncharted, and hurricanes and cyclones that have made matchwood of many a ship.

Here, then, was the real test. We wanted to prove that the Incas and Huancavilcas could have navigated these waters, some of the most difficult in the world, on balsa rafts like ours.

"The *Kon-Tiki* started to fall apart about here," Gabriel reminded us. "How can we be sure about this raft?"

We decided to have a look at the logs. Three hours later, after carefully puncturing each one below water level and examining bits of balsa from inside, we were happily assured that they were in excellent shape, having absorbed almost no water.

As dangerous as any reef or hurricane were the boredom and personal tensions of our crew. It was inevitable that we would become restless and edgy, repeating the same monotonous routine day after day. There were days when nothing seemed to go well, when the *craack* and *rassp* of Gabriel's spoon was more grating than ever, and even Normand's quiet nature made me uneasy. On such days we stayed clear of each other, consciously expanding our bubbles of privacy.

Another problem was fresh water. Marc told me our supplies would probably run out before we reached Australia. "Then we'll have to chew raw fish to quench our thirst," he said.

My own reading about the Huancavilcas and Incas had reassured me on this point. Aside from chewing raw fish, they would squeeze the moisture from pieces of fish by twisting them in strips of cloth. They would also extract juices from the lymphatic glands of larger fish like dorados and tuna. When I tried it, the ooze tasted terrible, but the percentage of salt was so low that my thirst quickly vanished in spite of the acrid taste.

Of course, we needed a certain amount of salt in our diet, so Marc provided us with salt tablets, which we took on especially hot days when the temperature would rise to 115 degrees in the cabin and perspiration drained our bodies of salt. He also occasionally added salt water to our regular drinking water, in a ratio of one to five.

Gabriel screwed up his face after every swallow. "If we had some coca leaves to chew on, this would be easier to take," he said. "That's what the Incas did. They found that cocaine would kill the taste of anything. I should have brought some."

"And you might have become addicted," said Marc.

"You old fogies think everything's addictive," answered Gabriel. "Look at all the nonsense you hear about marijuana. Yet some studies show that it's less addictive than ordinary tobacco, and less harmful than alcohol."

Drugs, politics, and the Vietnam war were the principal topics of conversation, and, of course, we never reached a consensus. When our talk got too serious, Normand would start singing the chorus of a song he had picked up somewhere.

"He sings better in the bath," Marc observed one morning as Normand lay on the rear deck, the waves washing over him.

We all took baths that way, grabbing a rope looped around a crossbeam to keep from being swept off the raft. The water was cool and refreshing, but our bodies were always left with a residue

In mid-Pacific, Vital and Normand adjust the rigging as *La Balsa* proceeds under full sail.

of itchy salt. Gabriel was bothered most by it. "The first thing I'm going to do in Australia is take a long hot shower to get rid of this damned salt," he said, scratching his back. "And then I'm going to eat the biggest meal I've ever eaten."

For some reason, he had developed a great fear of starvation. Every morning he would ask Marc about our food supplies.

"We're doing all right," Marc would say, trying to reassure him.

"Are you sure?" Gabriel would ask.

"Of course. Even if all our rice and canned foods are used up, we still have all the fresh fish we can eat."

"But what if we hit another dead spot in the sea?"

To allay his fears, I told him we could eat plankton if worse came to worst. Fortunately we never had to, but we did collect some in a cone-shaped cloth suspended from the bow.

Marc makes an entry in the log. Behind him is *La Balsa's* "amphibious toilet."

"*Aach!* It looks like a mess of fat, slimy germs," said Gabriel. "I'd rather starve than eat that stuff."

"Don't worry, Gabriel," said Marc, nudging me. "I'll make us a nice casserole with it—with a fine wine sauce."

Plankton, seaweed, barnacles, and crabs gradually accumulated on the bottom and sides of *La Balsa*. Gabriel explored the underside of the raft, with Normand and Marc keeping a sharp lookout for sharks. "We've got a botanical garden down there!" he exclaimed. Thick long strands of seaweed, like creeping ivy, threatened to climb onto the deck, but we managed to keep them under control by scraping them off periodically.

We had less success combating legions of small ants that fed on the seaweed. In spite of all our precautions, the ants had hidden inside the porous balsa logs before we left Guayaquil, surfacing when we were out at sea. Now they swarmed all over the

303

raft, burrowing into our sleeping bags and keeping us awake with mean little stings. They crept up our legs and arms as we sat on deck during the day, sharing our food at every meal.

"Don't these ants ever sleep?" asked Gabriel, scraping one off his breakfast plate.

"In shifts," said Marc. "The morning shift has just come on."

Our best weapon against them was provided by nature. During a good heavy storm some ants would be washed overboard.

But, of course, we were also susceptible to the same danger. One such storm struck us early in August. Dark ominous clouds rushed toward us from the east, blotting out the sun and rumbling along with the harsh driving winds.

"All hands on deck!" I yelled. "Here comes a big one. Tie everything down!"

As the wind howled like a demented demon, we started to pull in the sail with all our strength. Two or three times Normand was nearly swept overboard as he struggled to fold the lower flap. Battling with the ropes for almost half an hour as successive waves drenched us, we finally got the sail in. Then, just as we were tying it down, a huge wall of water swept toward us. The raft heaved sideways, up and over the wave's back, just as it broke, hissing and foaming at the crest. Riding through the churning foam which engulfed us, we slid down into the broad trough. Then the next wall of water came at us, tossing the raft into the air, carrying it through another curtain of foam.

"Here comes another!" shouted Marc, grabbing the mast.

"Ooooh b—" I heard Normand say, but a deafening clap of thunder drowned out his voice.

A sheet of rain washed over us like water from a fire hose, slashing the deck and cabin for ten or fifteen minutes. Holding on to the mast, I looked up at the dark clouds and began to shout, "Chisco!" (My nickname for my favorite saint, San Francisco.) "Listen to me, Chisco! Why did you double-cross us this way? Why didn't you give us fair warning?"

Somehow *La Balsa* managed to withstand the onslaught. Then suddenly, as if an unseen celestial referee had blown a whistle, the storm eased and the raft started riding the waves like a gull.

An hour or so later Gabriel approached me with a serious expression. "You shouldn't have talked that way to Saint Francis," he said, fingering his good-luck coin. "It wasn't his fault."

Actually my presumed blasphemy was a convenient mask for a deeply felt belief in a supreme being. Chisco was merely His surrogate. I suspect that most sailors—even those who pride themselves on being tough, hard-drinking womanizers—have a streak of hidden piety in them. Facing the elements of nature day after day, they must inevitably question the reasons behind those gigantic forces which, for the landlubber, are simply lines on a map on a television weather forecast.

5

BOTH the winds and the currents were sluggish during the rest of that first week in August, but we made some progress to the west. The listless water was coated with scum, seaweed, and man-made debris—beer cans, paper plates, even a bamboo cane with a plastic handle. Fortunately, a stiff wind soon pushed us away from this ecological graveyard.

On the afternoon of August 8, as we were moving out of the Polynesian longitudes toward Melanesia, we had a staticky radio conversation with Rafael Corcuera in Guadalajara, Mexico. Just before we signed off, he asked about our food supplies.

"Gabriel thinks we're going to starve," I answered with a chuckle. "And I'm dying for a good steak and some French fries—but Marc says we'll have to eat raw fish for the next two months."

Unknown to me, we had a terribly faulty circuit, and all Rafael had heard were the words "starve," "dying," and "raw fish." Fearing the worst, he put in an emergency call to Admiral Fernandez in Mexico City. Together they contacted the U. S. Naval Station at Pearl Harbor, telling them that a raft was in distress somewhere between the Polynesian and Melanesian islands.

On the morning of August 11, as we were enjoying a breakfast of flying fish, we had a frantic message from Guadalajara, informing us that "a ship is on the way." I tried to tell Rafael to leave us alone, but our transmitter was apparently dead.

"Why in God's name does he want to send a ship?" I asked.

"Don't let it bother you, Vital," said Marc. "Rafael means well. He's just a worrywart."

No one seemed to share my determination to remain totally independent, and since I was a minority of one, I eased up.

"Now let's have a little contest," Marc said. "Whoever sees the ship first will get an extra ten thousand points on his canasta score." We had been playing a continuous day-to-day game of canasta since our departure from Guayaquil, and most of our scores now exceeded the million mark.

It was Normand who, late that afternoon, sighted a small speck to the northeast. "There's the ship," he said, obviously thinking of the extra points he had just won.

As the speck grew larger we could see it was a good-size naval ship. Still several miles away, it managed to establish radio contact with us. It was the USS *Granville S. Hall*, a special project-and-research ship weighing 11,600 tons. I could imagine how primitive our raft must have looked to them.

When the *Hall* got within a mile of us, it stopped and lowered a motor launch, which roared toward *La Balsa*, spewing a V of white foam. Less than three minutes later it pulled alongside the raft and two crewmen came on board. They greeted us warmly and told us their captain had invited us to dinner.

"We do not want to trouble you," I answered in my halting English. "You are too kind."

They smiled. "No trouble at all. Everyone wants to meet you."

They attached a towrope to our bow and started tugging *La Balsa* toward the ship. Meanwhile I went back to the cabin to answer a signal on our radio, which seemed to be working better. It was Joe Megan calling from Guayaquil.

"Vital!" he exclaimed. "I can't believe this, amigo. I've been in touch with an American ship that's close to you, the USS *Hall*. They say you're west of the Polynesian longitudes."

"Of course," I said. "I reported that several days ago."

"I know," he said. "But I didn't believe you could transmit messages from anywhere beyond the Galápagos on that lousy radio I fixed for you."

Then the low, resonant voice of Admiral Fernandez broke in from Mexico City. "I've always believed in you, Vital. Congratulations and a warm embrace."

I was so absorbed in my conversation that I failed to notice a commotion outside the cabin. Then I felt a tremendous jolt. Rushing out, I saw the huge gray bulk of the *Hall* looming over us. The launch had pulled us too close to the ship.

"Watch out!" someone cried, as the hull rammed us again, with a loud splintering crunch.

Our trip is over, I told myself, with a sick feeling in my gut. The raft will be smashed to pieces.

Pushing against the hull with bamboo poles, we somehow managed to shove the raft away. Then the ship moved some distance off, the captain having seen our danger.

"We heard something crack down here," said a crewman.

"That was only the toilet," I said, attempting to conceal my disappointment as I looked at the mess of crushed balsa wood.

Waving good-by to Minet, who was standing at the cabin doorway with an aloof, go-ahead-and-leave-me expression, we jumped into the launch for the short trip to the ship.

The reception we got was tremendous. The entire crew shook our hands, patted our shoulders, congratulated us, and asked a hundred questions about *La Balsa*. Finally someone cleared a path for the captain himself, W. P. Karmenzid, and he shook hands with each of us, a smile lighting his bronzed, finely chiseled face. He was an Indian from the Navajo tribe. What a marvelous coincidence: here in the mid-Pacific a giant modern naval vessel commanded by an American Indian had encountered a small raft of the kind used thousands of years ago by Indians who might have been indirectly related to his ancestors.

"Welcome aboard," Karmenzid said. "Our ship is yours. And please forgive us for the damage we caused. You must be tired and hungry. We were told that you're nearly starving."

"Who told you this?" I exclaimed, scarcely believing my ears.

"Senor Corcuera, the man from Guadalajara. We got the alert from our command in Pearl Harbor two days ago."

"I don't understand," I mumbled. "We eat very well—plenty of fish all the time." Then, as I remembered my conversation with Rafael, I began to smile. "Poor Corcuera," I said. "He didn't realize I was making a joke. I said to him, 'Gabriel thinks we are going to starve. And I'm dying for a good steak and some French fries.' But the static was so bad he must have caught only bits and pieces."

The captain was smiling now, as were his three officers.

"Well, even if there is no emergency," he said, "we're glad you're here, Captain Alsar."

We gladly accepted, and hungrily devoured, a banquet of steaks, French fries, creamed asparagus, marinated beets, hot biscuits with butter, apple pie, and ice cream. "We must be eating like sharks," I apologized, accepting a second serving of pie.

"You're welcome to everything we have," said the executive officer in a soft Southern drawl. He meant it, too. Later, when we boarded the launch, we found several crates of canned food and a container of gasoline for our radio generator.

When we got back to *La Balsa*, Minet was waiting for us on the cabin roof like a haughty gargoyle. "These Americans are incredible!" said Gabriel, as he hauled in a large box of canned fruit. "No one is more generous than they are."

Recalling his previous statements about "money-grubbing materialistic gringos," I answered with a restrained smile, "Yes, Gabriel, they have that reputation."

But when the *Hall* had disappeared below the darkening horizon, I said, "We'll have to dump it overboard, amigos. They're gone now, so they won't see us."

Gabriel was dumbfounded. "But why?" he asked.

"Because we have to make it on our own," said Marc.

"It's also too cumbersome," I added. "We have to travel light."

Reluctantly Gabriel helped us dump our American bounty into the sea—though he did manage to salvage some gasoline and a few cans of peaches and pineapple, persuading us that their use wasn't enough to invalidate our theory of self-survival.

Three or four days later, as we were approaching a passage between the islands of Tongareva and Vostok, Gabriel sat with me near the bow, his eyes squinting at the lowering sun. "We shouldn't have thrown away that food," he said. "I think we're going to need it."

I tried to make light of his worries, though I knew they were genuine. "But we have all kinds of fish, Gabriel."

"Not as many as yesterday," he persisted. "The wind is going down, and the current's slowing. I think we're headed for another dead spot." His blue-gray eyes were staring beyond me, his jaw muscles twitching as he tightened his chapped lips.

I was suddenly reminded of the famous Donner Party that got trapped in a snowstorm in the High Sierras and finally resorted to cannibalism. Sitting there in the immense loneliness of the Pacific, knowing that it *was* possible to starve if we were stranded on a lifeless, fishless sea, I tried to visualize myself eating the flesh of one of my companions. I decided that I would rather starve, yet how could I be sure?

"Well, at least Minet won't starve," Gabriel said. "He'll eat anything, even that lousy plankton."

We had been watching Minet play a new game. He was crouched on the portside log, his right paw batting at the water as if teasing a fish. Just then he lost his balance, splashing into the water with a loud meow! Gabriel reached the edge of the raft just as I did. "My God!" he said. "Look at that!"

Minet had surfaced and was now swimming back to the raft, paddling with his forepaws and meowing furiously.

We fished him out. "He swam at least five feet!" I exclaimed.

"More," insisted Gabriel, cuddling the drenched and shivering cat in his arms. "It was at least six feet."

By now Normand and Marc had joined us, laughing with pride. Minet shook off the water with a charming arrogance.

"Now that we know this cat can actually swim, we must give him some lessons," I suggested. "Starting tomorrow."

"You're crazy, Vital," said Gabriel. "He'll drown."

"He may have to swim someday to save his life," I said. "Especially through the rough seas we're expecting."

The first lesson began after my morning watch. With Normand and Gabriel poised on the starboard log like short-distance swimming champions, I took Minet and gently tossed him into the water six to seven feet away. Almost instantly he bobbed up, meowing angrily, then started swimming toward us.

"*Bravo, gatito!*" said Gabriel, pulling him in.

A few minutes later I tossed him about twelve feet out. Once again he paddled back to us, his strokes more measured than before. This time he accepted our praise like a seasoned champion, strutting around the deck with his tail straight up.

We repeated the experiment twice more that day, using the dinghy to row him out to twenty feet, then thirty. "He'll go even farther tomorrow," I said, drying him off with my shirt. I was determined to test the outer limits of his survival power.

So after lunch the next day, while the others sprawled on the rear mat for a short siesta, I got into the dinghy with Minet and rowed away before they could object. Gabriel spotted me when I was about ten feet away. "Don't!" he yelled. "He'll drown."

I kept on rowing, whispering encouragement at Minet as he sat on the edge of the rubber boat with cool assurance. Finally, when I had rowed fifty or sixty feet, I put aside the oars and shoved the cat toward the raft, saying, "*Buena suerte.*"

Without the slightest hesitation he started paddling with his tiny white forepaws, meowing softly to himself like a coxswain calling the stroke for a long row. He started so well that I immediately felt a sense of relief.

Then, abruptly, Minet paused. Thrashing the water for a second or two, he let out a loud meow and started paddling furiously back to the dinghy. With my oars already in the water I surged toward him with two desperate strokes as I spotted a six-foot shark racing toward us. Lunging forward, nearly capsizing the dinghy, I grabbed Minet as the shark closed in with its mouth wide open. It missed Minet by less than two feet. As I rowed toward the raft with Minet on my lap, the shark made a U-turn and came back at us. Twice it snared an oar in its teeth, but each time I twisted it away. The shark finally dived out of sight as Minet and I boarded the raft.

"I'm sorry," I told the others. "That was really stupid of me."

"It's okay," said Gabriel reassuringly. "Minet learned something from this. He got exposed to the worst danger—and survived."

AT NOON ON August 25 I took a sextant reading and found that we were passing the 160th meridian—two-thirds of the way toward our goal. On this trackless, signless sea it was just another invisible milestone, but to us it had special, almost metaphysical, significance. We were beating the odds, doing what everyone had thought was impossible.

"This calls for a celebration," said Marc. "I've saved something for this occasion. It's under the mat behind the cabin."

We crowded around him as he lifted the bamboo mat and pulled out an object wrapped in several layers of banana leaves. It was a bottle of champagne. "There's another one," he said. "For the day we reach Australia."

Normand produced some yellow plastic cups, and we drank a toast to *La Balsa*.

Several hours later I decided to inspect the logs again. I was particularly concerned about the possible absorption of water through the grooves we had made for the ropes. Leaning over the portside log, I studied a groove just below the water level. It was soft and foam-rubbery around the cut edges, but when I pressed it with my thumb, the wood yielded only half an inch. Not bad, I thought. To make sure, I carefully punctured it with an ice pick and brought out several tiny particles of balsa wood. They looked dry—fluffy white and dry as sawdust.

"*Voilà!*" I said to Marc, showing him the samples. "It's still dry inside." A check of the other six logs yielded the same results. The ropes were in equally good condition.

The favorable diagnosis of *La Balsa*'s health gave our morale a considerable boost. We sang more, joked more, ate more, and played more canasta. Even the winds and currents were in our favor, propelling us in a southwesterly direction at an average of 130 miles a day. The islands of Samoa were not far off, prompting Gabriel to speculate about the women we might see.

Pursuing this train of thought, he suggested that we try to contact Liliana on our radio and listen to her lovely voice. After considerable fiddling, we finally heard her.

"We'll soon be in Pago Pago," whispered Gabriel during an interval of static, "where they have the most fantastic women in the world. But they're only for Normand and me. You old married men will have to stay on the raft." He talked on about how he would teach them to sing Chilean love ballads, to dance the *cueca*, to say "I love you" in French, Spanish, German, and Greek, and to scratch his itchy, salt-powdered back.

Suddenly the radio went completely dead. "This damned machine," I said, slapping it. "Something snapped inside."

For several hours Marc and I tried to repair it, but the radio still wouldn't work. "Joe Megan was right after all," I said. "It couldn't work forever. We'll have to finish the trip without it."

The next day I took it apart again. Still dead. On the third day Gabriel took over, periodically spanking the top and sides with a few coaxing phrases in Spanish and French. Suddenly the set responded with a low, whining noise.

"It works!" shouted Gabriel. "Listen to that beautiful static."

A few moments later we heard the half-garbled voice of Admiral Fernandez. "Are you listening, are you listening?" he kept saying. "We've been trying to contact you for two days. Your voice was cut off on Wednesday. Now I'm getting a clicking sound from your transmitter."

I shouted into our microphone, but apparently all he heard was the clicking.

"If you hear me," said Fernandez, "disconnect the main transmitter coil and use it like a telegrapher's contact signal."

I followed his instructions, holding the tip of the coil close to the contact screw, waiting for his next order.

"Okay," he said, "apparently you hear me. Now make three long clicks."

"Cliiick cliiick cliiick."

"That's fine. Now remember that a long click is 'yes' and two short clicks are 'no.' I'm going to ask you specific questions. Answer yes or no. Are you making twenty to thirty miles per day?"

"Click click." (No.)

"Are you going faster?"

"Cliiick." (Yes.)

"Are you going more than fifty miles?"

"Cliiick."

"More than one hundred?"

"Cliiick."

"Between a hundred twenty and a hundred thirty miles?"

"Cliiick."

Fernandez then got specific data regarding our position, approximate direction, the speed of the current, the amount of food and water on board, and our health. He promised to contact a ham operator in Australia and teach him our system. "You will be much closer to him. The signals will be clearer."

I knew, however, that he would make every effort to remain the key man in our communications setup.

Our system almost went awry a few days later. While I operated the radio, Normand usually watched the generator, taking it outside the cabin so its noise wouldn't interfere with my hearing. On this particular afternoon he was perched on the starboard log, with the small motor resting on his lap, when a huge wave knocked him overboard. Clutching the motor to his stomach like a fullback, Normand grabbed a rope with his free hand. Gabriel scrambled across the deck and snatched the motor with one hand, pulling Normand aboard with the other.

"That's a great act," I said. "In and out of the water in ten seconds flat."

"We'll charge admission next time," said Gabriel. "Sorry about breaking the no-touch rule, though," he added jokingly.

"That doesn't apply in emergencies," I said.

At the beginning it had not been easy to observe our rule of no physical contact. We were all *Latinos*, accustomed to touching people during conversation, to greeting friends, male or female, with affectionate *abrazos*. But now we were acquiring a reserve more characteristic of Englishmen. I began to feel so comfortable in my self-imposed bubble of privacy that I wondered if I would ever recover my penchant for demonstrative affection.

But there were other conditions to which we could never become reconciled. The ants seemed to grow more numerous every day. Sometimes I prayed for a hurricane that would wash them away.

One evening early in September, as we were approaching the

islands of Samoa, the gods apparently decided to respond. The sunset had been startlingly beautiful, an ocher and tangerine splash of color illuminating a vast tumult of clouds drifting across the horizon. The sea itself was like a rippling flame that cast a warm glow over us. But as the colors faded the clouds looked menacing, and the water became ominously dark and choppy.

Then suddenly the winds came up, whipping our sail around and slashing it against our heads as we hastily pulled it in. "Grab your ropes!" I yelled, as a fifteen-foot wave sent the raft hurtling along on the foamy crest. "Tie yourselves to—"

Astern of *La Balsa*, rising seas warn of a coming storm.

A second wave deluged us before I could finish. My crewmates had already secured themselves, and I quickly grabbed a rope to do the same. But before I could reach the mast a huge wall of water caught us broadside, crashing over the cabin and slamming me to the deck. Dazed and stunned, I managed to grab the mast as an even larger wave gushed through the cabin doorway and spilled out the windows, carrying a sleeping bag with it.

We were like blind men in a house of horrors, not knowing where the next assault would come from. Tossed in all directions, we clung to the mast and crossbeams like frightened crabs, and attempted feeble jokes to keep up our courage.

"The gods heard you, Vital," shouted Gabriel. "Three ants went overboard with that last wave."

"They didn't go overboard," I said, between mouthfuls of salt water. "I swallowed them."

Finally, after two hours of relentless punishment, the winds subsided, leaving us numb with exhaustion.

The next morning we surveyed the results. The deck and cabin

314

Wearing oilskins and secured by a rope around his waist, Vital adjusts a *guara* in rough seas.

were a shambles of water-soaked debris—Marc's torn sleeping bag hung limply from a crossbeam, my tattered shorts flopped over the portable stove, and a shredded red shirt was wrapped around the starboard log like a blood-soaked bandage. Our radio cable was tangled around the damaged boom, and bamboo splinters jutted from the cabin roof like stubborn cowlicks on a schoolboy.

"It could have been worse," I said, falling back on that cliché.

"I'm afraid it *will* be," cautioned Marc. "We're coming into the cyclone zone."

We had known this all along—Admiral Fernandez had clearly marked the climate changes on our map—but that baptismal night storm was a most emphatic reminder of the dangers ahead.

Two more squalls assaulted us before we reached Samoa. During a few sunny interludes we tightened the beams of our wobbly cabin, repaired the splintered boom, and washed and dried our sun-faded shirts and pants. We were down to twelve pieces of laundry: four shirts, four pairs of pants, and four sleeping bags. But since we spent most of the time in the nude, except for loincloths, our clothing needs were minimal.

At sunrise on September 12 we sighted the green-tipped fringe of the 60-mile-long Samoan island of Savaii—the first land we had seen since passing the Galápagos Islands more than thirteen weeks before. Marc, Gabriel, and I shouted, "Saaamoooaaa! Saaamoooaaa!" while Normand contented himself with a bubbling "Oh booooy!"

Through our only pair of binoculars, we could see the spire of a neo-Gothic church, surrounded by glittering green palm trees. We visualized beautiful girls in sarongs dancing on the beach.

"The girls will be fully dressed and Christianized," said Marc. "Anyway, you won't see them."

"Why not?" asked Gabriel.

"Because there's a reef between us and them. We've got to stay clear."

Momentarily dejected, Gabriel looked longingly at the fertile beauty of the island. "Maybe there's an opening in the reef."

"Maybe," I said. "The maps can't show everything."

As we drifted along Savaii it was a tantalizing sight, with tall coconut palms gently bending in the breeze, multicolored birds flitting among the trees, the white-capped surf swelling toward sandy beaches. At midday we were level with the church, a jagged reef partially obscuring the lower half.

Then the wind changed, carrying us too close to the reef for comfort. We pulled in the sail, but continued to drift closer. I scanned the water for the telltale sign of foamy surf beating against the reef, which here lay submerged like a waiting trap. However, the only surf I saw was washing against the distant coastal beaches.

By sunset we were about three miles offshore, still drifting southwest toward the island. Flickering lights and gentle spirals of woodsmoke appeared along the shore.

"Smell that cooking," said Gabriel hungrily.

"That's only your imagination," said Marc. "The wind is blowing the other way. You're smelling the fish in this pan."

"Why don't we signal them?" suggested Gabriel. "Perhaps they'll come out and tell us about the reefs, Vital."

Marc fired two flares. A half hour later we saw a motor launch coming our way. There were three men on board, a New Zealander and two Samoans; they assured us the wind would be changing soon. I asked if they could possibly bring us some fruit.

"It might be too late to go ashore and come back again," said the New Zealander. "Why don't you let us tow you ashore, and you can get all you want. I'm sure these good people would love to see you. They're very kind—and curious."

"How about reefs?" I asked.

"None between you and the bay," he said.

Yielding to smiling, soft-spoken pressure from the Samoans, we agreed to go into the bay for an hour or two. We hadn't reckoned on the extent of the hospitality. The moment we reached shallow water a laughing swarm of people, mostly women, climbed onto the raft and poked into every corner, peering into the cabin, stooping down for a close look at the rope grooves, frightening Minet into hiding.

"Please! Please!" I yelled at last. "We're very tired. We have to sleep a little."

317

Most of the women were so striking that Gabriel was stunned into silence. Later he recovered enough to say, "Someday I'm going to come back here and get better acquainted with them."

We were finally left alone about 3:00 a.m., more exhausted than if we'd been through a storm. Taking the night watch, I told Marc we should leave as soon as we got a proper wind. But early morning visitors came before the hoped-for winds and brought us piles of fruit and hot food. After greedily devouring the native dishes, we waved good-by to our friends and continued our journey.

Minet had come out of hiding and was playing with some crabs near the stern, faking a hurt meow whenever one of them snapped at his paws. We were so fascinated by his ham acting that none of us noticed hovering over us a large hook-billed albatross with a wingspread of seven or eight feet and clumsy webbed feet.

Catching us unawares, it swooped down like a shadow and grabbed Minet in its beak. Thrown off-balance by its squirming prey, the albatross tried to continue its flight. When they were about seven feet in the air, Minet twisted furiously and forced his kidnapper to drop him just behind the cabin.

"Assassin," screamed Gabriel, running toward Minet, who had, in true cat fashion, landed on his feet. "I'll kill that bird!"

There was a large gash in Minet's neck; a two-inch hunk of fur had been ripped off, but he seemed more angry than injured.

"I'm glad he had webbed feet," said Marc, inspecting the wound. "If he had had claws like an eagle or a hawk, Minet would be done for. He was just too heavy for the bird's beak."

We wiped the wound clean, applied an antiseptic, and gently wrapped a bandage around Minet's neck. But in a few hours he had clawed the bandage to shreds.

Marc found a solution. "Let's put gauze mittens on his paws," he suggested, "or that wound will never heal."

So with four puffy gauze feet and a ruff around his neck, Minet crept about the deck, occasionally licking one mitten and washing his face and body with the tongue-wet gauze. Somehow, it never occurred to him to rip off the foot bandages with his teeth.

"That would ruin his act," observed Marc when I mentioned it. "Minet is too much of a ham to spoil a good comedy."

6

ALTHOUGH we were well over two-thirds of the way to Australia, most of the dangerous reefs and banks were still ahead of us, as were the heavy storms. Now we would have to steer our way past ten major reef barriers, nine of them, according to our calculations, by night. If my navigation was faulty, the first we would know about it might be a terrible crash in the dark.

We had wanted to come down in latitude after leaving Savaii, but a stiff south wind on the afternoon of September 15 kept us going northwest. Blowing stronger and stronger as the day wore on, creating waves twenty feet high, the wind threatened to push us toward the dangerous Pasco Bank, less than sixty miles ahead.

But suddenly we had more immediate worries. On our radio (still receiving but not transmitting) we got a report from a New Zealand meteorologist, predicting winds of forty-five to fifty miles an hour. Yelling "Batten down the hatches," I sealed the radio in plastic bags and lashed it to the ceiling of the cabin, while Gabriel pulled in the sail and Marc and Normand secured various other items. Just before sunset heavy clouds gathered, and a long moaning wind came out of the east. As its velocity increased, it started to screech. The sound chilled me to the bone, reminding me of the *lloronas* I'd been told about as a child, demented witches running through the night with bloodcurdling screams.

"I've never heard such strange winds," said Gabriel.

They were now blowing at full gale force, up to fifty miles per hour, pushing waves more than thirty feet high and whirling *La Balsa* around like a matchbox. The waves made a strange whirring sound.

"That's the bigger waves curling in on themselves," shouted Marc. "The big ones don't break—they curl inside like a wheel."

Thinking it might be safer than outside, we crawled into our fragile cabin. All we could see through the doorway was the gush of waves, slashing at us from all directions, turning the raft with a slapping up-and-down motion that bounced us around like loose dice. The cabin floor would tilt forty-five degrees, first sliding us

319

into a helpless heap against one wall, then slamming us against the opposite wall as huge masses of water poured through the doorway and out the windows, drenching us again and again.

At one point an enormous wave hurtled through the portside window and smashed Marc's head against the radio. His mouth opened in a soundless scream, then he crumpled to the floor.

"Marc!" I yelled, reaching for him in a sudden rush of fear.

. To my great relief, he'd only been knocked unconscious, but it took me some minutes to revive him. Finally, he shook his head groggily. "Where am I?"

"On *La Balsa*," I said. "You were knocked out by a wave."

He pondered my answer for a moment. Then his eyes cleared, and he gripped a corner beam for support. To my shouted "All right?" he nodded a vigorous affirmative.

By some miracle our bamboo cabin held fast, bending with each fierce gust of wind, straining at the ropes that held it together. No modern cabin would have withstood such pressure—not even a conventional metal structure.

An hour or so before sunrise, the storm subsided to a mild uproar, and we were able to determine the damage. "The boom has split again," said Marc, running his hand over a previous crack that he had bound with heavy rope. "But it's not a new crack, thank God." He moved more slowly than usual; obviously, he had not totally recovered from the blow on the head.

Two supply boxes were splintered, the bamboo deck mats badly shredded, and banana leaves ripped off the cabin roof. Minor debris was everywhere, and scores of walleyed sardines flapped between exposed logs. Inside the cabin our water-soaked sleeping bags smelled worse than ever.

"Time for spring housecleaning," said Gabriel.

"It's mid-September," I reminded him.

"I know that," he answered. "But this is the southern hemisphere. And it's springtime here."

Occupied with such trivia that day, we found it easier to ignore the danger that was still there in the ominous gray clouds coming from the east. We housecleaned our raft as it roller-coasted from one wave to another, and we kept a wary eye on the horizon.

The second gale struck us a few hours after sundown. Once again the waves swelled to heights of up to fifty feet. With water rushing in and out of our cabin, we tried to joke our way through the night. We laughed—at times maniacally, the way people laugh when they're dead tired or terribly frightened, though I can honestly say that I had gone beyond the point of fear. I felt the danger, yes, but also a conviction that we would pass this awful test, that otherwise our journey would be meaningless, that perhaps Saint Francis himself had sent these winds.

"Chisco," I said half aloud, "you're a true rascal."

"Are you talking to that saint again?" asked Gabriel.

"Thanking him," I answered, "for this fine storm."

Gabriel was sure the winds had driven me crazy.

In our preoccupation with the storm, nobody noticed that Minet had disappeared. It was Marc who first asked about him.

"Normand has him," said Gabriel, unable to see in the dark.

"No, *you* have him," said Normand.

Gabriel jumped up, calling "Minet! Minet!" as he staggered through an incoming mass of water at the doorway.

"Grab him, Vital," called Marc. "He'll be washed overboard!"

Yanking with all my strength, I managed to get Gabriel back, with Normand's help. "Minet will be all right," said Marc with as much conviction as possible. "He's a tough cat."

But Gabriel wouldn't be consoled. "He's drowned," he said, making his way back to his corner. He said no more for the rest of the night, but we knew he was miserable. I too felt sad.

The gale was gone before dawn, and an eerie calm greeted us when we went outside at daybreak. As I stood there, accustoming myself to the sudden quiet, I heard an anxious meow. Minet was clinging to one of the slanting mast posts, his limbs wrapped around it like those of a baby bear on a tree.

"Minet! Minet!" yelled Gabriel. "Come down."

But Minet was too frightened or too exhausted to move. So Gabriel shinnied up the pole and brought him down, tears welling in his eyes. Forgetting our fatigue, we cheered and laughed and caressed our tenacious little mascot. He had proved himself an awfully tough *hombre*.

The storm came back at midafternoon. Marc was tossed over-board shortly after he assumed his regular watch at 6:00 p.m. He had been nervous and tired following his concussion, and his fingers were blistered from tightening the knots on our cabin. Consequently, when the raft lurched abruptly, he lost his grip on the starboard *guara* and tumbled backward off the stern, yelling "À *l'aide!*" Normand and I quickly pulled him in by the rope around his waist, straining every muscle in our weary arms.

I realized I should have insisted (rather than merely urged) that he let one of us take over his watch. "Marc," I said, "as captain of this ship I must order you to quarters. We can't afford a tired chief cook. You're liable to poison us."

He smiled, and crawled into the cabin for whatever rest was possible on that miserable choppy sea.

My reference to his cooking was ironic, for none of us did any cooking during those three days of stormy weather. We subsisted on what remained of the fresh fruit and native bread we had gotten at Savaii. How we yearned for fried, or even raw, fish.

Aside from the hunger, we all felt an enormous weariness, a soreness in every muscle of our bodies, and, like Marc, our hands were swollen and cut from handling the ropes. The cordage, as one might expect in such volatile weather, would be slack one minute, then tight enough to snap a few minutes later.

On September 18 we finally got a spell of good weather, enabling me to get a fix on our latitude and longitude. The storm, I discovered, had been pushing us northwest, toward an area clotted with banks, but we had apparently skirted Pasco Bank on the night of September 15. Now we were safely bypassing Isabella Bank, another treacherous reef. It was strange to see Spanish names way out here in the middle of the South Pacific. We Spaniards had dropped names everywhere.

I wanted us to come down as close as we could to the northern coasts of Vanua Levu and Viti Levu, two of the principal Fiji Islands, then head south, and finally west, so as to pass south of New Caledonia. My intention was to avoid the New Hebrides, a chain of volcanic islands between the Fijis and New Caledonia, some four hundred miles long, and a nightmare even for vessels with sophisticated navigation instruments. There would be fewer islands and reefs this way, and we would also miss Australia's famous Great Barrier Reef.

We had now been some fifteen weeks on the high seas and had acquired a new kind of courage, the cool, tested-by-fire courage of the seasoned matador, as opposed to the defiant courage of a young *novillero* who is still trying to convince himself that he's not afraid of bulls. Like good matadors we were trying to maintain that "grace under pressure" which Ernest Hemingway described so well.

Marc responded to my Hispanic analogy with typical Gallic skepticism. "But you've got to remember," he said, "that even Manolete finally met a Miura." (The famous matador Manolete was killed in 1947 by a bull from the Miura ranch, which reputedly raised the most dangerous bulls in Spain.)

"Then we shall die like Manolete," I said. "And with grace, I hope."

As my log indicates, the next few days were free of actual danger, but we seemed to be headed for serious trouble.

September 23:

We have come down a few degrees in latitude, but not enough. A rather stiff current pushes us west. The navigation chart indicates this current goes south at half a knot, but for us it is going west at two and a half knots. I don't like it.

October 1:

To clear the southern tip of New Caledonia we will need a course of 200 degrees, and to do this we need a wind from the east or northeast—*not the south wind that blows today!*

We cry against the Devil, against God, and against nature! And where is Chisco now that we need him?

NORMAND had spent several hours trying to catch a large swordfish which had been trailing us since daybreak. It would dive and swoop under *La Balsa*, its seven-foot sword piercing the water with menacing speed. Then it would churn and thrash about like a playful dolphin. "He won't take my bait," Normand said.

"He's not hungry enough," I said. "Though he soon will be, with all that thrashing around."

Eventually it snagged Normand's bait without touching the hook itself. But as the swordfish turned away from us, a huge gray shark torpedoed out of the depths and chomped off its tail in one fierce bite. Mortally wounded, the swordfish was soon devoured in a bloody turmoil just below the surface.

"There goes our dinner," said Normand glumly.

"How about some shark meat?" suggested Marc. "Plenty of nice fillets out there."

"Not today. That killer's too big. I couldn't handle him."

I knew what Normand meant: our lack of sleep and nourishment during the three-day storm had weakened us. The sharks we had caught were generally six to ten feet long. Tough-skinned and muscular, they were difficult to slice. Some were covered with remoras, black slippery fish that fastened themselves to the larger fish by means of a vacuum disk on top of their flat heads.

Strangely enough, Minet showed no interest in the remoras; perhaps he was repelled by them. But his fascination with crabs finally got him in trouble. One afternoon he was batting at a large crab Normand had caught, when suddenly the crab snared Minet's left forepaw in one of its large claws. He let out loud meows as he scrambled around the deck, slapping it with his free paw in a vain attempt to break the viselike grip. Finally Normand chopped off the crab's claw and pried it loose.

"Minet," he said, "you're a damned fool."

Apparently chagrined, Minet disappeared from sight, and all we could hear was an occasional faint meow coming from somewhere behind the cabin. "He's punishing us," said Marc. "He's hiding, hoping we'll think he's gone or dead."

He continued to punish us for several hours, but as the sun began to set he left his hiding place and strutted up and down the deck. "Don't laugh," I said with a straight face. "Or he'll go into hiding again."

We wouldn't have had time for an encore of Minet's act; another storm was brewing. We barely had time to haul in the sail before the stronger winds came, rattling the boom against the mast. We bounced around for several hours in the darkness, listening to a symphony of different sounds as the escalating winds twanged on the taut ropes. (When the thin ropes vibrated in high pitch, you knew the wind was strong; when the half-inch ropes *thummmed,* the wind was very strong; and when you heard the inch-and-a-half ropes *thooong-g-g* like a giant bass viol, it was time to batten the hatches.) Bracing our legs for the onslaught of waves, we could feel the logs jostling up and down beneath our feet like piano keys rhythmically accommodating the rumbling seas.

Framed against an expanse of ocean, a crew member checks *La Balsa*'s rigging.

"Let's keep the watch all night," Gabriel suggested to me. "The other two need a rest—especially Marc."

"Good idea," I said, noting that the squall was already subsiding.

In the morning Marc and Normand crawled out of the cabin to relieve us. "Why didn't you call us?" scolded Marc. We happily accepted his grumpiness.

"We're going to have a great dinner tonight," Gabriel predicted before falling into deep slumber. "Marc looks like a new man."

At midafternoon the next day Marc told us he was feeling much better, but that the raft was in failing health. "The logs seem looser, Vital. All these storms have stretched the ropes and made the grooves deeper."

We checked, and found that the ropes had indeed carved much deeper into the balsa wood, accounting for some looseness between the seven main logs. This was cause for considerable worry as we headed on our zigzag course through the dangerous reefs ahead. A tight firm raft would have been far easier to maneuver.

On October 5 we realized that we wouldn't be able to pass south of New Caledonia, so I decided to steer between the islands of Eromanga and Tana in the southern New Hebrides. "That passage will be narrow and dangerous," I explained to Gabriel, who had been studying the maps with me. "There are all kinds of uncharted reefs there."

We stood at the prow of our little raft as it bounced and dipped toward the lowering sun, searching for some sign of the two islands we had to pass between. The sunset was beautiful that afternoon, fluffy flame-tinted clouds escorting a bright orange disk beyond the horizon. I could have sworn the earth was flat, that the sun was falling off the edge into endless space. But when it was gone, we had not seen a trace of Eromanga or Tana, and the wind was beginning to shift.

"Damn it, Chisco," I muttered. "We'll be sailing blind. Why must we always face these dangers at night?"

None of us could sleep—we all stood watch. Marc and I stood at the corners of the bow, peering into the darkness. Normand and Gabriel were stationed at the stern, alternating turns at the starboard *guara*, prepared to shift course if necessary. Near midnight I thought I saw a splash against a dark reef, but it was only a shark's dorsal fin cutting a foamy circle around the raft. He was soon joined by another. They trailed us for hours, like vultures.

"Eromanga and Tana," mused Marc. "Are you sure they exist?"

"They do on my map," I said.

Just after daybreak Gabriel verified the existence of Eromanga. Pointing to the tip of an island on the horizon behind us and slightly northeast, he said, "Look, we passed it last night." Tana, behind us to the southeast, was not even visible.

Late in the afternoon of the following day we skirted the northern fringe of the famous Astrolabe Reefs, coming close enough to see the jagged coral blocks jutting from the waves for several miles. I studied a nearby submerged reef through my powerful binoculars. It looked like an immense rock garden dotted with anemones and branches of coral, having the appearance of fossilized plants in purple, yellow, green, and red; there were dark green mosses here and there, prickly objects that resembled cacti, and fish of all sizes, shapes, and colors—a fantasy of strange flora and fauna that only the sea can provide.

"Now we'll have to go northwest of the D'Entrecasteaux Reefs and Huon Islands," I told Gabriel. "That ought to test the raft. It's one of the trickiest seas in the world."

On the evening of October 10 we contacted Rafael Corcuera. Using our time-consuming click-click system, we told him our approximate position, not knowing we were less than nine miles from the dreaded D'Entrecasteaux Reefs.

Then, as we were signing off, I heard the voice of a New Zealand ham operator named Gus. He was talking to Rafael, but we could hear him quite clearly. "They're in danger!" he said. "They're headed straight for the reefs."

Then Admiral Fernandez's voice broke in. "New Zealand, New Zealand, I agree with you. . . . They are in great danger. . . . The wind is from the east and pushing them hard toward the reefs. . . . We've got to warn them. . . . Their radio is out. . . . Can you have a plane sent?"

It was already quite dark when we heard the urgent plea from Mexico City. Once again we were headed for a possible disaster in the moonless night. We spent another sleepless ten hours standing watch.

But by daybreak the D'Entrecasteaux Reefs were far behind us, barely visible through our binoculars.

Around 11:00 a.m. we heard a small plane in the vicinity of the reefs. Five hours later, when we again made contact with our ham-radio network, I heard a voice say, "The plane didn't find anything, so I think they made it okay. If they had hit a reef, there would have been some wreckage."

I tried to reassure them, but they were apparently unable to hear my clicking from the not-too-reliable transmitter. After a half hour of futile tampering, I went back to my navigation charts to ascertain our next move.

October 12:
We have passed the Huon Islands and their reefs—again during the night. Incredible! I think somebody is pushing us. I can no longer sleep at night. I'm afraid to be awakened by the crunching of the raft against a reef.

The wind is from the east, but we cannot go south as far as we would like because the current is flowing due west. We would like to go almost due south so as to miss Chesterfield Reefs and Islands, which are between 5 and 17 feet high.

At night we would have to be within half a mile of a reef to see the surf breaking on it, and by then it would probably be too late for a raft with no motor to change course. With each new test, however, we became prouder of our raft's performance.

October 13:
No wind today. We can rest and let the small current take us south from the Huon Islands. We sang songs all afternoon, ate a fine lunch of flying fish prepared by Marc, played Parcheesi for high stakes.
Gabriel says, "We are lucky for once." And Marc says, "If we are lucky now, I am afraid of what will happen tomorrow."

Marc was right, but it would be a trouble different from the kind he expected.

7

ON THE following day we drifted into a dead sea again. There was no current and no breeze. The sun was unbearably hot, forcing us to seek the meager shade of the cabin. Nothing seemed to be moving except a few cockroaches and ants.

There were no fish anywhere; they had disappeared along with the current. So we had fish from the day before, eating it raw so as not to produce additional heat from the stove. It tasted warm and bitter. Neither Marc nor I could eat it, but Normand and Gabriel chewed the tough pieces with a stubborn, joyless determination, as if this were their last meal.

Sunset brought some relief from the heat, but there was still no breeze. Nor was there the following morning. My sextant indicated that we had moved less than a mile in twenty-four hours.

Finally, just after the burning sun slipped over the horizon, we got a gentle breeze from the north. Two hours later we drifted into a southerly current, and the increasing wind pushed us along at a comfortable five miles an hour. We sang "La Cucaracha" and

"La Marseillaise," our voices tumbling over one another like care-free waves.

The next few days were almost perfect, as we headed for a passage north of the Chesterfield Reefs. "We're less than seven hundred miles from Australia," I told Marc, after checking our position on my sextant. "And the raft is still in fine shape."

"A bit loose here and there," said Marc, "and needs a shave."

The ragged beards of seaweed had grown up again on the out-side logs.

"We ought to take some pictures before we cut them off," said Gabriel.

Gabriel and I hopped into the dinghy and rowed for several hundred yards. From that distance *La Balsa* looked terribly frag-ile and primitive, and I thought how little we had realized the extent of the dangers or the meagerness of our protection.

"I've been thinking about that last big gale," mused Gabriel, as if reading my thoughts. "It was worse than I imagined."

"How so?" I asked.

"I don't know how to say it exactly. It's just a funny feeling I got a minute ago, a strange sort of cold chill when I looked at the raft. Silly, I guess."

"We all get that," I said. "It's called shell shock. A soldier con-vinces himself that he's not scared when the bombs are exploding all around him, but the fear comes back later on."

We started snapping pictures of the raft, Gabriel rowing while I worked the camera, and vice versa. There was a comic elegance about *La Balsa* as we came closer, a sort of quixotic flair in the billowing sail that contrasted with the shabbiness of the cabin. I felt that the legendary man of la Mancha would have been proud to sail on our little raft.

"She's the most beautiful raft in the world," said Gabriel.

I had to agree. It was a good little craft and had held up through remarkably severe conditions. Nevertheless, I couldn't help fretting about the looseness Marc and I had detected. I especially worried at night. Lying there in the cabin, I could feel the logs jostling, as if the ropes were wearing away. Even the *guaras* had become slightly wobbly, making it more difficult to steer through narrow passages. Would the raft suddenly disintegrate as we were approaching the Chesterfield Reefs, or would it wait until we got to the more dangerous Great Barrier Reef?

"WE MUST be near an island," Gabriel said one day, nodding toward the distant funnel-shaped cloud in front of us.

"It must be the Chesterfield Reefs," I said, studying my chart. I quickly calculated how long it would take us to reach them, and concluded we would have to pass them in the dark.

Once again we stood an all-night vigil, but detected no slashing of waves that might indicate invisible reefs. According to my calculations, however, we must have passed the first of the Chesterfield Reefs around midnight, and the last just before dawn. We were elated when we got a strong morning wind from the east which, combined with a southerly current, would carry us in a southwest direction.

The next few days and nights were spent on a zigzag course through other reefs. Some, not even charted, were lying just below the surface—particularly dangerous for minor craft without radar.

"*La Balsa* has its own radar," observed Marc as we twisted through a jagged mass of coral five feet below the surface. "I think she uses the seaweed on her belly as antenna."

Minet, like other sea cats, had also developed an internal radar, enabling him to anticipate bad weather long before it developed. The sky would be clear, but suddenly he would creep into a corner of the cabin. Several hours later a squall would come, surprising everyone but Minet. My log testified to this.

October 26:
Minet was right again about the weather yesterday. It suddenly rained like hell.

Today we heard for the first time a ham operator in Sydney named Sid Molen. This makes Australia seem much closer. He has a strong voice, and is very brief and practical.

Now we were headed for the Great Barrier Reef, one of the most dangerous areas in the world for any kind of vessel. With Marc peering over my shoulder, I spread our chart on the matted deck and studied the jagged profile of the immensely long reef, searching for a possible passage at high tide.

"This light-shaded area might be an opening," I said, with more hope than conviction.

"I doubt it," Marc responded. "I've been told that there are no safe passages. We'd better prepare for a crash."

"There's still one possibility," I said, pointing to some wavy lines on the chart. "There's a current that runs south along the eastern face of the reef. We might have a fifteen percent chance of drifting with it."

Marc smiled. "How did you reach that precise calculation?"

"Very simply," I answered. "Thirty percent is a fair chance. I figure we only have about half a fair chance."

Once again I felt like a matador on the morning of an important bullfight, wondering how the bulls would behave at four o'clock. Perhaps the Great Barrier Reef would be like the Miura bull that killed Manolete.

The sky darkened before we could get within sight of the reef, and the wind switched from east to south-southeast. Normand had gone up to the crow's nest to scan the horizon with the binoculars, but could see nothing but the amber afterglow of sunset on the choppy waves. Marc and Gabriel were at the boom, trying to swing the sail just enough to change our course without losing the wind. Finally, when it was too dark to see farther than three hundred feet, I told them to take in the sail.

"We're liable to hit that reef before we see it," I said, holding the compass close to my eyes. "We'd better slow down and drift awhile. I hope the current is strong enough to save us."

But even with the sail down, the wind kept pushing us to the west. Having tied down everything in preparation for a crash, there was nothing to do but pray for a miracle. "Call your saint, Vital," said Gabriel. "We need him." There was no jest in his voice, only the fervor of a determined but ambivalent atheist.

We all stood at the bow, peering into the darkness, each one lost in his own thoughts. Had we come all this distance—nearly eight thousand miles through the worst obstacles—simply to fail on the last lap?

It wasn't my nature to accept defeat gracefully. Chisco! I yelled inwardly, not wanting to show my desperation to the others. Give us a fair chance. Not a miracle, damn it—just a fair chance.

We kept drifting closer to the dreaded reef, bracing ourselves for the collision, straining our eyes for the white-capped lashing of waves against the invisible barrier. The sea became choppier and darker as the moon drifted behind a bank of clouds, and the tension on board mounted with each passing minute.

Then suddenly the wind died down. "We're awfully close," said Marc. "I can hear the surf beating against the barrier. I can also see spray," he added. "Over there, to your right. About three hundred yards away."

Sure enough—it was to my right! We had turned somehow. We were drifting south now, with the reef on our starboard side. "We're in the current!" I shouted. "We're going to make it."

Shortly before midnight we got a fairly good wind from the north, which prompted us to hoist our sail again. As dawn crept over the eastern horizon, the reef emerged in a dazzling display of bright coral and multicolored plants.

By October 28 we were clear of the Great Barrier Reef and still moving south, with the last obstacle—the Saumarez Reefs—coming up to the southeast. We had a brisk wind and clear blue skies, a perfect day for fishing and sunbathing. Minet was perched on the cabin roof, watching Marc as he hauled in a wildly flapping dolphin. He waited until the first blood spurted, then leaped from the roof in one fluid motion and neatly lapped up the puddle at Marc's feet.

"Minet has developed better manners," observed Marc. "He doesn't slurp anymore."

"He's over five months old," I said. "He's maturing."

We were interrupted by Normand calling from the crow's nest. "I see a ship—a big red ship over there."

Looking through the binoculars, I saw a motionless ship. As we drew closer, I noticed a gaping hole in its side. I unfurled my navigation chart and saw a wreck symbol right on one of the Saumarez Reefs. As I later learned, we were looking at the wreck of the American Liberty ship *Francis Blair*, which had foundered on the reef in 1942. Subsequently, it had been used for bombing practice by the RAF, which explained why it was painted red.

Checking my chart again, I said to Gabriel, "If this is the right wreck, then there should be some huge rocks visible at a hundred and twenty degrees southeast."

Sure enough, there were two slender rocks sticking up like sharks' fins about three miles away. Beyond them we could just make out the foamy white line of surf breaking on the reefs.

"There's also a white line to our port side," said Normand. "And another one behind the ship."

"We're headed for trouble," I said to Marc.

Suddenly, we realized we were in the middle of an immense curving reef, and the wind was blowing us steadily toward the deadly white lines in the distance.

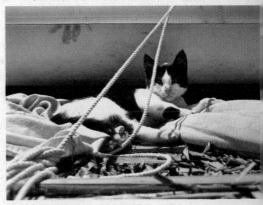

Minet—ham actor and "born delinquent"— catnaps by the dinghy.

Now I could see the rocks beneath us, about sixty feet below the surface.

"If we escape this one," Marc said, "we're damned lucky."

My feelings as we approached that first barely submerged coral formation were a mixture of cold fear and sheer delight at the incredible spectacle below. The water was a clear emerald green, the convoluted coral shimmered with the bright colors of an artist's palette, and thousands of fish darted in and out among dreamlike underwater plants. It was to be the most beautiful—and the most dangerous—moment of our entire voyage.

Angry waves were breaking on two big outcrops of coral half a mile apart. We zigzagged between them, sometimes missing a coral trap by less than three feet. From his perch in the crow's nest, Normand kept warning us that we were still heading for a white line of breakers.

Rushing back and forth between the four *guaras* behind the cabin, I would push down the starboard boards one moment, then pull them up ten seconds later as the raft veered toward a new reef. Meanwhile, Marc was running up and down in front of the cabin, frantically adjusting the forward *guaras* to coincide with my maneuvers. It was a kind of split-second acrobatics.

Suddenly we found ourselves in a pocket of reefs. "We're trapped," I told Marc. "We'll have to try that gap."

We steered toward a gap in the churning foam. As we came closer, we saw that the gap was barely wide enough for the raft, but it was too late to turn back. Here was the supreme test of *La Balsa's* maneuverability. I shifted the starboard-stern centerboard about six inches to correct a slight list to the left. We started through the gap, catching a spillover of spray on both sides. Then we heard a loud grinding underneath us. A jolting crunch knocked us off our feet, as the *guaras* bumped over rocks and coral. Three *guaras* broke, but in a few more breathless and terrifying seconds we were over the reef and out into blue water.

We were on the last lap to Australia.

8

The moment we cleared the Saumarez Reefs, Normand started singing his song at the top of his lungs. The rest of us joined in, laughing boisterously, relieving the tension. The only one who didn't enjoy our foolishness was Minet. He just sat twitching his whiskers, like a disapproving schoolmaster at noon recess.

"He feels left out," said Gabriel.

"But he used to meow when Normand sang, remember?"

His sudden silence disturbed us. But then, just before sunset, he snuggled into Gabriel's lap, purring softly. That night he kept the watch with me, never leaving my side for three hours, and when Normand relieved me around 3:00 a.m., Minet immediately climbed into his lap. He had obviously decided to stay up with anyone who was standing watch.

Then it dawned on me that our little cat was afraid to be alone. He had somehow sensed we were near journey's end and that we would soon leave *La Balsa,* the only home he had ever known. My daily log reflects my continuing concern about our "fifth crew member."

October 30:
We have traveled south about 40 miles today, and we think we've reached the first Australian currents. Everyone is happy except Minet. He's still moping around like a child expecting to be abandoned by divorced parents.

Now our canasta score is: Marc, 1,617,380; Vital, 1,331,525; Normand, 1,268,905; Gabriel, 1,257,350. Though I hesitate to make judgments about comparative ability, I think we can assume that older codgers like Marc and me are more patient in such games than youngsters like Gabriel and Normand.

November 1:
We're picking up speed. We made 62 miles south today. We can safely say we're practically in Australia. Fraser Island is due west of us, although we can't see it. Our bad luck seems to be disappearing. I guess we left it behind us on the Saumarez Reefs.

ON NOVEMBER 3, shortly before 3:00 p.m., we established contact with Sid Molen in Sydney. A senior television technician, Molen had been in radio contact with Rafael Corcuera for several months. On October 24 Rafael had asked him to take over the coordination of the raft's communication system, teaching him our click-click technique. Consequently, when Molen called us that afternoon, he had alerted ham operators in Queensland, Victoria, and New Guinea, all of whom were listening as he questioned us.

"Do you need urgent assistance? Is anyone sick?"

To which I answered with a "click click." (No.)

"Do you have enough food and water?"

"Cliiick." (Yes.)

"Would you like a ship to stand by?"

"Cliiick."

We hoped to land at Brisbane, and I wanted a boat standing by in case a wind threatened to blow us ashore. After 8000 miles, I didn't want our raft broken up in a crash landing.

"Can you wait until tomorrow?" asked Sid.

"Cliiick."

I gave him a fairly accurate longitude, but because of cloudy weather, I had not been able to gauge our latitude, so I gave him an approximation. As it turned out we were thirty-seven miles north of the position I reported to Sid. My mistake caused considerable confusion. On November 4 everyone believed we were farther south, headed for Brisbane, where Captain E. Whish, the Air-Sea Rescue Coordinator, was preparing to meet us.

At about 3:30 a.m. on November 5 Normand saw a light on the horizon, blinking every seven and a half seconds. Checking my chart with a flashlight, I identified it as the beacon light from Double Island Point, just south of Fraser Island.

When the sun came up three hours later, we saw the southern tip of Fraser Island, and I got out the radio and started clicking away. Our network of ham operators were all on the line in less than five minutes. When the information about our position was relayed to Captain Whish, he replied, "That's not possible, according to where they were yesterday."

We were asked: "Are you south of Danger Point?"

"Click click." (No.)

"All right, are you northeast of Double Island Point?"

"Cliiick, cliiick, cliiick." (Yes, yes, yes.)

"Okay, Vital, we're sending a plane to spot you right away!"

The first plane flew overhead at 9:20 a.m. and dropped a beer can with a message: "Welcome to Australia!" Then came another plane packed with journalists, followed by several others that buzzed over us like friendly bees.

Either frightened or resentful, Minet hid in the cabin, refusing to join the wild celebration we were staging on deck. After a while I crawled in and found him huddled in Gabriel's sleeping bag, meowing softly like a heartsick child. I held him in my lap, stroking his back and trying to console him.

Had Minet somehow realized that our raft family would soon break up? Obviously, he could go away with only one of us—and we all assumed it would be Gabriel. In any case, whether or not the little cat would actually miss us once he left the raft, we knew we would miss him. He had given all of us a profound lesson in the art of survival against heavy odds, and he had defied all dangers with the élan of a soldier of fortune.

I took him outside to join his family, and they invited him to share the lunch Normand had cooked. As we sat down together, I noticed that Marc no longer disdained Normand's amateur cooking by lowering his jaw. I also noted that Gabriel was eating quietly, without his usual *craack* and *rassp*. It was the first pleasant meal I had eaten since leaving Guayaquil.

I thought of the many things we had proven on this voyage. We had shown that four men can live on a "floating prison" for more than five months without succumbing to the urge to kill. In fact, by carefully adhering to our two rules, we had managed to avoid even a serious dispute. A raft or boat on the high seas is really a small world unto itself. Each man must be responsible for the welfare of the whole group. Survival depends on the total cooperation of *all* men—whether their world is a raft, a village, a country, or a planet. The voyage of *La Balsa* had shown that such cooperation is possible.

Moreover, we had demonstrated that it was possible to navigate a raft with considerable accuracy, that one need not drift with the caprice of winds and currents. We had come through some of the most dangerous seas in the world and successfully maneuvered past nine treacherous reefs at night. We had also shown that a balsa raft of good female logs retains its buoyancy over long distances. Now, at the very end of our voyage, the logs sat only slightly more than one inch deeper in the water than they had in Guayaquil. Had we wanted to sail the raft back to South America, I was sure we could do so after tightening the ropes. The French raft explorer Eric de Bisschop, who died in 1958, believed there had been circular migration from Peru to Polynesia and back again to South America via west-to-east currents. Someday I may undertake that round trip myself.

These were my thoughts as we sailed the last few miles to Australia, accompanied by an escort of small planes and scores of pleasure craft. The people gave us fruit, candy, and beer, and asked hundreds of questions about the raft. We were headed for an area known as the Sunshine Coast. I was particularly fascinated with the name of its port, Mooloolaba, a musical rolling of full vowels and soft consonants that spoke of mystery and beauty.

When we came into the estuary of the Mooloolah River, it was too dark for us to see any dangerous obstacles, so we agreed to let a motorboat tow us into port. Shortly before midnight we drew near the dock, which we could barely see through the darkness.

Then, suddenly, there was an explosion of light and noise. Sky-rockets, Roman candles, blue flares, and all kinds of fireworks shot up from the docks, and hundreds of well-wishers shouted and cheered as *La Balsa* pulled into port: "Welcome to Australia!"

THE tumultuous welcome was soured when two quarantine officers boarded the raft and took Minet away in a metal cage. Australia has strict regulations on the importation of animals, but we hadn't expected their officials to arrive at midnight. We planned to spring Minet next day.

We left the anchored raft and climbed a wooden ladder at the end of the dock, telling each other how good it felt to be on land again. Crowds of people lined the dock, stepping back to form a passage for us. Waving to their welcoming shouts, I started walking through the gap. Then, suddenly, before I had taken even three or four steps, my legs buckled. Gabriel and Normand fell in a heap beside me, and Marc wobbled into the arms of two men. We were experiencing the punch-drunk effect that all sailors go through when they first step on *terra firma*. In fact, ours was worse, because the motions of a small raft are more exaggerated than those of a large vessel.

In spite of the wobbliness we shook hands with hundreds of men, women, and children, but we found it almost impossible to autograph the notebooks, slips of paper, menus, and napkins that were shoved into our hands. "I can't stand still," I kept telling them in my heavily accented English.

About an hour after our arrival I talked with my wife and two little daughters. Admiral Fernandez had arranged for them to greet me on his ham radio set. My wife, Denise, sounded wonderfully happy and excited, and my elder daughter, Marina, asked me to bring her a mama kangaroo "with a baby in her pocket." But four-year-old Denise seemed subdued, perhaps confused by the complex dials and knobs on the admiral's transceiver. Suddenly I felt sad and guilty, a lump rising in my throat as I visualized her standing in front of a cold metal radio apparatus, trying to sound affectionate toward a long-absent father she couldn't see.

"Did you drown?" she finally asked.

"No, I'm still here, *mi corazón*," I said. "Everyone's fine."

"Is the little kitty still there?" she asked.

"Yes, Minet's still with us."

"Bring him home, Daddy," she said with sudden enthusiasm.

I would have promised her the moon wrapped in cellophane, but our conversation was abruptly terminated by shrill static that stabbed my eardrums like an invisible knife.

About one in the morning we had a press conference at the crowded Mooloolaba Yacht Club. We felt less woozy as we sat on solid wooden chairs, facing a jumble of microphones and television cameras.

"How do you feel, Captain?"

"Tired and happy."

"Also hungry," added Gabriel, evoking a burst of laughter.

"Were you ever afraid?"

"Quite often," I said. "But I managed to hide it. Mostly from myself."

Later a local radio ham told me he'd just been contacted by Rafael Corcuera, who wished to congratulate us. Our conversation was lighthearted and friendly, yet I detected a strange note of sadness in Rafael's voice.

The next morning we arrived at the waterfront office of the Australian Quarantine Department at ten o'clock. Twenty or thirty reporters and television cameramen were there ahead of us, crowded into the gray-walled reception room, apparently hoping to photograph "the cat who had learned to swim among the sharks."

"We have come for the cat," I said to a pleasant-faced man behind the desk.

"I'm sorry, sir," he said, nervously eyeing the red light on a TV camera. "She's got to stay in quarantine, you know."

"For how long?"

"Well, it will be thirty days, sir. She's got to be checked for communicable diseases. Same as all animals."

"Then what happens?" asked one of the reporters.

The official cleared his throat and shuffled some papers, his worried blue eyes avoiding ours. "I'd rather not say," he said.

"We want to know," I insisted, leaning across the desk.

"Well . . ." he said, with great reluctance, "I'm afraid she's got to be disposed of."

Everyone gasped—even the supposedly callous newsmen.

"You mean kill her?" yelled someone at the rear of the room.

A bedlam of angry protests broke out. Several police officers from the nearby immigration department rushed in to quiet the uproar, and the official disappeared into an interior office.

"We won't permit this!" shouted a woman reporter. "We'll raise hell with all of you."

Within a few hours the news had spread to every province and town in Australia. The wire services carried angry articles condemning the quarantine department and asking for new laws prohibiting the slaughter of innocent animals. Minet's picture appeared on front pages everywhere. The evening telecasts carried filmed coverage of our morning encounter at the waterfront. Vehement editorials demanded that the government release "the cat heroine who had survived the toughest sea journey in all recorded history."

"They keep referring to him as *her*," Gabriel observed.

"Minet sounds like a feminine name in English," I said. "But let's not correct them. A female cat arouses more sympathy."

She did indeed. Thousands of letters, mostly from women, poured in to newspaper and government offices—"save Minet"; "free the heroine"; "don't let her die"—a blizzard of protests that no government with any political sensitivity could afford to ignore. Within twenty-four hours several elected officials had asked the administration to reconsider its regulations. The next day a government spokesman announced that the "Minet matter" was under review by higher authorities.

Fortunately the government was spared further embarrassment by the wife of a sea captain whose ship was about to sail from Brisbane. "I'll adopt Minet," she announced in a telegram that relieved the quarantine officials. "She'll find a home on the ship *Sued,* which will leave your country within five days."

Since we would be traveling through Australia, attending receptions for two or three weeks, we decided to let her have Minet, with the agreement that Gabriel would pick him up at some port along the *Sued*'s route. But when the captain's wife later informed Gabriel that Minet seemed "wonderfully happy" aboard the huge ocean liner, he reluctantly agreed to let him stay.

"That little cat is a born sailor," he subsequently wrote me. "I don't think he could adjust to Chile. And where would I get him enough blood to drink?"

After our "heroes' tour" of the major cities (our hands swollen from handshakes, our jaw muscles worn out from smiling), Marc, Normand, Gabriel, and I parted company. We had a farewell party on the raft, a boozy, sentimental affair that lasted until dawn. We talked about Minet and about all the dangers we had overcome, laughing and hugging each other as we discussed the difficulty of keeping my two rules.

"I wanted to punch you every time you cleared your throat, Vital," said Gabriel. "One afternoon—sometime in August—you cleared your throat twenty-nine times in a single hour! I counted."

Normand spoke up about the way Gabriel had *craack*ed and *rassp*ed, "finally forcing me to eat outside the cabin because I couldn't stand it anymore."

"I guess I was nervous," explained Gabriel rather sheepishly. "Anyway, I'm glad you didn't criticize me. I would have stopped eating altogether if I'd known how awful it sounded."

Marc grinned and slowly shook his head. "No, Gabriel, nothing could keep you from eating. I envy you your stomach, my friend—and also your ability to sleep when nobody else could. With that kind of gift, you can survive anything."

Thus praising and forgiving each other, we cemented a friendship that is rare—the profound comradeship of men who have traveled far and faced death together, thumbing their noses at the gods of chance.

341

Leaving Australia on a 707 jet two days later, after arranging for *La Balsa* to be shipped to my home in Spain, I looked down at the sparkling waters of the Pacific with affection and awe. Had we really crossed that huge mass of water in a primitive raft? It hardly seemed possible.

Stranger still was my reaction when the stewardess informed me that it would take us twenty-three hours to reach Mexico City. "Twenty-three hours!" I exclaimed, forgetting we had taken nearly six months to travel a shorter distance. "I'll get claustrophobia."

Even with the long stopover in Tahiti, I felt imprisoned inside the huge, almost empty jet. How I longed for the freedom of *La Balsa*, the nearness of the pulsating water, the friendly fish trailing behind us, the satisfaction of controlling one's own destiny.

When we landed in Mexico City the following day, my wife and children and several friends were waiting for me, and there were tears and laughter and warm embraces all around. But this stopover was brief. My wife and I had to board another plane almost immediately. The president of Ecuador, José María Velasco Ibarra, had invited us to a homecoming celebration in Guayaquil. Within a few hours we were reunited with such friends as Don Cesar Iglesias, Senora Paladines, Joe Megan, and the many Ecuadorians who had given us aid and comfort from the beginning.

Then we flew back to Mexico City. The next morning I took my little daughters to an amusement park to celebrate. Wearing bright new dresses, with saucy beribboned pigtails bouncing off their shoulders, they led me hand in hand from the merry-go-round to the scooter to the funhouse, and to several refreshment stands in between. But at the roller coaster I balked.

"It's too dangerous," I said.

"Mama takes us all the time," said Marina, squeezing my thumb in her tiny hand.

"She must be crazy," I said under my breath. "Only a fool would get on one of those deathtraps."

"What did you say, Papa?" asked Denise.

"Nothing," I said. "I was just thinking that we ought to take another ride on the merry-go-round."

They followed me without protest, but I distinctly heard Marina whisper to her sister, "I think Daddy's afraid."

Realizing they were too young to understand the difference between rational and irrational risks, I bribed them into silence with popcorn and cotton candy, and saved the lecture for my wife, who had just arrived to join us.

"There's nothing wrong with being afraid of roller coasters, Vital," she said, missing my point entirely. "Everyone has to be afraid of something. I hear that Manolete was afraid of cats."

The next day I made a quick round-trip flight to Guadalajara to visit Rafael Corcuera. Hoping to surprise him, I had not called him in advance. But when his wife answered the door, her expression told me that something tragic had happened.

"Rafael is dead," she said in a hushed voice, leading me into their modestly furnished living room. "He died just after you finished your voyage. He had been awfully sick for a long time, but he wouldn't let himself die until you had reached Australia."

She paused, touched her graying hair with trembling fingers, tears brimming in her dark brown eyes. "Your wonderful voyage kept him alive. He seemed to be sailing with you as he charted your progress day by day. He kept worrying about your water supply and about the terrible storms near Samoa. And when he heard of your emergency—when you were almost starving—he couldn't sleep for forty-eight hours. When your radio went dead, he would often stare at the map, mumbling, 'Where are my sons?'"

"He was very kind to us," I said, not wanting her to know that the "emergency" was simply a misunderstanding.

"We finally moved his bed down to the basement, where his radio was," Senora Corcuera continued. "He was too weak to climb up and down stairs." She took me down and showed me the log he had kept, and the much-marked maps. I felt a mingling of pride and sadness when I noticed how his writing had grown fainter toward the end.

"We loved your husband," I said, looking at the neatly folded covers on his bed. "And we always felt his presence. You might say he was the fifth man on *La Balsa*."

"Rafael would have been proud to hear you say that," she said

343

in a soft whisper. "And I'm grateful that you kept him alive as long as you did."

The following week, in Madrid, the Spanish government gave me an elaborate reception at General Francisco Franco's ornate palace. It was a splendid ceremony, and I was presented with a beautiful bronze medallion. But I couldn't help feeling a certain pity for General Franco. Here he was, surrounded by everything money could buy—exquisite tapestries, gleaming marble floors, oriental carpets, Etruscan vases, red velvet drapes, discreet servants to answer his slightest need. Yet it seemed like a gilded prison. He had no free access to that world that is most real to me. He could not take a solitary walk down a tree-lined avenue, or eat in one of those marvelous gypsy taverns on the Plaza Mayor. Like any other head of state, he had to be escorted everywhere by a bodyguard, having long ago sacrificed the precious privacy that even the most humble Spaniard enjoys.

"It must be wonderful to sail on a raft," he said to me. "How nice it would be to get away from all the humdrum problems of this world."

Had it been possible for him to use it, I would have given him *La Balsa* then and there. Instead, with his financial assistance, we established a sailors' museum in Santander, my hometown and that of Columbus's map maker, where *La Balsa* can remain on permanent display.

Perhaps it will encourage someone else to take up the challenge of the sea—as the Huancavilcas did—and sail freely toward the western sun.

Vital Alsar

By the time this volume goes to press Vital Alsar should once again be in mid-Pacific, sailing westward on a course about eight hundred miles to the south of *La Balsa*'s. His latest expedition, which left Ecuador in May, consists of three rafts—the other two skippered by Marc Modena and Gabriel Salas—and twelve men.

Alsar's purpose this time is twofold. He wants to test different currents, those "moving roads of the sea" which, he maintains, the ancient mariners knew as a modern motorist knows road maps; and to show that the original expeditions, directed perhaps towards trade or colonization, may have comprised small fleets of balsa rafts. If all goes well, his rafts will reach Mooloolaba, Australia, where *La Balsa* made her landfall, before the end of 1973.

When not at sea, the thirty-nine-year-old Vital shares a busy homelife with his young wife, Denise, who is one of Mexico's top classical Spanish dancers, and their two daughters. They live in a Spanish-style house in the quiet Mexico City suburb of Etchegaray, where the girls are in kindergarten and first grade. Alsar, a physical fitness enthusiast, finds time, every day he's ashore, for two hours of swimming and Swedish gymnastics.

It takes Alsar about a year to recover from a long raft expedition, and another year to raise funds (estimated cost of the present voyage is $250,000) and prepare for the next one. Assuming that his current venture is successful, he expects to set out on a final journey—a circular trip from Ecuador, through Polynesia, and back again—sometime in 1975.

THE SHADOW OF THE FALCON
Ewan Clarkson

Illustrated by Victor Ambrus   Published by Hutchinson, London

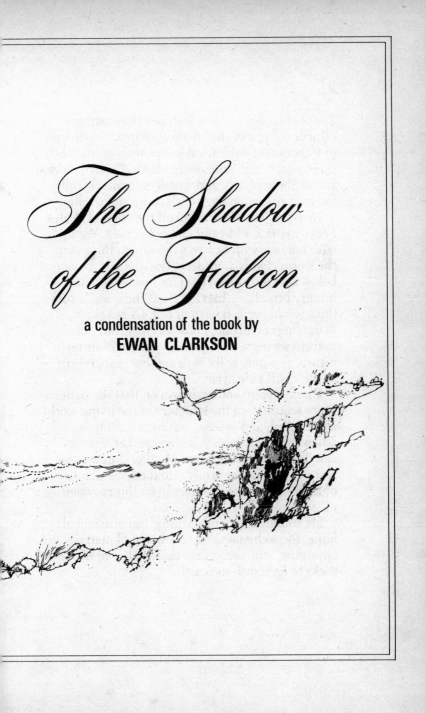

The Shadow
of the Falcon

a condensation of the book by
EWAN CLARKSON

For centuries men have watched the soaring, effortless flight of the falcon and dreamed dreams: of freedom, of wild, wind-swept seas, of limitless skies, of the high and lonely places. Ewan Clarkson knows these places, and writes of them with all the magical immediacy of the born story-teller.

In a desolate island eyrie off the coast of Wales Freya mates for life and makes her nest. We fly with her, see with her eyes the sun on the water, the storm clouds' approach, the smallest movement below that may mean food for herself and her hungry brood. . . . Inevitably, as the seasons pass the age-old perils take their toll. Of her three fledgelings finally only one survives. But the pattern seems secure. Just as spring will surely return, so surely will Freya and her mate return to their cliff-side eyrie.

Clarkson also knows, however, that the pattern is *not* secure, that the structure of the living world is beautiful, and precise, but so delicately balanced that Man in his greed and arrogance can do it irreparable harm. He therefore sets his story of the falcons firmly into the wider context of life both animal and human on this crowded planet.

He sounds a note of warning, but also one of hope, for, as he says, "A new breed of man is emerging, who recognizes the sanctity of life and seeks to replenish the earth."

CHAPTER ONE

A shadow flickered fork-winged over the cliff. For a moment it hung dark against the jade-green of the sea. Then a small cloud drifted over the sun, and the shadow faded and was lost in a wilderness of crumbling, weatherworn rock and wind-rippled water.

Many eyes marked the passing of the shadow. It was seen by the buzzard, wheeling a thousand feet above the cliff, and by the raven, motionless on a crag high above his brooding mate. Even the tiny kestrel, hovering twenty feet over a newly ploughed field, caught the flicker of movement. Herring gulls shouted a warning, and the red-billed chough screamed as he dived for the safety of the stones. Freya the wanderer, the peregrine falcon, had returned to her island stronghold.

A minute later a jackdaw died, its life blown out in an ash-grey cloud of feathers that drifted away on the wind. Freya flapped away with her prize to a convenient rock, where she alighted and began to plume it, stripping the feathers away from the plump dark breast. Then she fed, cutting long strips of meat from the breast-bone with her sharp curved beak, and bolting them down. From time to time she paused, to gaze skyward with wild dark eyes and to crouch ready for instant flight.

351

She was a large bird, some twenty inches from beak to tail, weighing just over thirty ounces. Her back and wings were coloured the bluish grey of slate, so that she was almost invisible against the cliff. Chest, legs and the underparts of her wings were a deep cream, with chestnut markings. Her talons and shanks were bright yellow, matching her bill, and she wore a helmet of black with dark moustaches and sideboards offsetting her white neck and throat. When at rest her long, pointed wings reached two-thirds of the way down her tail.

Hunger satisfied, Freya wiped her bill with meticulous care, and, leaving the corpse to the buzzards and crows, she walked in an awkward, hobbling fashion to the edge of the rock. Her talons, with their long, curving, razor-sharp claws, were instruments of death rather than locomotion, and, as always on land, she moved with extreme care lest she should damage the needle-like points. Looking out to sea, she stretched her neck and gave a high-pitched, staccato yelp. Then she waited, head half-cocked.

The answer came, faint but clear, from a speck in the sky. Lofting her wings she flew towards the newcomer, calling again. The two birds met and circled, fell apart and climbed again, wheeling and spinning in the soft, golden light of the March sun.

The land was warm and the air was rising, drawing a cold breeze off the sea. The peregrines rode the thermal, and looked down on their territory, an island crouched in the Atlantic like a beast of prey, separated from the Welsh mainland by a narrow gut or Sound of turbulent water. Except in the north, the mainland was flat, a carpet of brown and green fields, over which a few small buildings lay scattered like the discarded toys of a weary child. To the north, a chain of hills shaggy with gorse and heather reared skyward, while three miles to the south lay the great bay of St. Brides.

In the spring twilight the two birds flew together to the west of the island, to pitch and roost on the high cliffs.

Morning dawned cloudless. The sea was calm, and a light frost spread over the sleeping land. A gull's sobbing cry echoed among the caves. The peregrines heard it as they perched motionless but alert on their separate ledges. The ecstasy that had sent them spiralling together skyward had faded with the night. Now each

352

was withdrawn, unaware of any need for the other. Yet the need was there. It was this need that had brought them back to the little island of Ramsey and its cliffs.

Before Bronze Age men, with their herds and womenfolk, had come seeking the gold and copper in the ground—before the sea came, when the cliff was an inland crag towering above forest and plain, peregrines had nested here. High above the ancient plains where bison and elk roamed, a peregrine had killed. Primitive man, gripping his stone axe, had seen, and envied the bird its skill in hunting. In that moment perhaps, an idea had been born that was to lead to a strange relationship between man and bird, a bond so finely wrought it was invisible, yet so strong that a man could take a falcon on his fist, and it would sit there without fear. Unleashed, the falcon would fly free and kill, as free as the quarry it pursued, yet at the end it would return to the gloved fist.

Over the centuries men took and trained many species of falcons and hawks, from the noble peregrine to the dainty hobby and merlin, from the mighty goshawk to the diminutive sparrow hawk. Men scoured the earth in search of new varieties, taking gyrfalcon from the cold hills of Norway, lanner and saker from the dusty plains of Persia and Africa, and shaheen from the hot lands of India. There was more to the quest than mere pride of possession. It was as if, through his hawk, earthbound man found a new dimension of freedom, a chance to share the thrill of the flight and the breathtaking stoop that preceded the kill.

The peregrine, of all the falcons, became the most treasured prize of royalty and nobility. Vast sums were paid for one, and the penalties for illegal ownership were harsh. The primacy of the peregrine may have been the result of a voyage made by an English king across the sea from Wales to Ireland. As the ship passed Ramsey Island, the king stood on deck, bored and idle, surrounded by his courtiers, and nursing his favourite goshawk. A peregrine flew low over the rigging and with a shout the king launched his bird in pursuit.

The engagement was brief. The peregrine sideslipped, skimming the waves as the goshawk dropped, talons outstretched to kill. The peregrine then rose vertically and dived in its turn, a steel grey arrowhead that struck home. The goshawk crumpled and spiralled down to the waves, where it drifted half-submerged, like the wreck of a once-proud galleon.

There was silence on board ship as the courtiers waited, wondering how their lord would take this public humiliation. Their answer came in a mighty shout of royal laughter. From that day the king would own no bird save descendants of the Pembrokeshire falcon that had slain a giant goshawk in fair combat.

Yet from his proud perch on the fist of a king, the peregrine fell to an ignoble end, hanging head-down on a keeper's gibbet. For the shotgun was invented, and with it the concept of raising

huge flocks of game for the winter entertainment of shooting parties. Any natural predators which presumed to take what man considered his were ruthlessly destroyed by keepers.

At the same time the spread of railways opened up new territories for the Victorians and Edwardians to explore. With their insatiable appetite for collecting, and their interest in natural history, they plundered the falcons' eyries, frequently taking the entire clutch of eggs.

Young birds too were taken, for although the art of falconry had declined, there were still many men prepared to pay a handsome price for a bird that was once the proudest possession of a king.

Freya, the falcon, was a direct offspring of the Pembrokeshire line. Her mate Frika, the tercel, had drifted down from northwest Scotland. His grandparents had come from Norway, for the peregrines were great wanderers, and over the centuries had populated almost every country in the world. Most of them settled down to breed in the land of their birth, and so in time distinct races became established, but all wore the black helmet and steel-grey livery that were the badges of their lineage.

Now, without warning, the tercel crouched and slipped off the ledge, diving almost to the surface of the sea before vanishing round ·the headland. The falcon watched him go, and then began a thorough examination of the eroded cliff face. A great fissure ran down it, terminating in the roof of a cave. Above this cave were three narrow chambers which tunnelled far under the cliff.

355

Each of these Freya visited in turn, waddling sedately round and inspecting walls, roof and floor. Yet always, on this first morning and on future visits, she returned to the first chamber to scratch the soil that lay hard-packed on the ledge until she had excavated a shallow, cuplike depression. A strange alchemy was at work in her, a driving force, to be obeyed as implicitly and innocently as she followed the inner orders to kill.

THE TERCEL FLEW out across the Sound. The air was clear and cold, drying the bare brown soil of the fields, where already the farmers were busy planting potatoes. Frika avoided the fields with their bustle of activity, and flew on southeast over heathland. A young cock blackbird panicked at his approach, breaking cover from a gorse bush and swooping low over the rough tussocky turf. Instantly Frika darted in pursuit, but the blackbird was too quick for him. With a shrill scream of alarm, it dived headlong into a mass of bramble and briar thorn. Chittering angrily, Frika flew on and at last came to the marsh.

In summer the marsh was a yielding green mat fringed with yellow flag irises and leafy bushes of sallow. Now, after the winter rains, it was a clear shallow pool of fresh water. A noisy chorus of gulls splashed and bickered in the morning sun, and a moorhen crept for cover, its head ducking nervously and its tail jerking as its broad-vaned toes propelled it through the water.

Frika ignored the gulls. They were hard to catch, and their stringy, rancid flesh a poor reward for so much effort. Avoiding the open water, he skirted the margins, darting from side to side in an endeavour to flush out some unwary bird.

At the top of the pool he was rewarded. A lonely green sandpiper, probing the mud for insects, was startled into flight, his white rump flashing in the sun. Frika pursued and was soon climbing above him with short, chopping wing beats. The sandpiper swung in a wide arc and dropped in a desperate attempt to gain the safety of the marsh, but Frika had closed his wings and was diving for the kill. As he swept past his victim his talons, bunched tight against his chest, shot out, striking the sandpiper at the base of the neck, then catching it in mid-air.

356

Fifteen minutes later little was left of the sandpiper save the intestines, fastidiously drawn aside, the keel of the breastbone, and one foot which remained obstinately outside Frika's beak. After a few moments he threw it away. He wiped his beak, stretched luxuriously, shook himself until all his feathers were ruffled, and then dozed in the sun and wind.

The croak of a raven passing overhead woke him. Immediately he remembered Freya, and with rapid wing beats flew back to her on the island. She was still pottering amongst the crevices and barely noticed Frika's return. He pitched on a ledge, and sat motionless, surveying the surrounding seascape.

The sea was largely empty. The plankton had just begun to grow into the rich sea pastures that would support a vast wealth of marine life, which in turn would feed the sea birds soon to arrive. At the foot of the cliffs a small colony of herring gulls squabbled noisily over nesting sites, but for most of the residents, those who had not migrated, it was a time for relaxation, for lazing in the sun before shouldering the responsibilities of raising a family. The cormorant, perched on a rock, his wings outstretched to the sun, looked like some ancient symbol of heraldry, and a bull seal rolled lazily before sinking back into the clear green water.

A shrill scream split the air, dying abruptly, like the ricochet of a spent bullet, and from a low stone ledge that jutted into the Atlantic a black shape emerged, then another and another, until there were eight of them, rising and falling, dancing their court-ship ballet in the bright spring air. The birds were choughs, sable-plumaged with bright red beaks and legs, so delicately built that they resembled big black butterflies.

The flock split into two groups, and their cries grew more excited. They divided again, each pair flying in close unison, black blossoms blown on the wind. Then it was over, and for a brief while the dark dancers settled sedately on the rock. Then one by one, the pairs vanished among the tumbled masses of slate and granite, seeking some dark crevice in which to build their nests and raise their young.

Fate had dealt harshly with this, the most graceful of the crow family. Once their screams had echoed around the high cliffs from Sussex to Land's End, but now only a few remained, sheltering in the remote cliffs of Wales, Ireland, and northwest Scotland.

The day wore on, and Freya began to feel hunger. She slipped off the ledge where for the past hour she had sat preening, coaxing each dishevelled feather until it sat tight and clean in its correct place. Frika joined her, and together they climbed over the island to circle above the Sound.

At first the thrill of flight and joy in the company of her mate made Freya forget her hunger and wheel and soar in the clear evening sky. Throughout the centuries the peregrines had flown thus, their breasts burnished by the evening light. Warriors of old, watching, had seen their resemblance to axe heads, sickle-shaped, lethal, forged by the fire of the sun and gifted with the power of flight. So they came to be called falcons (from the Latin word, *falx*, meaning a sickle), the curving crescents of their wings distinguishing them from the round-winged hawks.

As they soared together, the difference in size between Freya and her mate was obvious. He was fully three inches shorter, smaller boned and less powerful, weighing not more than twenty ounces. So he earned his title of tercel (from the Latin word, *tertius*, meaning third), being a third smaller in size than the falcon.

The light was fading. The peregrines ceased their soaring and hung motionless, alert for the weary birds winging their way to roost, their crops full. Three pigeons flew down the Sound, making for the cliff. Frika scattered them as he dived and climbed rapidly among them. Two pigeons flew for the cliffs, the third turned out over the Sound with Frika in pursuit.

Freya waited five hundred feet above the waves, then came in on a long shallow dive. At the last moment the pigeon twisted aside, and Freya's talons kicked empty air. As she turned and came chopping back above her quarry, Frika, in a sudden explosion of energy, passed underneath, and, turning on his back, plucked the bird out of the skies. It flapped madly for a second, then hung limp.

Frika bore his prize skyward as Freya, shouting her frustration, climbed in hot pursuit. When she was a few feet below him he released the bird and Freya caught it as it spiralled downwards.

Frika followed her to the ledge where she was already at work, tearing at the hot flesh, mantling her prey with hooded wings and hissing jealously. Frika was unconcerned. As the light went, his head sank, and he slept.

CHAPTER TWO

April came, and as the days lengthened the sun warmed the land. Gorse ringed the fields with gold, while on the cliffs pale primroses spread like stars amid the yellow blossoms of the cowslips. Dips and folds in the cliff held early hyacinths spread in a thin purple veil, while still a few late snowdrops lingered nearby.

Each evening at sunset, the peregrines flew their courtship flight. Frika grew more ardent until Freya accepted his caresses, prostrating herself with drooping wings and widespread tail.

One dawn, as the sea lay oily and calm beneath a thick grey mist, Freya slipped into the niche she had chosen as her eyrie and remained hidden for a long time. When she emerged an egg lay on the soft brown earth of the hollow.

The next morning there was another, and on the following day a third, slightly smaller. The eggs were large and round, sharply pointed at one end, the creamy shells heavily blotched with russet markings. They lay without touching in the dim light of the eyrie.

Frika was intrigued, but when he attempted to enter the eyrie, Freya drove him off with such asperity that he flew yelping to the furthermost ledge on the cliff face. There he sat, shaking his feathers and scratching at the lice that infested his head and neck.

Gingerly, Freya stalked into the eyrie, and settled on her eggs, fluffing her feathers and letting her wings hang loose. On her breast were patches of bare skin, brood patches which were swollen and hot. It was comforting to feel the cool hard surface of the eggs pressed smooth against them. She fell into a doze.

Frika went hunting, to return after a short while with the limp body of a thrush, its beak still stained with the mud it had been gathering to line its nest. He carefully plumed it before feeding Freya with slivers from the plump breast, then, when she slept once more, he ate the head and legs and left the remains to drift off the ledge down to the waves. Patrolling herring gulls marked their flight, and swooped down to the sea to tear the carcass apart. Nothing was wasted.

The day wore on, and the rays of the sun inched over the cliff face until they pitched warm and yellow on the entrance to the eyrie. Easing herself off her eggs, Freya walked onto the ledge and stood blinking in the strong light. Slowly she stretched, then shook her feathers and called, an urgent, high-pitched summons. Frika answered. Together they lofted high above the cliffs, riding the sea wind. The eggs lay in the eyrie, cooling a little, but guarded against a sudden chill by the warmth of the sun.

The eyrie Freya had chosen had many qualities that made it superior to other nesting sites on the cliff. It was virtually inaccessible to other than winged predators, for the cliff below rose vertically from the sea, while above it was protected by an overhang of rock. It commanded a wide view, which gave early warning of the approach of an enemy, was dry and well drained, and sheltered from the worst of the winds. Most of the time it lay in shadow, thus ensuring Freya's comfort, though in late afternoon the sun shone in, giving Freya a chance to leave her eggs for a brief while.

For these reasons the eyrie had been chosen not only by Freya, but by countless generations of peregrines. Each spring, century after century, the returning falcons had guarded their domain with jealous pride. But the very permanence of the eyrie proved its weakness, for once a man had established the whereabouts of a nesting site, he could return year after year to take the eggs and young. Although the peregrine and its eggs were protected by law, illegal egg-collecting still went on.

Freya was also not entirely safe from other dangers, and if she left her eggs unguarded for too long they could be discovered by some marauding raven or black-backed gull. Now, as she grew increasingly anxious, she dropped out of the sky and swooped down almost to sea level, before sweeping up the face of the cliff to land on the ledge. All was well. Crooning softly she settled down once more.

Frika flew off to the mainland. Halfway up a low cliff of crumbling rock an oak tree grew. It had been planted by a peregrine. One gusty October evening over a century ago, a wood-pigeon had hacked its way over the valley, its crop laden with acorns. A peregrine had come in on a long shallow dive, hitting the pigeon squarely on the back of the neck. The blow burst open the pigeon's crop, spilling the acorns over the valley. Some were damaged, others eaten by rabbits and sheep. One survived, lodged deep in a crack in the rock, where the rotting debris of centuries provided a soft bed. The tree grew to the top of the cliff and then the crown flattened out, eternally cropped by the searing salt wind that blew over the headland. Yet the tree never quite relinquished its hold, and each year a crow nested in its branches.

Frika lighted on the oak, close by the massive black bulk of the crow's nest. Barely had he settled before the parent birds were all around him, beating and buffeting him. Frika fled but the hen crow pursued him. In exasperation, Frika fell back and below her. Then, climbing, he stooped and kicked out as he passed.

The crow fell in a tumbling dive, only regaining her level flight a few feet above land. Shaking her head and cawing dismally, she flew back to the oak, where she sat, hunched and shivering, one eye tightly closed. Frika's claw had pierced her right eyeball. Though the wound healed, the sight blurred and as the days passed it faded altogether, and the eye became a dead, chalky white.

Frika flew on, skirting the cliffs and dropping down into the rocky cove at the foot of the valley. Whimbrel were coming in on the tide, to probe for small shellfish and crabs or dig in the sand for worms. They were on their way north to their breeding grounds in the Arctic circle, after a winter by the shores of Africa. Singling out one bird, Frika killed it skilfully.

Back at the eyrie, Freya scolded him for his long absence, before gorging herself on the whimbrel until little remained for the tercel. The light was fading, but there was still time for a quick kill. Frika skimmed the thick heather that bordered the hill, where a young rabbit was cropping the grass near the shelter of a gorse bush. Frika dropped, and its dying squeal was muffled by the beating of his wings.

TO THE CASUAL OBSERVER, the rocky cliffs seemed a grim environment for survival. Yet this was not the case. For the peregrines and the sea birds, and the sleek grey seals that lay on the rocks below, the cliffs were at once sanctuary and fortress.

For the sea birds, the ocean poured forth an endless supply of rich and easily obtainable food. Above all, sun, wind, and rain preserved an atmosphere of antiseptic purity without which such densely packed communities would swiftly perish from disease. So the auks and gulls and the kittiwakes not only survived but enjoyed a health and vigour such as most men in their squalid cities had forgotten.

Other creatures shared the life of the sea cliffs. Most of the crow family were there, the jackdaw, the raven, the crow, and the chough. Only the rook preferred to nest in the high tops of elms, and to till the fallow fields with his great ploughshare of a beak.

From a sea cave came the soft cooing of a dove. Inside, on ledges just below the roof, were five untidy nests of heather stems and dried seaweed, each containing two white eggs. In the semi-darkness, the parent birds brooded their eggs, or perched close by, crooning. Their history and the story of their association with mankind was as old, if not older, than the story of the peregrine, and in many ways stranger.

Of the five pairs of birds in the cave, no two were exactly alike. Some were cinnamon and white, some piebald, some varying shades of dove grey. Only two wore the true livery of the rock dove, the white rump, the black wing bars, and the iridescent neck patch of green and purple. Even these two were not descended from pure wild stock, for the true rock dove had long been extinct on these cliffs, and every bird had either been born in captivity, or was the descendant of domesticated stock.

When man the hunter became man the farmer, he was quick to notice that these fat grey birds, so delicious to eat, came readily to his settlements to feed on the grain and scraps that lay around. So he began to capture and domesticate the rock dove, and long before travellers to the Far East returned with chickens—the domesticated offspring of jungle fowl which laid such a plentiful

supply of large eggs—the dove was a familiar sight in ancient cities. Indeed, several of the birds in the cave were descended from ancestors once reared in the dovecotes of the monastery at Saint David's on the mainland.

Soon man discovered another useful trait. The dove had a strongly developed territorial instinct, and could fly free for forage each day, and return each evening to its cote. It soon occurred to man that this homing instinct could be put to further use, for even when transported long distances the pigeon would return home, flying hundreds of miles without stopping. So when travellers set off on a long journey, or armies went to war, pigeons were carried, and when released with a written message strapped to their legs, would fly home, bearing news of safe arrival, victory or defeat, or summoning help if need be. In time much of the world's commerce and trade came to depend on the services of the carrier pigeon.

In the latter half of the nineteenth century the workers of an industrial nation turned to the breeding of pigeons as a cheap and absorbing hobby. Particularly exciting and widespread was the practice of racing pigeons. Considerable sums of money were at stake, and a good homer could be worth hundreds of pounds to its owner. But frequently they failed to return from a race, even when weather conditions were favourable. The answer was to be found in many a peregrine eyrie. Buried among the debris on the ledge lay numbers of aluminium rings, each bearing the legend N.U.R.P. (National Union of Racing Pigeons).

So, in addition to the attacks from gamekeepers and egg collectors, the peregrine had to face the wrath of pigeon fanciers. Then, as the shadow of the swastika fell across Europe, the peregrine was declared an ally of the Axis powers. The British fighting forces still relied on carrier pigeons to convey messages in time of war. In particular, planes spotting enemy submarines off the coasts had to maintain radio silence. They used pigeons instead to carry information, and a pigeon flying over the coast from the sea was a prime target for a peregrine.

The Air Ministry decided that, in the national interest, all peregrines should be destroyed, and so thorough and ruthless was the ensuing persecution that in many areas, particularly in the south where eyries had existed for centuries, the annihilation of the falcons was complete. Over six hundred birds were killed, and countless eggs destroyed.

Yet, even before the end of the war there were signs that the destruction of the peregrines was not altogether a good thing. Pigeons, free from harassment by their ancestral enemy, multiplied at an unprecedented rate. Colonies from the cliffs raided coastal farms, while in the towns and cities pigeons fouled buildings and pavements and blocked gutters with their untidy nests. Inland, wood-pigeons stripped the fields of grain and greenstuff to such a degree that pigeon shoots were hurriedly organized to combat the menace.

About this time too, the Air Ministry itself became interested in the idea of using falcons on and around aerodromes as a deterrent to other birds which had been flocking to the aerodromes, colliding with aircraft, causing damage and even crashes. So a search began for eyas peregrines suitable for training, and by the end of the war, the peregrine was placed on the protected list. It was feared at first that they would never recover as a breeding species. Yet in many remote areas of moor and mountain, they had lasted out the war, and from these strongholds they came back, to recolonize the empty eyries and prosper on the abundant stocks of pigeons. Within ten years they had almost regained their previous numbers, and, though still rare, it seemed they would survive as a breed.

CHAPTER THREE

The island of Ramsey was large enough to support a small farm, and tucked away in a sheltered cove to the northeast stood the house, a long low-roofed building of whitewashed stone. Here lived a widower, Owen Thomas who, when the war ended, had left the sea and settled on the island.

He lived there alone, but was not lonely, for he had a deep and abiding interest in the island and the wealth of wild life it supported, and over the years his experience as a naturalist had made him many friends.

He grew hay and some corn, raised beef cattle and sheep and kept chickens and ducks. The farm brought him little profit, but he was self-supporting and his needs were few, a glass of whisky in the evenings his one luxury.

He was equally at home on the sea setting lobster pots at low tide or spinning for mackerel on a summer's evening. Regularly he rowed across the Sound to the mainland and walked a mile and a half to the tiny cathedral city of Saint David's for his few provisions. Although near retiring age, he was fit and hale, and his sight was as keen as a hawk's.

Owen Thomas knew about the peregrines on the eyrie, and had noted the date of their arrival in his field diary. Each evening, from the headland opposite Freya's nesting site, he watched them through his old brass telescope and chuckled to himself at their occasional bickering.

All the same he was anxious. The rougher element among the labourers on the mainland would not hesitate to take the eggs if they knew there was money to be made from such vandalism.

Up to a point he could protect them. The only safe landing, a sheltered cove, was in view of his home, and he could send anyone packing whom he did not trust. Yet in fine weather a yacht could anchor off the beach below the peregrines, and a small boat row ashore. A short scramble up the cliffs would put an intruder right above the eyrie. They would need ropes and stakes, and an hour or two in which to work, but he could not always be on guard. At night he lay awake, wondering how best to protect "his" birds.

He found the answer in a yellowhammer's nest. One morning, as he drove the house cow out to graze on the fresh new grass of the cliff tops, he found the delicately woven cup of plaited grass on the ground beside a low stone wall. He stood for a moment, admiring the pale pink lustre of the eggs and the curious markings that looked as though someone had scribbled all over them with a pen. And suddenly he knew that he had found a way to safeguard the peregrine eggs.

After supper he set off to the cliffs with a weighty bundle—two stout iron stakes, a sledgehammer, a coil of rope, a length of cord, a sack, and four wooden stakes. As he had hoped, the peregrines were flighting.

Freya, a thousand feet above the waves, had seen him toiling up the hill, but he was a familiar figure, and the peregrines had long accepted him as harmless. Freya slanted away on the wind and vanished behind the cliffs.

Because of the overhang, Owen Thomas could not tell from above exactly where the eyrie lay. So, dropping his load on the cliff above the eyrie, he took the four wooden stakes and walked round to the headland opposite, to set markers to give him its exact location. He pushed two of the stakes into the ground, exactly in line with the eyrie, and about twenty paces apart. Then he walked fifty paces to the right, and did the same with the other two stakes. Now returning to the cliff above the eyrie, he looked back across the bay. The point where he had dropped his bundle was a little too far to the left. Moving it, he stood at last at a point from which, as he looked across the bay, the two farthermost stakes were directly in line with the ones in front. This point was right above the eyrie.

Swiftly he drove the iron stakes into the ground, lashed them with the cord, and anchored the rope to the stake below the lashing. He slung the free end down the cliff, slipped the sack under it to prevent fraying, and began to lower himself, hand over hand, down the cliff.

At first the going was easy, but at the overhang the rope began to bind against the rock, crushing his knuckles, and his boots lost their purchase on the cliff face. His arms also were beginning to feel the strain. Once he had passed the overhang, however, he made rapid progress down to the ledge. It was only a few feet below him when the rope began to twist, spinning him slowly round and round. For a moment he panicked, and almost fell. Then, with eyes tight shut, he thrust his feet out against the rock and the spinning stopped. Next moment he was on the ledge. He rested before kneeling and peering into the eyrie.

He knew then, for a brief instant, something of the motives that

367

drove men to plunder the nests of rare birds. The eggs looked so beautiful, so solid and rich and rare as they lay on the bare soil, that it was like gazing on hidden treasure. He picked up the first egg. It even felt valuable, as if made of gold, and he felt a curious reluctance to put it down.

But there was no time to waste, for at any moment the peregrines might return. They were unlikely to attack him, but their rage and fear over his presence might cause them to desert their precious eggs. He produced an indelible pencil and moistening the eggs with saliva he printed on each the word: INDELIBLE. They were thus ruined as collectors' items, for the writing could not be erased without also destroying the magnificent mottling that identified the eggs as those of the peregrine falcon.

Carefully he arranged the eggs exactly as he had found them. Then he gripped the rope and swung himself free of the ledge to climb swiftly to the cliff top.

He was just gathering up the wooden stakes from the headland opposite when he saw the falcon return. She swooped straight into the eyrie, and settled down, totally unaware that anything had changed.

He felt light at heart as he walked back down the hill. The eggs were safe, and once they were hatched, the eyasses were also safe until they were ready to fly. An eyas taken too soon from the eyrie would not prosper, or train easily, instead spending its days in senseless, hysterical screaming. For the brief time that the eyasses were at risk he could mount a special guard. Until then Owen Thomas could relax.

THE CLEAR SKIES and bright sunshine of early spring gave way to cloud and rain, as a series of depressions swept in from the Atlantic. Gales were sudden and savage, often bringing stinging showers of cold rain.

The peregrines, like the sea birds, were impervious to the cold, and the wind was their ally. Riding the invisible currents of the air with effortless grace they were able to stay aloft for hours on end, hanging in the sky without any more exertion than the merest curve of a wingtip or a slight flexing of their tails. The burden of pregnancy would have been intolerable to a species so finely attuned, so delicately in balance with its environment. So peregrines, throughout the slowly evolving millenia, in company with other birds, continued to produce their kind by way of the egg, a way having many advantages over that adopted by the mammal.

Each of Freya's eggs was a miracle of miniaturization, perfectly programmed for the pattern of its future life. The germ cell hung suspended in the yolk, a concentrated soup of fats and proteins to nourish the growing embryo. The yolk was encapsulated in a sac, attached to the shell by twisted cords, so that when Freya moved the egg, the cords could rotate, allowing the germ to rise to the top of the yolk. In turn the yolk was cushioned, insulated, and protected by a layer of albumen, which also prevented the egg from losing moisture through the porous shell.

The shell itself consisted of crystals of calcium carbonate laid around a network of protein fibres. This arrangement made the egg extremely strong and resistant to external pressures, for when compressed, the crystals locked together like the stones in an arch. When the time came for the egg to hatch, a relatively small pressure from inside the shell would cause it to break.

Each egg cooled slightly after laying, and the contents shrank a little, allowing a bubble of air to seep through the shell. This air would be the first the chick would breathe, a tiny reservoir of life in which the chick could exist as it laboured to break through the shell into the harsh and variable environment that lay beyond.

After the first flush of possessive pride, Freya, with extreme caution and reluctance, allowed Frika to take his turn at incubation. Frika, a little nervous at assuming so responsible a task, would position himself with exaggerated care and remain absolutely motionless, his small body barely covering the clutch, until Freya returned. By the fourth week of incubation, however, she grew more reluctant to leave her eggs. She could feel the fully formed embryos move, and hear faint sounds, and she knew that her vigil was almost at an end.

The chicks were aware too of the warmth that was Freya. They could also sense light, and this made them more active, twisting and kicking away from the lifeline that still attached each embryo to its

369

rapidly shrinking yolk. This exercise helped to develop the strength the chick would need to break free of the shell. For most of the time, however, they slept.

THE PRESENCE of the peregrines in no way deterred sea birds from nesting nearby, and the cliffs were a scene of indecipherable confusion, as thousands of birds congregated in close-packed colonies.

Highest on the cliff were the razorbills and guillemots, but while the razorbill hid its single egg in a crevice, the guillemot laid its egg on an open ledge. Below them nested the fulmars, choosing the bare soil of wider, less precipitous ledges. Below them again, almost within reach of the waves, the dainty kittiwakes built nests of weed. All around, the watchful gulls hovered, ready to pounce on any unguarded chick or egg.

Chough and raven, jackdaw and dove, all made their homes on the cliff face. A colony of shags, bottle-green fishermen of sardonic countenance, built their untidy nests in a sheltered corner of the cliffs. One, scavenging the flotsam in search of building material, had found the top half of a hot water bottle. This, protruding from beneath the brooding bird, gave a misleading impression of comfort.

Birds came and went, whirring upwards from the waves, hovering round their nests, or floating on the sea. Amid the squawking and the chattering, the screaming and wailing, anarchy reigned supreme. Eggs fell into the sea, and the bereaved mothers, waiting their chance, stole other eggs from some absent parent. In time, too, a chick might wander away from its parent, to be lost in the milling throng. Sooner or later it would be fed by a passing bird, and thus survive.

Yet in spite of the seeming chaos, each bird recognized its mate, and defended its own small breeding territory. And in spite of the apparent squalor of the cliffside slums, each bird was immaculate—free from the ordure that limed the rocks. The sea birds had little to fear from the peregrines, for, apart from picking off the odd straggling razorbill or guillemot from a flock, the falcons found the black-backs and the herring gulls too big and powerful to be easy prey, the fulmars and petrels too rancid-fleshed, oily and unsavoury, while the auks hugged the waves, and at the first sign of danger dived below the surface.

Occasionally, however, discord marred the harmony of cliffside co-existence. One evening Freya, on a hunting expedition, killed a wood-pigeon as it flew up from a potato field, and she flew heavily back to the eyrie, the pigeon clasped firmly in her talons. As she passed a herring gull colony below the eyrie one young bird, hungrier or more foolhardy than the rest, was seized with an impulse to mob the falcon, in the hope that she might drop the prize.

Freya waited until the gull was almost at her wingtip and then, shaking one foot free, she raked the gull's chest, tearing loose a cloud of feathers and etching a red raw line across the skin. The gull gave a yelp of fear, and others of his kind, obeying the age-old command, flew to his aid.

Next moment Freya was weaving and dodging in an effort to throw off her pursuers. Frika saw her plight and flew to join battle. Between them they bulldozed their way through a snowstorm of screaming gulls, Freya to pitch the corpse of the wood-pigeon onto the ledge, and Frika to land near, crouching over it with mantled wings, and gazing skyward with eyes that blazed with a merciless anger.

The gulls hovered for a moment over the two falcons shouting defiance, then began to drift back to the colony. Freya, however, had no intention of letting them off so lightly. The gulls had actually invaded her territory; her supremacy had been challenged. Screaming, she launched herself off the ledge and flew straight at the gulls.

There were seven of them in all, and it took her a little under two minutes to clear them from the sky. She aimed to punish rather than kill. Kicking, swerving, diving and swooping, she drove them all down, and when at last they huddled, cowed and shivering, on the nearby cliffs, each one carried the scars of her whipping.

As she flew back in triumph to the ledge, she heard a strange cry from the headland opposite. Their guardian had watched, and now he cheered her victory.

CHAPTER FOUR

May came, bringing sun and rain to bless the soil. The air was heavy with the scent of hawthorn and gorse and fresh sweet grass. The cuckoo called, flitting hawklike along the low stone hedges of the fields, and at dusk the grasshoppers warbled amongst the tussocky jungle of the cliff tops.

In the grey, pre-dawn light, Freya heard the piping cry, faint and muffled from inside the shell, that heralded the hatching of the first chick. She stirred and answered, crooning encouragement. The tapping began, as the chick pecked at the chalky walls of its prison, using, for the first and last time in its life, the specially adapted egg tooth it had grown to cut itself free. At the same time it kicked and struggled in a convulsive effort to shatter the shell. From time to time it rested, but at last a crack appeared and in a short while the chick lay on the bare earth of the eyrie, surrounded by the yolk-stained fragments of the shell. Its plumage of down clung in sticky strands to its naked skin and its eyes bulged grotesquely under closed lids. The minutes passed, and with a shuddering heave it stood upright, swaying and weaving, before crawling under Freya's protective wing.

When the chick emerged, her down had dried and whitened, fluffing out to form a warm, insulating coat, and that evening she took her first feed, flesh from the breast of a skylark, brought to the eyrie by Frika.

Twenty-four hours later her sister kicked and clawed her way into the world, and on the third day their brother joined them. He was smaller and lighter than his sisters, and, in order to survive, he had to battle for every meal in competition with them.

For the first few days Freya rarely left the eyrie. The young eyasses still needed the warmth of her body, and they slept for long periods nestled beneath her, waking to instant hunger whenever Frika, the breadwinner, arrived with the partly plucked carcass of a bird. Frantic with greed and excitement, they snatched and pulled until, replete, they dozed in a warm huddle of contentment, as Freya demolished the remainder of the meal.

Another breadwinner was Larus, the black-backed gull, whose mate had just hatched three chicks in their great messy nest of heather and seaweed, built behind a rock stack on the cliff top less than a hundred yards from the eyrie.

Larus had no friends, and no near neighbours. He was a killer, a stealer of eggs and chicks, and even the adults among the smaller sea birds feared his great snapping bill.

Once he and his kind had been mercifully few, but during the past century they had increased tenfold. Marksmen no longer shot seagulls for sport. Gulls' eggs, once considered a delicacy, were now regarded as not worth risking life and limb to collect. So the gulls enjoyed immunity from attack, and the expanding fishing fleets around the coasts provided a flow of fresh offal. Inland, near every town and city, garbage heaps created fresh foraging grounds. The gulls were not fussy about what they ate.

It was to the garbage dump that Larus made his way one blustery Monday morning. Experience had taught him that on this day tons of edible refuse found their way to the dump, following the orgy of eating and waste that took place every weekend among men.

The dump was already crowded when Larus arrived. A cloud of herring gulls flickered white around a bulldozer that was busy levelling the latest load of waste. A group of starlings bustled about, snatching crumbs of offal. A cock chaffinch seized a morsel of bread and carried it off to his young.

Larus landed amid a litter of paper, plastic, and empty food cans. He found bread crusts, bacon rinds, a slice of ham. Soon his crop was bulging, and he stood for a moment, his webbed feet slipping and sliding among the debris, waiting for the contents of his crop to settle.

Among the citizens of Saint David's was a conscientious house-wife whose dustbin was as clean inside as out. This weekend she had opened a large can of peaches. As always, she had rinsed the can, and then carefully pushed the lid, still hinged by a scrap of metal, back inside the can. She had a horror of anyone cutting himself on it.

The can now lay on the dump. As Larus stood on it, he felt his foot slide over the lid and slip inside. The lid sprang back and trapped his foot. He shook it and felt the first stab of pain as the edge of the lid nicked his skin.

Startled, he spread his wings in flight, and the wind gripped the can like a sail, throwing him off balance and making him fly harder while the lid's edge sawed away at his leg. Herring gulls watched Larus's drunken flight, and circled round, mobbing him, as was their custom with anything strange to them. Larus threw up the contents of his crop to lighten his load, and the herring gulls followed the noisome mess as it fell to earth.

Larus wore the can for eighteen hours, moping disconsolately by the cliff. Each time he moved, the lid sawed a little farther through his leg. When he tried to fly his wings were too weary to carry him. He planed down to the sea, and the can filled with water.

He felt easier floating on the sea. He bathed a little and sipped some of the sea water. Then he tried to rise. The waterlogged can held him fast, though by now it had sliced through his leg, leaving the foot attached by a mere fragment of skin. Next time Larus tried to fly, the skin snapped, and the can sank slowly down to the sea bed, followed by a shoal of pouting.

Larus was free, but he was lame. The antiseptic action of the salt water soon healed his stump, and as the days went by he learned to alight on one leg without pitching ignominiously onto his beak, wings a-sprawl. But he was slower, and an easy target for irate parents when he went raiding a colony of herring gulls. The garbage dump, cause of all his trouble, he avoided.

JUNE ARRIVED, and the long period of unsettled weather came to an end. Each day the sun blazed from a cloudless sky, and the land soaked up the heat, drawing cool winds from the sea. Each evening the wind died, and the stars glittered in the canopy of the sky. Frika hunted during the day. Prey was now so plentiful that he had no difficulty in keeping up with the demands of the youngsters, and stored unwanted carcasses in a convenient crevice on the cliff face where many rotted away or dropped in the sea.

Larus soon took to hanging about beneath the eyrie, paddling with his one leg and waiting for the carcasses that fell from the sky. Before very long he began to plunder the peregrines' larder, drifting quietly along the side of the cliff when both birds were away, to snatch and swallow his prize.

Now over a fortnight old, the young peregrines were beginning to develop distinct personalities. Aya, the eldest, was placid and complacent. Wayee, her sister, was more aggressive and quick to seize the best portions of food. Chek, the tercel, small and lively, seemed to need less sleep than his sisters and often spent his time pattering round the eyrie, poking into corners, snapping at the flies that buzzed round his head, or toying idly with the remains of a jackdaw's wing that lay among the debris of past feasts.

Early one morning, as his parents were quartering the cliffs to the north of the island, Chek wandered out of the eyrie and began to explore the ledge. To the left the narrow rock shelf dropped abruptly to the sea. Chek peered down, then retreated back along the ledge, past the mouth of the eyrie and along the cliff face to where a white feather, caught in a bunch of sea pinks, was waving in the breeze. Chek pounced upon it and turned to make his way back along the ledge. A rush of wings made him look up. Perched on the ledge and blocking his way, stood Larus the Lame, his yellow eye glinting hungrily, his great red bill open in anticipation.

A black-eyed ball of fury, spitting and hissing like a snake, Chek fell backward, his talons spread wide in the age-old defence position of birds of prey. Tentatively, Larus sought to grab Chek with the tip of his beak. Chek kicked out, and his talons raked the gull's head.

Larus jumped back and shook himself. He was nervous, for at any moment the falcons might return. He was determined to make one more attempt. A sudden lunge, a quick flick of his beak, and Chek would go spinning down into the sea where Larus could devour him at his leisure.

At that moment Frika hit him. The blow pinned him to the ledge, splintering one wing and tearing a great flap of skin from his neck. Larus tore himself free and launched himself into space, one wing frantically fanning the air as he spiralled down to the waves. Freya came up from below, hit him hard, and swooped past, turning to drop and hit him again. But Larus was already dead, his head half-severed from his body.

For some time Freya and Frika hovered and wheeled above the corpse, until at last, waterlogged and sodden, it was pitched up on the shore by the waves, for the herring gulls to find and tear apart.

THEY EYASSES WERE now fast replacing their baby plumage with feathers. Their heads were quite dark, and on their backs two narrow bands formed the shape of a figure eight. They spent a great deal of time worrying at their plumage and flapping their wings, and their appetites were more voracious than ever. Every hour or so they clamoured to be fed.

At dawn, Frika slipped off the ledge and flew northwest, out over the sea, to a pinnacle of rock a mile and a half away. Hugging the face of the cliff, he surprised a small black and white sea bird. He kicked out, clutching the bird across the back, so that it died almost instantaneously. In giving its last scream it opened its enormous varicoloured beak, and dropped its load of small silver fish in a shimmering rain down into the sea where they were seized and swallowed by a herring gull and a fulmar.

Frika bore the dead puffin back to the eyrie, and within fifteen minutes all that remained were the wings and the head with its massive, clown-like beak of vermilion, gold and grey. One pink, webbed foot still hung like a grotesque swollen tongue from Wayee's beak. Chek attempted to pull it away and got a hearty kick for his pains. Retiring, he found the head of the puffin, and tried to swallow it, unsuccessfully, whereupon he shook it, and the head flew down into the sea. For a long time it floated, like a gaudily coloured buoy, until the waves cast it up on the shore. It lay for several days among the flotsam, providing many a meal for the small denizens of the tideline, and finally the empty skull became a home for a colony of sandhoppers.

Once the puffins had swarmed on Ramsey in their thousands, returning each spring after a winter wandering the Atlantic Ocean, to share their cliff-top burrows with the rabbits. Then the rats came to the island, perhaps from some cargo being landed on the island or from one of the frequent shipwrecks around the coast. They prospered and bred, and the fate of the puffins was sealed, for although the rats did not molest the adults, they took the eggs and butchered the young birds in the burrows when the parents were away. The puffins came no more.

A few pairs nested on the North Bishop Rock where Frika had killed his bird, but their last great stronghold on the Welsh coast lay at Skomer, the island to the south of St. Brides Bay. And even here their numbers were decreasing. Oil pollution took its toll and black-backed gulls haunted the puffinries, slaughtering adults and chicks indiscriminately.

Occasionally, it seemed, the puffin was its own worst enemy. Far to the west lay the island of Grassholm, and here in the late nineteenth century the puffins had thronged by the hundreds of thousands. The thick green thatch of turf proved ideal for their burrows, but gradually they so undermined the fescue grass that it dried out and died, and the labyrinthine network of burrows crumbled away.

The puffins left, never to return. Instead, the island was colonized by gannets, which over the years grew to such numbers that their droppings bleached the island white. On a clear day its shimmering, snowy crown could be seen from Ramsey.

Perhaps this was the natural way of the sea birds, part of a long, slow cycle, whereby the puffin, like man, destroyed the environment on which he depended by sheer weight of numbers, only to leave it for another species to colonize and restore. One day the gannets too would probably depart, and on their rich guano deposits grass would grow anew, laying down a thick mat of turf for the puffins to repopulate.

CHAPTER FIVE

Throughout the ages those species have survived which were best able to adapt to a changing environment. For thousands of years in Britain the environment altered slowly, giving all forms of life time to adjust. Then, suddenly, all was changed, as the industrial revolution brought about alterations as swift as they were dramatic.

These were man-made, and so it followed that the species which flourished were those best able to adapt to the ways of man. The house-fly, the rat, the sparrow, the herring gull, learned quickly. They came to dine on the leavings of the most wasteful and destructive species ever to inhabit the earth.

Of the birds of prey the tiny kestrel alone had some success in learning to live with man. Raptors, and falcons by right of their hooked, notched beaks and long, pointed wings, they survived, and even flourished, picking a frugal living wherever opportunity presented itself. They were quick to discover new hunting grounds, disused aerodromes, railway embankments, even the new multilane highways with their central reservations and grassy embankments on either side.

Like the peregrines, the kestrels build no nest, but they are more adaptable in their choice of site, a hollow tree trunk or an abandoned crow's nest being as acceptable as some crumbling cliff. They even nest in the cities, and in London one pair successfully raised a brood on a ledge high above the Houses of Parliament.

Some kestrels, however, lived on in the wilder regions where the impact of man had little or no effect. Such a bird was Cree, who shared an eyrie high on the crumbling slate cliffs to the south of the mainland with his mate and three hungry youngsters. He knew little of man until chance and a high wind carried him into the grounds of an old house three miles from the sea.

For two days the wind had blown a gale, setting all in turmoil and confusion. Cree went hungry. To hover was impossible, and to quarter the ground in the teeth of such buffeting proved pointless because every potential quarry was under cover. He turned inland, seeking the shelter of the wooded valleys, and so came to the garden.

The owner of the house was an old man, a recluse who kept birds —rare pheasants and parakeets, ornamental waterfowl and pigeons. He kept them, not for their beauty or fascinating ways, but for the prizes they won at shows.

He kept pigeons—Birmingham Rollers and Flying Tipplers. The tumbling ability of the rollers, originally bred in Birmingham, was so highly developed that they would climb to a great altitude and then spin back to earth in a lightning-swift succession of somersaults, levelling out just above the ground. The tipplers had lost this ability, but were renowned for stamina, being able to stay aloft for hours at a time.

The pigeons, kept in a loft on the roof of the house, were allowed the freedom of the garden in order to supplement their diet of corn with weed seeds and young greenstuffs. Some weeks ago Frika had sighted one of the rollers, and, intrigued by its curious fall, he had sped over to the house and killed the roller in full view of the old man. It had been an isolated incident and Frika promptly forgot the house and the odd pigeon.

The old man did not forget, and for a while he kept his pigeons shut in the loft while he watched to see if the peregrine would return. He knew nothing of the Wild Birds Protection Act and did not recognize Frika as a peregrine. To him all hawks were vermin, to be destroyed without compunction before they murdered too many of his feathered possessions.

He fed his captive birds too well, so that much of the grain soured or sprouted among the unkempt flowerbeds and shrubberies. This waste food attracted rats and mice, which bred in the outhouses and grew fat and bold. They began to appear in daylight, scurrying bright-eyed among the pecking birds, and from time to time they took eggs and young birds from the nests of the waterfowl on the lake. Although the old man set traps and laid poison, he could do little to control them. A few cats would have solved his problem, but these he dared not keep.

So, on this wet and windy morning, Cree found what seemed to be an ideal hunting ground. He caught two mice in quick succession and carried them off to the top of a tree, where he perched on the sawn-off stump of a branch to dismember and swallow his prey. Then he surprised a short-tailed vole at the foot of the tree. He dropped on it, and bore it away to the eyrie. One vole did not go far among his hungry youngsters, so he returned once more to the garden, and this time the old man saw him as he swooped low over the lawn.

He did not see the kestrel carry off a young rat, nor did he know about the two mice and the vole. He felt sure that this was the same hawk that had stolen one of his prize pigeons. The following day he saw Cree perching on the dead stump. The gale had blown itself out, and Cree could have returned to his old hunting grounds, but having found such plentiful food he was reluctant to abandon it. He paid several visits to the garden that day, and never once returned to the eyrie without a full crop, and food for the young kestrels dangling from his talons.

That evening the man went into one of the outhouses, and from an old chest pulled out a trap, of a curious half-moon shape, its jaws stiff with rust and disuse.

He got to work with oil can and wire brush, and then carried the trap into the garden. He set it on the flat stump, its jaws spread in a circle, securing its chain to the tree trunk with a staple. Dusk was falling as he put away his tools and retired indoors.

Night came, mild and dry, with low clouds drifting over the face of the moon. On noiseless wings an owl swept over the lawn, listening with large, offset ears that could locate with pinpoint accuracy the slightest sound. Once he swooped on a young rat, but the moon betrayed his presence at the last moment and the rat escaped. The owl swooped up, and, closing his wings, alighted on top of the stump.

There was a dry, metallic click, and the crunch of breaking bones. Held by both shanks, the owl screamed and flapped his wings in anguish. For a moment he hung in the air, frantic with fear and pain as he tried to fly away. The chain held fast. The trap slid from the top of the stump and fell, dragging the owl down.

From time to time during the night he attempted to struggle free, but the jaws of the trap bit deeper until at last the spirit of the owl faded into the shadows of the night.

At first light the old man hurried over to the stump, thinking he had caught his hawk, but when he saw the reproachful brown eyes of the owl he tore the corpse down in disgust and reset the trap.

In the chill of early dawn Cree left his ledge, circled the eyrie once, and flew confidently away. Noon passed and dusk fell, but Cree did not return. He too hung head-down from the stump in the garden, and the stars had gone out of his eyes.

The old man, his birds, and the rats and mice were left in peace. Soon the rats gained access to the house, and six months later an apparently healthy rat contaminated some ham with a drop of its urine. The old man ate the ham, not knowing that it now contained the spirochetes of infectious jaundice.

After his death, his birds were destroyed. The house stood empty and derelict, and the following spring a pair of owls took up residence in the garden.

CHAPTER SIX

In the heat of the summer afternoon the full-fledged eyasses dozed on the ledge outside the eyrie, beaks agape, wings spread wide to catch the air. Freya and Frika perched in the shade, engrossed in the lengthy process of preening.

A fishing boat slid slowly past the cliffs and came to anchor off the beach below. Boats were a familiar sight to the peregrines, and after a sudden sharp stare of inquiry, they ignored the vessel.

A man sat in the stern of the boat studying the cliff through powerful binoculars. He scanned every ledge until at last he focussed on the peregrine eyrie. Chek, roused by a fly that buzzed around his head, caught the flash of sunlight on the lens.

TINKER SMITH was well known along the south coast. Some said he was half gipsy. The police knew him as an inveterate smuggler and dealer in protected birds and eggs.

Now, Tinker knew of a rich Italian who would give him seventy-five pounds a bird for young peregrines. So, after he had located the eyrie, he arranged a secret rendezvous at sea with the Italian's yacht, and waited for the weather he required. For three nights it continued misty, but on the fourth, a fresh breeze kept the fog at bay. The trip was on.

That evening the peregrine's self-appointed protector, Owen Thomas, lingered on the cliffs until long after dark, for the fully fledged eyasses might at any time attempt their first flight, and he fervently wished to see it. Also now was the time when the young peregrines were most vulnerable, most likely to be stolen by falconers.

Although he knew nothing of Tinker Smith and his plans, he had resolved many weeks ago to keep vigil during this time. The mist had afforded the peregrines better protection than any he could offer, but now the skies were clear. Stars glittered in the clean cold night-sky, and already the moon was silvering the waters of the Sound. He decided to return to the farmhouse, snatch a few hours' sleep, and be back on the cliffs by first light.

Away to the south Tinker Smith sang as he stood at the wheel of his boat, watching the dark coastline slip by. Tinker had no doubt the police would be waiting for him when he got back to port, but all he would have on board would be a few mackerel and a wad of used and dirty notes, his life savings, he would stoutly declare. So he sang at the wheel and the short night passed.

The clamour of gulls, roused by the rattle of an anchor chain, woke Freya, and she raised her head. It was an hour before dawn, and the boat was a dark mass against the light of the sinking moon. There was no sound or movement, and after a few minutes' intense scrutiny Freya decided that all was well. Once more she slept.

Sounds of splashing roused her a second time. A black shape had detached itself from the boat, and was drawing near the shore. She watched uneasily as the dinghy grated on the beach and a man got out. She heard the crunch of footsteps as Tinker Smith shouldered a dark burden and set off towards a point where the crumbling cliffs gave access to the headland. Dawn was breaking.

The sun sent a long finger of light through the tiny window of Owen Thomas's bedroom. He woke, and, cursing himself for having overslept, leaped out of bed and dressed. Pausing only to grab his telescope, together with its heavy tripod, he ran out of the house.

The eyasses woke to the sound of dull thudding on the cliff above them. Their parents flew overhead with high-pitched cries of alarm. Aya and Wayee crouched low on the ledge, not daring to move, while Chek huddled in the far corner of the eyrie, deep in the crevice with his back to the entrance, so still he might have been one of the rocks himself. He heard the rasp of the rope as it

came snaking down, and shortly after the grate of nailed boo
on rock.

Still Chek did not move. Shadow veiled the mouth of the crevice
there was the gasp of tortured breathing, the shrill cries and
flapping wings of his sisters, and then the shadow lifted and the
scrabbling sound of boots against the cliff gradually faded away
The rope was drawn up, and then there was silence.

"STAY WHERE YOU ARE!"

Tinker Smith swore as he saw the burly figure of Owen Thomas
approaching. It looked as though he was carrying a gun.

"Leave those falcons where they are, and get off this island,"
commanded Owen as he drew near.

Tinker chuckled as he saw that the "gun" was just a harmless

tripod. He set the basket containing the eyasses on the ground and spread his hands wide. "Look," he said. "Silly it is to get so angry about a couple of stupid birds. There's fifty pounds for you if you just turn round and go back to bed."

The tripod swung in a scything arc and crunched against Tinker's jaw. He dropped to one knee, waves of pain threatening to overwhelm him. He reached for a stone and Owen stepped warily aside. The cliff top gave way, and as his foot plunged into a rabbit hole he fell heavily and slid headfirst over the cliff to land with a thud amid a rattle of loose stones and shale on the grass below.

Horrified at this turn of events, Tinker threw his gear down on the beach and climbed down with the eyasses. Swiftly he examined the farmer. He was still breathing and his pulse was strong and regular. He lay above the tideline, on soft grass, and the day promised to be fine. Tinker decided to leave him where he lay. He loaded the dinghy and pushed off.

In a secluded bay off the little island of Skokholm the Italian's yacht lay at anchor. In the cabin Tinker sat drinking brandy and counting his money while the Italian crooned over Aya and Wayee, already hooded and jessed and perched on hawk blocks. Tinker got stiffly to his feet and pocketed the money. "A hundred and fifty pounds," he announced with satisfaction. "I thank you very much, and now I'll bid you farewell." Within minutes his fishing boat had drawn away from the yacht.

Back on the mainland the coxswain of the lifeboat station looked out across the Sound to the little farm on Ramsey. There was no sign of the flag Owen Thomas always flew each morning. An hour later he checked again. There was still no flag, and no smoke from the farmhouse chimney.

The cox phoned the coast guard.

Later that afternoon a pleasant-looking young man waited on the quay for Tinker as he tied up his boat and unloaded a box of mackerel. "Been fishing then, Tinker?" he queried.

"What does it look like?" snapped Tinker. He was dog-tired, stiff from his climb, and his jaw throbbed.

"Things aren't always as they seem," smiled the detective. "Like there's this old boy who fell over the cliff on Ramsey this morning."

"Nasty," murmured Tinker.

"Oh, it's not too bad," replied the detective. "He's in hospital, and conscious, although we haven't got a statement yet. Curious though. The local boys tell me they found a tripod slightly bent and smeared with blood. There's some skin and hair too, I believe. They've sent it to the forensic department for testing." The policeman took him by the arm. "Come on, Tinker, let's get that face fixed. Then we'll have a little chat."

CHEK SAT ON THE LEDGE outside the eyrie, gorged and drowsy. The weather had turned chilly, and a cold breeze whipped the waters at the base of the cliffs. Four days had passed since the plundering of the eyrie, and already Chek had forgotten his sisters.

He now received the undivided attention of both his parents. As a result he was suffering from a surfeit of food, for the peregrines could not adapt themselves to the reduced demands on their housekeeping, and still hunted as assiduously as before.

Chek hiccoughed violently, and brought up a pale grey casting of feather and bone. It plopped, soft and moist, onto the ledge and Chek eyed it, head on one side, as if its sudden appearance puzzled him.

The day wore on, and gradually he began to feel easier. He stood upright, legs stretched, and flapped his wings vigorously. The breeze was strengthening, sweeping up the cliffs in sudden gusts. Chek's feet left the ledge, and in sudden panic he closed his wings, alighting once more.

Abruptly his fear was replaced by pleasure at the recollection of the experience. He tried again, but the wind refused to co-operate, and in spite of much energetic flapping, his feet remained firmly fixed. He subsided, brooding, and then shuffled a little way along the ledge. Again he tried, this time instinctively crouching before springing upward and spreading his wings.

For a moment it seemed he would drop back, but as his wings frantically fanned the air the wind caught him, pushing against his chest with the pressure of a gentle, uplifting hand. For a full thirty seconds he hung in the air, a foot above the ledge, before tumbling down among the litter of bones. He shook himself and automatically began to preen the long pinion feathers of his wings. Ten minutes later he was trying again, his performance improving with each launching. It was late in the afternoon before he tired and dropped asleep.

An hour later he woke, refreshed, and exuberantly spread his wings. Now the wind was no longer playful. It slammed upward with the force of a clenched fist, flinging Chek aloft, and holding him pinned for a long moment against the overhang of the eyrie. He screamed, his wings stiff-spread over his head, as the wind released its hold and he began to fall. Then he was rising again, his wings working furiously as another gust swept him in a circle out over the sea, before hurling him back against the cliffs.

Chek saw the eyrie loom in front of him. His wings scrabbled the air, and his feet stretched out towards it, but at the last minute he was drawn up and dropped gently on a wide, sloping shelf of rock ten feet above the eyrie. There he lay, gasping and shaking, until his fear left him.

He stood up and shook himself. Then, his ruffled feathers trembling in the draught, he stalked to the edge of the shelf and peered down. A gust of wind tip-tilted him as it caught his broad tail, and he shrank back. Pressing close to the cliff wall, he crept back along the shelf and wedged himself firmly in the corner.

He was still hunched there when Freya flew onto the ledge outside the eyrie with a freshly killed lapwing. She called. Chek pattered across the shelf and gave a plaintive mew. Freya rose a foot above the ledge in astonishment. She called again, sharply and imperiously, then stalked into the eyrie to explore every inch of it. Only when she was convinced that no peregrine eyas was there did she emerge.

Chek continued to mew, his face now visible above the shelf. Freya flew up, still clutching the lapwing, and hovered over him. For a moment she almost alighted, only to rise again and fly back to the eyrie. Chek was hungry, but he refused to be tempted from the safety of his shelf. He marched resolutely back to his corner while Freya plumed and dissected the lapwing.

After she had eaten about half the bird, she relented, and carrying the corpse up to the shelf, she fed Chek, urging him with sharp impatient cries to hurry and finish the meal. By now it was almost dark. Black wispy clouds ran low across the leaden sky, bringing flurries of rain, and the sea crashed and thudded against the rocks with a menacing boom.

Chek passed a wretched night, for although Freya and Frika stayed beside him on the ledge and tried to shelter him, he was now too big to take refuge beneath their outstretched wings. Towards dawn the rain stopped and the wind dropped.

Several times during the next day Chek attempted to climb down into the eyrie, and each time his talons slipped on the smooth stone as it fell steeply away to the sea. He scrambled back, wings flapping madly, to scurry into the corner and crouch, as if the fear of falling made him sick.

Freya came with food, and circled above the shelf, calling loudly, but he refused to budge. Left alone, he preened himself a little, slept, and woke with the afternoon sun warm on his back. He called for food, and Freya launched herself from a ledge close by and flew past the shelf, to light like a giant moth on a sloping green stretch of turf, about a hundred yards away from Chek, and halfway down the cliff.

Three times she did this, each time passing so close to Chek that he felt the rush of air as she swept by. It was an exercise in mime, and after Freya had sketched the plan a few times, Chek got the message, and followed, launching himself into the air with winnowing wings. Suddenly he felt buoyant, floating, at ease with the element. He soared skyward, his wings still spread and his tail fanned out behind him. He moved a wing tip, saw earth and sky tilt and hurriedly corrected the manoeuvre. His mother called shrilly from the carpet of turf, and he planed down, intending to alight beside her. But he had not yet learned how to land. For a moment it seemed he might miss the turf altogether, and fall into the sea, but at the last minute he fanned the air, and pitched head-long onto the soft grass, close to the cliff edge.

His flying rapidly improved, as he progressed from short cliff-to-cliff hops to soaring flights out over beach and bay. On the second evening he climbed with his parents high into the sky, and the sunlight shone on the trio as they hung like stars above the ancient cliffs.

There was no one to watch their flight, for Owen Thomas now lay in hospital with a broken leg and massive damage to the nerves in his right shoulder. He might never move his hand or arm again, and unless he could work the farm he could not afford the tenancy of the island.

He tried to see himself attempting to fish and farm with a withered right arm, and he knew that it was better to let go, to say good-bye, rather than grow embittered with his handicap. So neighbours came and carried off Owen Thomas's stock, the house stood shuttered and barred. Save for the sea birds and rabbits, the island lay deserted.

CHAPTER SEVEN

Three falcons hung in the sky, two thousand feet above the white-capped waves. Each maintained station, wings stiff-spread, tails fanned out against the moving current of air, hanging like trout in the swift cold current of a mountain stream.

Daily, Chek had grown in mastery of the air, so that now it had become a highway, an intricate, shifting, changing pattern of currents and cross-currents, eddies and calms, great uplifts and downshutes, pathways to be followed and used. He had learned to slide down to sea level, to flatten out above the waves, riding the blast that carried him headlong, at thirty miles an hour, straight for the base of the cliffs, knowing that seconds before he crashed into the rocks the current would sweep him up the cliff face.

Now in the evening air the peregrines hung waiting in ambush. Several pigeons had gone by without attracting more than a glance. Suddenly Freya broke station, falling seaward in a wide, curving arc that carried her half a mile away. Frika and Chek watched her go, alert to the object of her manoeuvre. A rock dove approached from the northeast. To gain the cliffs it had to pass beneath the falcons, and Freya was intent on driving it up into the waiting talons of her mate.

The dove spotted Freya. It turned in panic as the falcon flew towards it, gaining on her prey. Frika closed his wings and stooped, Chek following, and Freya dropped back as the tercel hurtled down and hit the dove. Feathers exploded, the dove crumpled, fell fifty feet, and then righting itself flew on, passing below Chek.

Chek had yet to make a kill, for food he depended entirely on his parents. Now he did not hesitate. He saw the dove's feeble and erratic flight, and closing his wings fell towards it, talons stretched wide.

The dove heard the shrill whine of his approach and flung itself forward in a last desperate bid for survival. A split second later Chek felt the satisfying thump of impact, and instinctively he kicked out, adding more force to the strike. The dying dove spiralled down to the sea, and, screaming with excitement, Chek plummeted after it, catching it just above the waves and soaring up with it in his grasp. At five hundred feet he dropped it again and swooped down once more, to repeat the thrill of his first catch.

Frika and Freya followed sedately behind as Chek bore his prize back to the cliff. Alighting, he stamped hard on the carcass, pinning it down before he began to plume it. As his parents hovered near he mantled his kill with brooding wings, and hissed at them in warning.

Chek killed again several times in the days that followed, always in the company of his parents, and as summer swelled to full ripeness, as the combine harvesters began to clatter in the fields, and the sleek grey seals foregathered on the beaches of the island, he learned many things. It was a waste of time to chase the herring gulls that drifted to and fro in front of the cliffs—they simply tilted a wing tip and slipped away, avoiding his stoops as easily as if he were a lumbering buzzard. He also gave a wide berth to the fulmars. When attacked they ejected from their beaks a stream of vile, brown liquid over his head and breast which defied all efforts to remove it.

Then Chek began to hunt alone, and in earnest. He killed a jackdaw as it planed in to feed in a stubble field; he scooped a starling from under the nose of a surprised sparrowhawk, and at last, after many unsuccessful attempts, he killed his first pigeon, stooping on it in the grand manner, and knocking it out of the sky with such force that it bounced six feet above the heather. Mortally wounded, it was just crawling away when Chek fell on it.

Always he returned at sunset to the cliffs of his island home, but now, like his parents, he roosted on a ledge, impervious to wind and rain. The eyrie lay deserted, the bones, skin and flesh of many a meal waiting for the winds of autumn to blow them away and leave the ledge clean and bare.

WHEN AUTUMN CAME, with gales and rain, the sea birds had gone, and the cliffs lay deserted save for the drifting gulls and a solitary shag arrowing his way over the tumbling waves. An aura of unease and restlessness hung over land and sea. The days were shortening and the nights were full of the whisper of wings as the migrants passed, dark against the stars, blindly obeying the call of their kind.

Chek also heard the call, for Chek was a peregrine, a wanderer. Leaving his parents, he flew north, skirting the coast. He saw towns for the first time and veered off course to avoid their pall of smoke and stale air. As the setting sun stained the sky, he came to the mountains of northern Wales. Here, on a granite crag, over-hanging a waste of scree that slipped sheer down to the still waters of a lake, he slept.

Dawn came, and as the sun rose, Chek looked out, over the sea of mist that lay across the valley, to the mountain peaks beyond. Jackdaws were calling farther down the hill, and the sound woke hunger. He dropped off the crag and planed down to kill, clumsily, for he was still very inexperienced, and to fly back to his crag.

He had broken into the kill, and taken a few morsels, when he heard the high-pitched, chattering call of another peregrine. Instinct told him to beware, although he did not understand why. From time to time he paused in the act of tearing at his quarry to gaze up and around, and on the third occasion he saw the other falcon, a tiny speck high above the crag on which he perched.

The speck grew larger. Chek, satisfied that he had eaten the better part of the jackdaw, slipped off the ledge and sped away, hugging the side of the mountain. The falcon followed, still chittering angrily, but making no real attempt to catch him. Like all juvenile peregrines, Chek ran the risk of inadvertently intruding on another peregrine's territory, and when this happened, as now, he knew better than to stop and argue. The falcon followed him for three miles before abandoning the chase. Had Chek continued to trespass, she would not have hesitated to attack. As things were, each bird had obeyed the rules, and no harm was done.

Chek flew on, and the high mountains gave way to hills, and so to a flat, fertile plain, dairy country, tamed and thickly populated. None saw Chek as he passed overhead, for he flew high. Ahead of him lay the industrial north, with its mills and looms and steelworks, and the cold hand of pollution held the landscape in a grip of death. The rivers ran black and oily to the sea. No salmon forged their way upstream, and no herons fished by the water's edge. No trees grew, and on the heaps of poisoned waste the grasses had long since withered and died. Chek turned east, to reach a long spine of mountains, England's backbone.

These were the Pennines, a massive upland of millstone and grit and limestone, of peat bog and marsh grass, and untold acres of heather. The landscape looked as old and unchanged as the ancient hills, yet this was far from the truth, for these were grouse moors, strictly preserved and carefully maintained by the hand of man.

The red grouse was a bird found only in Great Britain. Slightly larger than a pigeon, it inhabited the high moors and mountains, feeding on flowers, seeds and berries, but mainly on the young shoots of heather. It was good to eat, and being a fast flyer, rising rapidly from cover, it had become a popular sporting bird with those landowners seeking something to shoot.

In their natural state grouse were few in number, each bird occupying about five acres of moorland, so landowners had set about increasing their stocks. Grouse needed heather, so heather was encouraged to grow. Heather needed dry conditions so the moors were drained. Heather was long-lived and slow in growth, taking a quarter of a century to reach maturity, by which time it was tall and woody, standing as high as a man. As it began to degenerate and die back, it made way for saplings of pine and birch, and, left to itself, the moor would have reverted to woodland and scrub. To prevent this, the moors were burned at carefully controlled intervals to ensure that at all times there was young heather to provide food for the grouse. At the same time predators were ruthlessly exterminated.

Thus cosseted and protected, the grouse thrived, until each square mile of moor might hold as many as three hundred grouse. Yet in spite of everything, there were years when numbers declined so drastically that the opening day of the shooting, "The Glorious Twelfth" of August, was a hollow mockery.

Like all birds, the grouse carried parasites, and in their natural state these caused little harm to their hosts. One was the threadworm, which lived on heather and was swallowed by the grazing grouse. Living in conditions of gross overcrowding, the birds soon fell victims to epidemics of over-infestation, and died.

The war years, when moors were neglected, added to the decline. Sheep grazed the heather instead of grouse, and so, except in a few places, the eastern highlands of Scotland and here on the northeastern slopes of the Pennines, the sport never regained its pre-war popularity.

On that October morning, Chek, riding a thermal high above the crest of a hill, looked down on a scene that might well have been the preparation for a battle. By the side of a sandy track stood a knot of vehicles and a group of men and dogs. Over the brow of the hill were a number of small semi-circular structures built of peat turves, spread in a wide crescent just below the ridge. The butts, as they were called, were roofless, and in each one waited a man with a gun, and his loader.

Far below them a long line of men and boys, the beaters, moved slowly up the hill, driving the grouse towards the butts. Chek, wheeling high above the ground, continued to watch.

The first covey of grouse burst from the heather, and flew toward the butts, shouting their barking call. As they passed over the heads of the shooters, Chek saw small flashes of light, heard faint pops and watched the grouse falling from the air.

He slid away to the east, checked, and waited as a second covey began their flight towards death. He marked a hen bird in the rear, and fell a thousand feet in a long shallow dive that made the air scream through his pinions. Even as he hit the bird he was climbing again on rapidly beating wings, bearing his prize away before the astonished eyes of the men.

The rest of the covey passed unharmed over their heads and Chek was a hundred feet above the butts and fifty yards away when someone took hasty aim and fired. The shot went wide, and the other guns were checked by a shout from the owner of the grouse moor, as he stood rapt in admiration for the breathtaking splendour of the falcon's stoop.

Chek vanished into the rock-strewn wilderness of the border country where the Roman, Hadrian, had built his great wall. Here wild goats roamed across the misty fells, and played among the ruins of a once-mighty fort. Chek flew on, the urge to wander still strong within him, over the lowlands of Scotland, past the spreading sprawl of the port of Glasgow, into the blue highlands, where lochs lay like pools of silver in the hollows of the glens, and the mountains towered to the sky.

On and on he travelled, north and west, until he came to the sea again. Here the coastline was split by long sea fingers probing inland to where the mountains climbed three thousand feet into the clouds. Here was the home of the deer and the wild cat, the eagle and the pine marten, a land untamed and free. At dusk of a misty autumn day, Chek flew up the eastern face of the mountain known as An Teallach, to fade, as the shadows spread, into a weatherworn wilderness of stone.

CHAPTER EIGHT

In Wales, the time of the harvest had now passed, and the land lay at rest, awaiting winter and the frost that would cleanse the ground of much of its burden of parasites and disease. The harvest had been good, and farmers shared the new affluence that was sweeping the country after years of war and post-war austerity.

With a speed unsurpassed in the history of mankind, traditional farming methods were washed away in a tide of innovation. The countryman plodding behind the plough learned to become a highly skilled technician, controlling thousands of pounds worth of equipment. To support him in this role a whole new industry was born. It supplied the farmer with the machines to sow and harvest his crops and the fuel with which to run them. It supplied fertilizers and foodstuffs, and it provided a network of transport to take away the produce and distribute it.

Yields grew to meet the ever-increasing demand. The only commodity that did not expand was space, and as land grew more valuable, so it became more overcrowded. Chickens, pigs, and calves were condemned to eke out their short existences in houses specially designed to ensure that each animal occupied no more room than the absolute minimum necessary for survival. Inevitably, under such conditions of overcrowding, pests and diseases increased, and to combat these a whole new armoury of drugs and chemicals was brought onto the market, many of them without being properly tested.

The crops also suffered from insect pests, and man tried to combat the menace, partly by rotating crops, and partly by dressing the seed with various substances noxious to the pests. A new product had appeared on the market, an organic chemical called Dieldrin, which proved remarkably effective against such old enemies of the farmer as wireworms, leatherjackets, and wheatbulb flies.

Soon farmers were using the substance over hundreds of thousands of acres. The seed merchants dressed the corn, the farmers planted it, and then waited for the rain to help the seed swell and germinate. But when the weather remained dry, the wind came and stripped the covering of earth from the seed, exposing it to the sharp eyes of birds, who flocked to the feast. Then the birds began to die.

The first bird to succumb in the gusty Pembrokeshire fields was a rook, a frugal bird who had toiled diligently year after year, helping to rid the land of the very pests against which the farmer now dressed his seed. Every spring he had walked sedately over the fallow land, probing and delving for every wireworm, cockchafer grub, and leatherjacket turned up by the plough. He and his relatives between them accounted for untold thousands of insects each year, and all he asked in return was a few handfuls of grain when it would least be missed.

This year he fed well, and several days passed before he began to feel the first effects of the poison. Then he grew drowsy and disoriented, and flew in circles for a while before falling to the ground, head and body shaken by violent convulsions. Before death came, his heart and brain had suffered damage from haemorrhages, his kidneys were totally destroyed, and the ulcerated walls of his bowels ran blood.

Now other birds began to die, some in secret places, others in the open, their beaks gaping, their bodies twisting and jerking, their heads shaking grotesquely. As, slowly, man began to realize that all was not well, and to cast around for some explanation of the suffering and death, the scavengers of the wild began to play their part in the grisly performance.

Then they too began to die. A buzzard lay in the heather, his head hidden beneath his outstretched wing. A vixen stumbled blindly along the cliff path, blundered into a rock, and fell mercifully to her death in the sea below. Magpies and carrion crows that had fed on the poisoned corpses of birds shared a common fate, for no bird or mammal seemed immune.

Wood-pigeons and rock doves were among the first birds to suffer, for they were greedy feeders, and regular visitors to the fields. Long before they died, they grew slow and lethargic, easy prey for Frika and Freya, and within a week Frika was showing signs of poisoning. For two days he clung to life, crouched helplessly on a ledge, the cliff face below him stained with the story of his indignity and suffering, until he too died.

Rain fell at last, and the green sprouts sprang forth, symbols of rebirth and eternal life. Yet in successive years the poison was to claim many more victims, especially when the weather was dry, and the seed lay for long periods without germinating.

Worst hit were the predators, particularly the birds of prey, and of these the peregrine suffered most of all. From the white cliffs of Kent, all along the south coast to the long rocky arm of Cornwall, investigators found the same grim story of eyries abandoned. By the early nineteen sixties the peregrine as a breeding species was virtually extinct along the south coast, and in Wales, northern England, and southern Scotland the situation was little better.

Frika died from Dieldrin poisoning, but this was only one of a wide range of toxins newly released on the countryside as the manufacturing chemists opened a Pandora's Box of pesticides. In response to pressure, the government introduced a partial ban on Dieldrin, but its use was still widespread, and other insecticides were used without any restrictions whatsoever.

Freya lived on. She suffered only mild ill effects from the poisons she ingested, and after a winter of wandering in the central mountains of Wales she returned to the Ramsey eyrie with a new mate, a young tercel from Finland. Their courtship was to be in vain, for the poison in Freya's system inhibited her calcium metabolism, so that of the three eggs she laid, one was infertile, and the other two had abnormally thin shells which broke beneath her as she lay incubating them.

The following year she tried again, and again failed to produce a sufficiently strong shell for her eggs. The eyrie joined a long list of others that now lay derelict. Although by 1962 the island of Ramsey had become a bird sanctuary, managed by the Royal Society for the Protection of Birds, only the sea birds returned each spring.

The island could provide sanctuary only for the eggs and newly hatched chicks. The adult sea birds, like the peregrines, were at risk from forces outside the island. Birds died, smothered in the thick oil illegally discharged from tankers. Others were found dead from a poison in the sea. Increasing amounts of a chemical called polychlorinated bi phenyl were being produced as a waste product of the growing plastics industry. Inevitably this waste found its way to the sea and into the flesh of fish, and so to the birds. In the Irish sea alone ten thousand sea birds died before man was even aware of the potential danger of his actions.

For the rock doves, however, the island provided an ideal sanctuary. The numerous survivors could now breed in peace, and fly with safety over the cliffs. The blackbird, too, sang on the fence-post above the gorse thicket, and no sparrowhawk came to knock him off his perch. Fewer buzzards threatened the young rabbits that came out in the evening to feed, and new generations of voles grew to maturity, without meeting the silent menace of the hunting owl.

Yet it was an uneasy peace, for over the living landscape hung the question: what new disaster threatened? One thing seemed certain. If the death and destruction of two world wars could not put a stop to man's arrogance and greed, the deaths of a few thousand birds were even less likely to make him change his ways.

CHAPTER NINE

Day was dawning, and Chek looked out from his lofty crag over a waste of snow and ice-clad rock. He shivered and hunched himself into a ball, ruffling his feathers against the chill. Three days had passed since he last fed, and it was snowing again. He could feel the dry flakes tapping against his plumage.

This was a strange sanctuary Chek had found, here in the western highlands of Scotland where once landowners had driven the peasant folk away from their homes and replaced their cattle with sheep, where sheep had given way to grouse, and grouse in turn to red deer. A few years earlier, Chek would have been exterminated on sight by men who believed that any living thing that could not be hunted, fished for, or shot for sport or profit, should be destroyed as swiftly and cheaply as possible. Now those times were passing. The Highlands were given over to fishing, forestry and the stalking of red deer, and a new tourist industry was growing.

The snowstorm passed, and as the light grew Chek saw that a herd of deer had moved into the corrie below to graze where the heather had been swept clear of snow by the wind. The majority were hinds, but here and there the dark outline of antlers revealed the presence of a stag. As Chek watched, a hind barked a warning. Beyond the stones and heather the snow lay broken and patchy. One patch moved slightly, and now Chek saw that it was a bird, its plumage as white as the snow around, one of a flock that, like the deer, was grazing on the meagre covering of heather.

The ptarmigan were hardy birds, dwellers of the mountain tops, rarely coming down below two thousand feet, even in the bitterest weather. They lived off heather and other mountain plants, and among the snowdrifts of a Highland winter their white winter plumage gave them excellent camouflage. The movement of a flock of ptarmigan alone would not disturb a herd of deer. Chek waited and a few seconds later saw exactly what had disturbed the hind—a fox stalking downwind of the birds. A situation was developing which Chek could well turn to his advantage, and he dropped off his perch, climbing rapidly to hang high above the corrie.

The fox was a mere few yards from the nearest bird, his jaws agape, white teeth bared in a grin as he crouched belly down in the snow for his spring. Chek closed his wings and hurtled groundwards as the fox pounced.

It was all over in seconds. Ptarmigan exploded like giant snow-flakes. The whistle of the falcon's approach, as Chek passed within a foot of the fox's head, the snap of the jaws, the solid thump of Chek hitting his bird, were followed by the thunder of hooves as the deer left the corrie. Chek flew back to his ledge, carrying his kill, and the fox trotted downhill, muzzle shrouded by white wings.

Not all kills were as easy, or as spectacular, for Chek still lacked the split-second timing and superb judgment of the mature falcon. The majority of his victims were either very young, very old, sick, lame, or simply careless. So Chek ensured the health and vigour of other species by weening out their weaker members.

Throughout the winter, the salt marsh at the head of the sea loch was Chek's favourite hunting ground. Always it was alive with movement. Dunlin and knot and bar-tailed godwit probed the shallow waters in search of small marine life. Teal and widgeon, wintering flocks of golden-eye and tufted duck, were joined by curlew, sailing in on massive widespread wings. On the waters of the loch were mallard and eider duck, sheldrake and merganser. A heron fished patiently by the shore, and from time to time a solitary great northern diver came in from the sea, rowing stealthily shorewards like a marauding Viking longship.

THE WIND BLEW from the south, bringing rain. Through breaks in the cloud the sun shone, melting the snows so that streams ran white and foaming down the mountainsides. Blackbirds sang in the birch thickets, and the rolling call of the curlew echoed over the windswept moors. After long months of darkness and ice, spring had broken free.

Among the first to feel it were the ravens, and long before the snows had left the high peaks the great black birds were flying high above the masses of rock and scree, tumbling and diving in their courtship dance, their elation growing until at times they flew upside down. On the ground the male paraded in front of his lifelong mate, bowing, neck-stretching, and ruffling the feathers of his throat.

The ravens were carrion eaters, and they had fared well through the winter on the sheep and deer that died of exposure. No death went unnoticed by these undertakers of the hills, but occasionally they could not wait for death, and were not above pecking the eyes from a living lamb. So they were not loved by the hill farmers, and many a sitting bird was shot on her nest, although they were protected by law. Yet it was always the weak and the helpless that the ravens took, and a healthy lamb, mothered by a strong ewe, had little to fear. The ailing lambs would die anyway, and it was bad husbandry that killed them. The beaks of the ravens were merely the instruments of death.

Chek was not aware that the mountain crag where he had passed the winter was the age-old nesting site of the ravens. The previous year's nest, a solid affair of heather stems, sheep's wool, moss and mud, had been broken down by the trampling of the young ravens and the gales and rain of winter.

One morning in April, a hen bird flew up on the ledge, closely followed by her consort. Chek, dozing in the sun, woke to hear the beating of wings. At first he felt no alarm, although he was dwarfed by their size, for normally ravens held a healthy respect for peregrines. The ravens, however, attacked, the hen bird in the lead knocking Chek off his perch with a powerful kick of her scaly black claws.

Chek had no strong sense of territory, and no real desire to dispute ownership of the ledge with the ravens. He dropped down towards the valley, only to find them hard on his heels. He peeled off at a tangent, and began to climb. The ravens followed. Seven thousand feet above the shimmering waters of the loch they closed with him, and Chek found he could not get past their guard. Buffeted by black wings, kicked and clawed, he was now in serious trouble. Desperately he twisted, striking out at their heads in an endeavour to stave off a lethal blow from their stabbing beaks.

The skies were growing dark. A squall had blown in from the sea, and now Chek was fighting for his life in a dense storm cloud. Lightning split the sky, and as the thunderclap broke, the three birds were flung hundreds of feet apart. Then Chek was spiralling down to the sea, only to be caught and swept inland by a gust of wind. The rock-strewn hillside rushed towards him, wearily he spread his wings to break his fall, and, dazed but otherwise unharmed, pitched down into the heather and crawled into a crevice between two rocks to rest and sleep a while.

In the late afternoon he woke and flew up onto the rocks to preen and stretch. Then, refreshed, he flew north, heading for the high peaks that stood sentinel against the sea.

These mountains formed a rough semi-circle around a vast arena of birch forest and marsh, interspersed with clear, rocky streams and dotted with tiny lochans. Beyond lay the shore, where sand dunes spiked with marram grass grew from the sea-scoured strand. Here Chek lingered. The hunting was good.

A ring ousel, conspicuous in black livery and white collar, piped

his song on a rock high upon the mountainside, and Chek swooped.
The ring ousel fled into a massive assemblage of pine and birch
branches piled on a rocky ledge. As Chek flew away it scolded him
from the safety of its hideout.

A month ago the ring ousel had arrived from Africa, found a
mate, and set up home here in the base of an old eagle's nest. A
week later the eagles returned, and began to repair the upper
storeys of the nest. Like the ravens, the eagles paired for life,
and this pair had three eyries, which they used in yearly rotation.
They ignored the ousels nesting below and the ousels, for their
part, seemed to have no fear of the great birds, with their hooked
bills, massive talons, and seven-foot wingspans.

The eagles were hunters, preying on grouse and ptarmigan and
the mountain hare. They also took lambs and deer calves, and for
this many were shot and their eyries destroyed. Their taste for
carrion also reduced their numbers. Each summer sheep suffered
from fly strike, as blow flies laid their eggs on wounds, and the
hatching maggots burrowed into the living flesh. To combat this
sheep were dipped regularly, and of late Aldrin had been introduced into the dip. If, in spite of the treatment, some sheep then
died, birds feeding on the carcasses were poisoned. Many birds
had to die before Aldrin was banned.

This pair of eagles had survived, to return to their old nesting
site, and it was not long before they began to harry Chek. Their
attacks were neither as concerted nor as vicious as that of the
ravens, but after a week his nerves frayed under the strain. The
eagles' great size, as they swooped down from the skies at speeds
up to ninety miles an hour, made even Chek's heart race with fear,
and several times he had to abandon a fresh kill, only to see it
borne away in the talons of the robber giant. The last sound he
heard, as he flew away from his tormentors, was the harsh scolding
of the ring ousel, safe in the dungeons of the castle of sticks.

During the following weeks there was no peace for Chek. A pair
of hen harriers pursued him down a mountainside, and from time
to time he strayed into territory occupied by other peregrines. He
fled east, across barren mountains, over dense forests of conifers
and wide straths to where the craggy peaks gave way to heather-

clad moorland, falling away in gently rounded slopes down to the sea.

Here a broad river flowed through parkland to the sea. In the park stood the laird's house looking out across valley and river and farms to vast game preserves and grouse moors. Pheasant stalked through the growing corn, and partridge called from the hay fields. Salmon forged their way up the cold waters of the river, and on the hills the grouse made their nests in the heather.

To preserve the game a small army of keepers was employed. There were bailiffs to patrol the river, keepers to tend the partridge and pheasant, and keepers on the hills to manage the herds of deer and preserve the grouse moors.

At the back of a wooden shed in the garden of the head keeper's cottage, nailed to the rough planking, hung the corpses of those predators classed as vermin by the keepers, shot so that the game birds might survive long enough to be killed by the laird and his guests. Of all the victims, hooded crows were by far the most numerous, but they shared the gibbet with owls and sparrow-hawks, buzzards and ravens. Goosander and merganser hung head down, their death the price they paid for fishing the laird's river.

Birds were not the only victims. Here were stoat and otter, wild cat, badger and fox. One corpse was fresh. It was a peregrine's, shot that morning.

Earlier in the year he had flown down from the far north with his mate, and in an outcrop of rock, high in the remotest part of the moor, the falcon scraped her eyrie, and laid four eggs. By the time they hatched the moor was alive with young grouse, feebly flying over the heather, and so the eyasses fed well.

For many weeks the existence of the peregrines went unnoticed, for the moors covered many miles, but, as the weather improved, keepers armed with shotguns ventured farther afield.

So the tercel died, his life blown out by a charge of shot as he flew up from the heather with a fledgling grouse in his talons. Later the keeper showed the tercel to the head keeper. Both men nodded in agreement. Somewhere, no doubt, there was on the moor a falcon with young, and the sooner she was found the better it would be for the grouse.

Ten miles away, the falcon waited by the eyrie for the tercel's return. The eyasses were hungry and yelped incessantly as they jostled and fought in the hollow of the heather.

In the late afternoon the falcon flew up and circled the eyrie, calling to her mate. Her cries grew more urgent as the long evening drew to its close, and only when it was quite dark did she fly down to the eyrie to gather her cold and hungry youngsters under her wings.

Chek heard her calls as he perched on a rock in the dying rays of the sun. The sound aroused strange sensations. He listened again, straining to hear. There was nothing, only the wind in the heather, and the distant bleat of a lamb.

He slept fitfully. By daybreak the spell had broken, and in the dawn light he flew low over the moor, hunger his only motive. A small covey broke to his left and he swerved in pursuit, picking off a bird in the rear and hitting it to the ground. He fell on it, wings spread wide for balance, and decapitated it with one deft twist of his beak.

Then he heard the call again, urgent, pleading. He hesitated a moment, then, snatching up his prey, flew off across the moors. A few minutes later he was circling the eyrie, and the falcon was flying below him her cries now soft and tremulous in greeting.

Chek pitched the grouse on the ground near the eyrie before landing to watch as the falcon tore the bird apart, bolting a few mouthfuls herself before stuffing great chunks of meat down the maws of the hungry eyasses. He lingered only a few minutes, then flew off, to return in fifteen minutes with another grouse. Soon the eyasses were content, collapsing in a sleepy huddle of white down. The falcon ate the remains of the grouse, and only then did Chek remember his own hunger.

So Chek became foster-father to a brood of four, and consort to the bereaved falcon. In the evenings they flew together high in the sky, establishing their territory, and enjoying each other's company. Though theirs was a union purely of spirit, they were, like all falcons, united until death.

Death came in the morning, a fortnight later. Ever since killing the tercel the keepers had been searching the moors for the eyrie. Now the falcon watched with growing unease two figures, a man and a boy, toiling slowly up the steep hill towards the eyrie. Chek was hunting far away on the other side of the moor.

An hour passed, and steadily the keepers drew nearer, but not until they were within yards did the falcon leave her post. Even then she did not fly far, but circled round screaming her anger. The older man watched, his shotgun ready, as the boy trampled the eyasses underfoot with his nailed boots. Then, as the falcon swooped low over their heads, he fired twice and at his second shot the falcon fell into the heather.

The boy ran over and picked her up. She was not quite dead, and her last act was to sink her talons deep into his hand. Even in death she did not relax her hold, and in the end the older man had to sever her toes with his knife and draw the claws out one at a time. By nightfall the boy's hand was swollen and infected. It was many weeks before he used it again.

The keepers had gone with the body of the falcon by the time Chek returned to the eyrie. He stood for a long time, the plucked corpse of a grouse in his talons, and looked at the bloody corpses of the eyasses. He called, sharply, but they did not move. He flew up, circling and calling for the falcon, but there was no answer.

All that day he waited by the eyrie, calling and listening for a reply. His vigil ended with the dusk. In the afterglow of the setting sun his grey form flickered ghostlike over the darkening hills and was lost.

CHAPTER TEN

Slowly, the long summer slipped away. Morning mists hung about the hedgerows, silvering the spiders' webs, and beside the shrunken rivers the wild balsam bloomed, and bees, white with pollen, buzzed among the pungent flowers.

Winter came early. Icy winds swept in from the north and east, bringing great flocks of migrant birds, seeking pastures free from frost and snow, and shelter from the bitter winds. Chek followed, harrying the migrants and impervious to the icy gales that brought blinding snow blizzards. At night he roosted wherever he could find shelter, and all the while he journeyed south, down the mountainous central spine of Wales across the sea until one morning he climbed out of cloud into bright sunshine and looked down on the mainland of Devon.

Snow lay thick on the high moors, but the coastline was clear. Chek quartered the cliffs, chased a wood-pigeon into a thickly wooded combe, crossed a broad white stretch of sandy beach, and so came to the estuary.

It was broad and wide and reached far inland from the sea, its mudbanks a rich feeding ground for hosts of waders. Once again Chek had found a winter larder, and in the weeks that followed he hunted the estuary every day. No one saw him, for the estuary was a wild and desolate place in winter. As the frost bit into the land even the sea began to freeze, and ice floes drifted into the estuary as the tide rose and fell. At night the stars glittered like great frost diamonds.

On a grey morning towards the end of January, Chek skimmed low over the frost-rimed saltings that bordered the estuary. His eye caught a flicker of movement. On the shore's high-tide mark a sandpiper fluttered and danced, leaping a foot into the air before falling back and scrabbling on the shingle.

Chek dropped on the sandpiper, and it died in his grasp. He began to feed at once. Several times during the meal he stamped in annoyance, hampered by a springy, slippery material that persisted in coiling itself round his shanks. At last, exasperated, he tried to fly away.

He rose into the air, and was pulled up short, held by the coils. He fell back on the stones and began to worry at his bonds, snipping at them with his beak, but each time he cut a strand, another enmeshed him.

The previous summer an angler fishing from a boat had got his line in a tangle. Impatiently he had cut away the snarled length of nylon and thrown it overboard, and the line had drifted ashore in the estuary, anchoring itself to the dried weed along the high-water line. It had snared the sandpiper, and now it trapped Chek.

The hours passed, and Chek gave up struggling and slept. The nylon caused him no pain, but already it was tightening on one toe, and beginning to cut off the circulation. Night came, and the dawn, and Chek was still a prisoner.

Days passed, and Chek grew weaker. Several times he was menaced by ravens and black-backed gulls, but even the boldest quailed when confronted by that indomitable glare and fierce, snapping beak.

As he lay, half-dozing, half-frozen by the cold, he was roused by the crunch of footsteps on the shingle. A man was coming, and fear woke Chek to one last effort. The feeble flapping of his wings attracted the man's attention. He made his way over to Chek, and stood for a few moments staring at the exhausted peregrine.

He was an old man, a retired doctor, and an ardent wild-fowler. He lived in the small town at the head of the estuary and spent many hours during the season waiting for the chance of a shot at duck or goose. He was also a conservationist, and a member of an association that believed in preserving the birds that offered them their sport. Throughout the winter the association provided supplies of grain to birds hard hit by the weather.

The old man carried a sack of grain on his back, and now he scattered it where the birds would find it. Then he returned to Chek. With a knife, he cut the line free, but left his legs still entangled. Then he wrapped Chek in the sack, and set off back to town. Chek, too weak to feel fear, gradually slipped into unconsciousness.

He was aware briefly of light and warmth and gentle hands cutting away the nylon that bound his legs. Then he was left alone in the dark and stuffy confines of a wooden box.

The old man took his gun and left the house. In an hour he was back with a brace of wood-pigeons. He hung one in the larder, and the other he split open, and cut thin slices from the breast. After wiping his hands, he took Chek from the box.

Chek offered no resistance as the old man gently forced open his beak and pushed a few morsels of meat down into his crop. Then he put him back in his box, and set him near the warmth of the stove.

Two hours later he prepared a second feed. When he opened the box Chek was on his feet, and his eyes were open. Each successive feed grew more of a struggle and by the time twenty-four hours had passed and the pigeon had been demolished, the old man was ruefully wishing that he possessed a strong pair of gloves.

By the end of the second day Chek was strong enough to be moved to the outhouse the old man had prepared, and he crouched in the semi-darkness, his talons gripping the rough perch, ignoring the pigeon the old man had left for him. The pigeon was newly killed, and the old man had split it open, so that its flesh steamed in the cold air. Chek made no move towards it. Outside the door the old man watched through a crack in the planking.

The slow minutes passed. Chek sat as though carved from stone. Then suddenly he stretched and raised his wings above his head. Subsiding, he extended one wing and leg, scratched his poll, and ruffled his feathers. Only then, as though he had completed a list of important tasks, did he sidle over to the pigeon. Delicately, he drew it towards him with the tip of his beak, glared all round, and began to feed.

Within a week he had regained his lost weight. His feet were frost-bitten but even they were on the mend, all save the toe where the nylon had bitten deep. It eventually withered and dropped off.

The weather was changing, and Chek could sense it. On a morning soft with the promise of spring, as a thrush shouted from the topmost branch of an ash tree, the old man opened the door of the outhouse and let in the sun. Chek spread his wings and flew to meet it.

High above the town he circled, and the old man watched him dwindle to a speck and vanish into the sun.

THAT SPRING CHEK was restless, dissatisfied. He hunted and killed, only to find that his appetite had left him.

Chek was lonely.

As the days lengthened, his fever grew. Planing high above the cliffs, drifting out to sea and then sweeping back inland, from time to time he called, a high-pitched staccato yelp, and after each call he hung listening and scanning the skies. Although they were full of birds, not one of his tribe came to his call.

The spring equinox passed. The winds softened and died, and

the blackthorn bloomed, a profusion of white foam among the leaf-less black branches. Country folk shook their heads, and spoke of a blackthorn winter. . . .

Now the wind blew from the east, sore and cold. Three frosts came in a row, and country folk prophesied rain. The wind veered south, and by late afternoon dark clouds rose over the moors. Out of them flew a falcon and Chek flew to greet her.

She was Vega, raised in an eyrie north of the Arctic Circle, where the sun never set. She had drifted south, following the coasts of Norway and Denmark, and crossing the wide and windy plains of Holland, where men still set their nets to trap the passage hawks, as they had done since the days when the kings of Europe fought against the Turks.

Vega had escaped the trappers and their decoy doves, and crossed the grey waste of the North Sea, wintering on the snow-bound estuaries of the Norfolk coast. With the coming of the thaw the search for a mate had drawn her west along the south coast of Britain, down to Cornwall, and back along its north coast to Chek.

Together they climbed into the turbulent air currents, fore-runners of storm, and rode the wild wind until the storm broke and they fell, to roost on the darkening cliff.

The night was long and arduous. Thunder hammered overhead, wind and rain lashed the cliffs and lightning filled the sky with forked tails of light. Stoically, the falcons endured the storm.

Their courtship was brief, and their union sealed on the second day.

From Hartland Point in the west, to Selworthy Beacon by Minehead, the coastline stretches about fifty miles, an intricate maze of cliffs and rocky shores, wide white beaches and estuaries. In the days that followed, Vega visited them all in search of a site for her eyrie. Chek followed, and hunted and killed and fed his new-found mate, and sat bored and disconsolate, as Vega inspected yet another dusty cranny in the rocks.

She was truly wild, and the proximity of man unnerved her to a far greater extent than it did Chek. Once she had almost settled on a particular cliff, when the sight of a lone observer on the opposite headland sent her winging on her way. Immediately

411

afterwards, the man hurried home to inform his bird-watching friends that the falcons had returned to Baggy Point. By the time the word got round, Vega and Chek were twenty miles away.

There came a morning in early April when Vega settled on a ledge, and began to preen. Twice before she had explored the same ledge, and a spacious cave formed by a leaning slab of rock. Three hundred feet below her the sea leaped up the old red sandstone rock. Above her the cliff towered two hundred feet to the green line of the turf. No cliff path wound its way over the top, no farm stood near. Vega's search was at an end. Here, in an environment unchanged since the last ice age, she and Chek would raise their young.

Author's Note

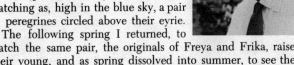

"Up there," said my friend, squinting out over the sea, towards the grey cliffs of Pembrokeshire. "About five in the evening. You should see them flighting."

Four hours later I stood on the dusty soil of a potato field, my back to the sun, watching as, high in the blue sky, a pair of peregrines circled above their eyrie.

The following spring I returned, to watch the same pair, the originals of Freya and Frika, raise their young, and as spring dissolved into summer, to see the endless everchanging pageantry of the seabirds and seals.

It was many years before I came to write their story, but at least I have been able to write it when, for once, in a lifetime preoccupied with trying to work out man's place in nature, I feel faintly optimistic. The peregrines may yet survive to share and add to the richness of the living world. Their fate is our fate, for we share a common destiny, and each species lost is a step back towards the time when the earth was without form, and void.

Fortunately a new breed of man is emerging, who recognizes the sanctity of life, and seeks to replenish the earth. Ospreys are returning to remote lochs in the Highlands of Scotland, and their nesting sites are closely guarded night and day. In the bleak mountains of mid-Wales the kite, once so common that it scavenged the streets of London, raises its young in a solitude made possible only by man himself.

So too each known peregrine eyrie is kept under unobtrusive guard, for the law now forbids not only the taking of eggs or young, but even imposes penalties for undue interference. Yet legislation by itself is not enough. The future of the peregrine can only be assured through a change in the hearts of men. I believe this change is on the way.

EWAN CLARKSON

THE TOWER
Richard Martin Stern

THE TOWER

A condensation of the book by
RICHARD MARTIN STERN

Illustrated by Tom Hall
Published by Secker & Warburg, London

It was the tallest structure in the world, brilliantly engineered, awe-inspiring . . . a tribute to human ingenuity and vision. A tribute also to human greed.

But whatever man's determination, backed by colossal scientific resources, can build, man's weaknesses can just as readily destroy. Here, ill-founded civic pride and ruthless personal ambition combine with the petty vengeance of a single workman to turn the Tower's dedication ceremony into a disaster of terrifying proportions.

Minute by minute, trapped on the topmost floor of the Tower, a group of favoured guests, the brave and the cowardly, the innocent and the guilty, wait as the great skyscraper, symbol of a city's faith in the noble future, becomes instead a blackened, twisted monument to past and present iniquity, and watch as their chances of rescue slowly but relentlessly diminish. . . .

FOR ONE HUNDRED AND TWENTY-FIVE FLOORS, from street level to Tower Room, the building rose tall and clean and shining. Above the Tower Room the radio-and-television spire thrust sharply against the sky. By comparison with the twin masses of the nearby Trade Center, the World Tower Building appeared slim, almost delicate, a thing of grace and beauty. But eight sub-basements beneath the street level its roots were anchored deep in the bedrock of Manhattan; and its core and external skeleton, cunningly contrived, had the strength of laminated spring steel.

When fully occupied, the building would house some fifteen thousand people in its offices and studios and shops; in addition it would accommodate twenty-five thousand visitors a day.

Level by level it had risen, a marvel for all to see. The great cranes hoisted steel into position and held it while the bedlam clamor of rivet guns gave proof that it was being secured; then, their work at one level completed, the cranes hoisted each other to new positions to repeat the process. As the structure grew, its arteries, veins, and nerves were woven into the whole: miles of wiring and piping; cables; heating, ventilating, and air-conditioning ducts, intakes, and outlets; as well as monitoring systems to oversee and control the building's internal environment. Sensors to relay information on temperature, humidity, airflow; computers to assimilate the data, and issue essential instructions: are the upper ten floors, still exposed to the setting sun's heat, warmer than

419

optimum? Increase their flow of cool conditioned air. Are the first ten floors now cooling too rapidly in the dusk? Reduce their air-conditioning flow, or, if necessary, feed in heated air.

Dull silver was the building's basic color—anodized aluminum curtain panels covering the structural steel; the whole pierced by tens of thousands of green-tinted tempered-glass windows.

It stood in a plaza of its own. At its base three-storey arches enclosed a perimeter arcade. Great doors led into the two-storey concourse, to the elevators in the core structure, the stairs and escalators and shops in the lobbies themselves.

On this morning, the building's uppermost tip caught the first rays of sunrise while the rest of the city still slept in shadow; and the thousands of men who had had a part in the building's design and construction were going to remember this day forever.

1

THE DATE FOR THE DEDICATION had been set months in advance.

Since dawn that Friday morning, the police barricades had been stacked in the Tower Plaza. Now city employees were setting them out in neat lines. The sky was clear, blue, limitless. A gentle harbor breeze swept the plaza, salt-smelling, fresh. The plaza flags rippled. Patrolmen Shannon and Barnes stood on duty by the arcade as a man approached.

"And where do you think you're going?" Barnes asked. Barnes was black, had his master's degree in sociology, was soon to be promoted to sergeant, and sought captaincy at least.

It was established later that the man's name was John Connors. He carried a toolbox. In testimony Barnes and Shannon agreed that he had worn work clothes and a shiny aluminum hard hat.

"Inside. Unless you're going to try to keep me out?"

"There's no work today," Barnes said.

"I know." Connors sighed. "It ought to be a day off for everybody while they make speeches here and drink champagne. Instead, the boss called me to come down to the job. I'm an electrician."

"Do you carry a union card, friend?" Barnes said gently.

420

Connors pulled out his wallet and waved it. "Satisfied?"

Still Barnes hesitated. As he testified later, for no reason, merely a feeling.

"Well?" Connors said. "Just standing here I'm already costing the boss—"

Shannon, an Irishman, said, "We don't have any orders to keep people out, Frank. Let him go."

UPTOWN IN NAT WILSON'S office, facing the walls covered with thumbtacked architectural drawings of the great building, Will Giddings said, "There are fifty things I want cleaned up before those stuffed shirts wander around like a flock of tourists."

Giddings was a big man, sandy-haired, blue-eyed, filling that ancient position of clerk of the works, the Tower owner's representative on the job. He was in his early forties. Somewhere, probably in the back of a drawer, he had an engineering degree and now and again over their years on this job Nat had seen him, slide rule in hand, doing his paperwork, but he always seemed more in character in his hard hat, riding an open hoist or walking a steel girder to see that the job was done right. "We aren't ready," he said.

"Agreed." Nat was the younger man, architect-engineer, middle-sized, solid, rarely excitable. "But the governor and the mayor and all those important guests—senators, congressmen, UN types, movie stars—are coming, and it was Grover Frazee who set the day. Your boss."

Giddings sat down and stretched out his legs, but there was no relaxation in the movement.

"Yes, my boss," he said. "We have to have businessmen, but we don't have to like them."

Nat could not resist glancing out the window at the distant Tower itself, clean and pure and beautiful against the sky, the result of his own boss's soaring visions.

"*My* building, sonny!" Giddings said. "Maybe it's part Ben Caldwell's and yours, but I watched the start of excavation, and I watched them top out the steel fifteen hundred and twenty-seven feet above grade and I know every grillage, every column, every

421

spandrel beam." Giddings's eyes went briefly to the distant Tower. "I lost some friends, too. On any big job you always do." He looked back at Nat. "Remember Pete Janowski?"

Nat shook his head.

"Walked out into air sixty-five floors up and splattered himself on a concrete ramp down in the bathtub."

"That one," Nat said, remembering.

"A good man," Giddings said, "never seemed to hurry, but he got the job done the right way, and that was what shook me. When you can't put a cause to something, that's when you worry." There was something uptight in Giddings's voice, his manner. "Take a look at these." He took a manila envelope from the inside pocket of his corduroy jacket, tossed it on the desk, and watched Nat pick it up and spill its contents on the blotter.

One by one Nat studied the Xerox copies. At last he said, "Design-change authorizations. All with my signature." Surprisingly his voice held steady. "Electrical changes. Not my bailiwick."

Giddings said, "But nobody would question your signature: Caldwell Associates, Supervising Architects—you're their man on the job, you say something's O.K., that's the way it is."

Nat still held one of the change orders. His hand did not even tremble, but it was as if his mind had gone numb. "Were these changes made?"

"I don't know. I never saw those orders before last night."

"How did you miss them?"

"I can't be every place at once. Where there are deviations from original specifications, I have records of legitimate approvals." Giddings paused. "But I'd have raised hell if I'd seen these."

"So would I," Nat said. The office was still.

Giddings said at last, "That means what?"

"Not my signatures," Nat said. "I don't know who forged them."

Giddings walked to the windows and looked downtown at the jagged skyline dominated by the Tower. "I figured you'd say that."

Nat's faint smile was unamused. "Of course. If I had signed those changes, I'd deny it anyway. But I didn't sign them. What reason would I have had?"

"I don't know. That," Giddings said, "is why I'm not beating the truth out of you here and now."

"Don't even try," Nat said. His voice was low.

Giddings said in a new, quieter voice, "What kind of rot have we got buried in the walls of my building? How many corners did we cut without knowing it?"

Nat's hands rested flat on the desktop. "I don't know the answer, but I think we'd better try to find it."

Giddings kept his eyes steady on Nat's face. "You try your way," he said at last. "I'll try mine." He indicated the papers. "Keep those. I have other copies. Ben Caldwell already has a set, in case you were wondering whether to plug him in." He walked to the door and stopped. "If I find out those are your signatures I'll be coming after you." He walked out.

Nat looked again at the papers. The signatures were plain enough: N. H. Wilson. Nathan Hale: the names had been his father's idea. The original Nathan Hale was hanged. And from the looks of things somebody was trying to hang this one, too. Well, if they thought he'd walk meekly up to the gallows, they were mistaken.

He phoned Caldwell's secretary, "Nat here, Mollie. I have to see the boss. It's urgent."

"I was just going to call you." Mollie's tone told him nothing. "He's expecting you."

Caldwell's office was the corner room, immense, impressive. Caldwell himself was slight, with slicked-down sparse gray hair, pale blue eyes, and small, almost dainty hands. He was neat, quiet, precise, and, in matters to do with architecture, implacable. He was standing at the windows, facing the downtown skyline, when Nat knocked and came in. "Sit down," he said, and remained at the windows, motionless, silent. Nat sat down and waited.

"The great lighthouse at Alexandria, the Pharos," Caldwell said at last. "For almost a thousand years it guided ships into the Nile." He turned to face the office. "I met the captain of the *France* recently. He said the first bit of America they see is the top of our Tower Building. He called it the modern Pharos." Caldwell walked to his desk and sat down. On the blotter in front of him, Xerox copies were strewn. "What have we done to it, Nat?"

"I don't know, sir."

Caldwell indicated the papers. "You have seen these?"

"Yes, sir. And I've talked to Giddings. For the record, those are not my signatures. I wouldn't have messed with electrical changes without Lewis's approval." Joseph Lewis and Company were the electrical engineers.

"Theoretically," Caldwell said, "nobody would have authorized changes without their approval. But somebody did, and on the face of it, it was with the approval of this office."

"Yes, sir." What else was there to say? Nat's anger was banked now, a strong, steady force. "But why my name? Why not one of Lewis's people? It would be less open to question."

"I agree," Caldwell said. "We don't know that the changes were actually made, nor how serious they might be." He was watching Nat's face. "We'd do well to find out, wouldn't we?"

"Yes, sir. And there are other things to find out, such as why they were written, why my name was put on them—"

"That can wait," Caldwell said. "My concern now is for the building and the integrity of this firm. Understood?"

"Yes, sir." Nat returned to his office. The implications were beginning to appear now, hints of the scope of the disaster that could arise because of deviations from the intricately woven electrical system. Nat didn't know where to begin solving the problems, but he knew there was only one place where the effects could be discovered. He gathered the change-order copies and stuffed them into his pocket. Outside he told the receptionist, "I'm going to the Tower."

2

THE SUN was high enough now and Nat walked the thirty blocks, in the exercise finding some relief from anger and stress.

"I guess some men play games for the same reason I take walks," he had told Zib once, "to let a problem churn around in the subconscious. When I was growing up, we fished, we hunted, we packed into the mountains on foot or on horseback; in the winter we skied

424

and snowshoed." The sense of not belonging here in the East still made itself felt. "A primitive life," he said. "I don't know a thing about sailing or golf or tennis."

And Zib had said, "Maybe those things were important to me once, but they aren't now. I married you for other reasons. Maybe because I was sick and tired of the prep-school stereotypes I grew up with." She smiled devastatingly. "Or maybe it was because you didn't try to get me into bed on our first date."

"Backward of me. Would you have gone?"

"Possibly. No, probably. I found you attractive."

"I found you stunning and a little frightening, so very sure of yourself, here in your own surroundings." True then; still true after almost three years of marriage.

He walked steadily, pausing only for traffic. He disliked the city, but if the dirt and noise and crowding, the unhappy faces were all around, so was the ferment and excitement, the satisfaction of talking with your peers. But most important was Ben Caldwell, with his artist's eye and his infinite attention to detail which some called genius. The seven years with that man made up for everything else. Oh, one day Nat would surely leave the city, go back to the big country where he belonged. And when that time came, he wondered if Zib would go with him or choose to stay behind. Hard to tell, and not pleasant to contemplate.

Near the main entrance to the Tower, a black cop was listening to his colleague, a big uniformed Irishman. The black cop looked at Nat and smiled politely. "Can we help you, sir?"

Nat took out the badge he wore on the job. "Architect," he said. "Caldwell Associates." He nodded at the bronze plaque beside the doorway. "Just going in to have a look around."

The cop's eyes were quick on the badge. "Is anything wrong, Mr. Wilson?"

"Routine," Nat said.

"Be our guest," the Irish cop said, as Nat went on inside.

In the concourse, he hesitated. He had no real destination. There was nothing he could do until work crews could tear into the structure to see what changes, if any, had actually been made.

He walked the empty concourse around the core of the building to the banks of elevators and pushed the button for a fourteenth-floor local. He heard the soft whir of the high-speed cable as the elevator began to move. Nat stepped inside as the doors opened, and there, his finger poised over the button, he stood motionless.

Faintly, within the hollow core that housed the multiple elevator shafts, he could hear another cable whirring, an elevator rising or dropping at its swift pace. Then it stopped.

All you can do is guess, he told himself. It could be anybody, and he could be on any floor between here and the mast. So? You are jumpy, Nathan Hale; those fake change authorizations have unstrung you. He pushed the button and the elevator began to rise.

He got off at the eighth floor and walked down to the seventh, one of the building's five mechanical-electrical floors. Here the cables, thick as a man's leg, brought up from the bowels of the building primary power from the nearby Con Edison substation, fourteen thousand volts—far above electrocution strength. And here the brooding transformers stepped down the voltage to usable levels for the heating, cooling, and electric-service needs of each of the building's vertical sections. The odor of the walled-off floor area was the odor of a ship's engine room: of heated metal and oil, of rubber and paint, of filtered air and wiring insulation.

Nat stared at the main electrical cable neatly spliced to give off its enormous power here and yet carry that same power, undiminished, to the next higher mechanical floor, and so on to the building's top. Here was the building's life center exposed. Without electrical power the building was without heat, lights, ventilation, operable elevators, computer monitors and their controls.

He was conscious of the bogus change authorizations in his pocket, and again his anger was steady and deep. He could understand Giddings's rage because its roots were in him too, and for the same reason: a job of work was a sacred thing. "Whoever," Nat said slowly, "has messed with this job, we'll find him, and hang him." That promise given, he felt a little better. He took the elevator to the next mechanical-electrical floor. He found nothing; he had expected no more. But he automatically visited each of the remaining aboveground mechanical-electrical floors.

He rose within the building, local elevator after local elevator, stepping out at last into the Tower Room on the top floor, just beneath the communications mast. The elevator doors closed and immediately he heard the whir of the high-speed cables as the elevator began to drop. He frowned. Summoned by whom? He tried to estimate how many floors it passed before the cable was silent. Ten? Fifteen? Impossible to tell.

He looked around the Tower Room. Tables were already set out along one core wall. Trays of canapés, bowls of nuts, bottles, glasses, all of the paraphernalia of the standard cocktail party would be along shortly, together with waiters, bartenders and maids.

The view from this top floor was unobstructed. He looked down on the flat tops of the twin Trade Center towers, the harbor, the Verrazano-Narrows Bridge, the shining ocean beyond. Northward the city lay in its rectangular pattern of streets and avenues, the midtown towers looking like building blocks in a tabletop model.

He turned from the windows at the faint sound of an elevator again. The red light over the doors flashed on. He watched it, suddenly tense.

The doors opened and Giddings stepped out. "I wondered if I'd find you here," he said. "Looking for something?"

"If you want to ask a question, ask it. If you want to say something, say it. I've decided that after five years I don't much like you, Will. I don't think I ever did."

"And now," Giddings said "since I waved the change authorizations at you, you've found a reason, is that it?"

Both men's expression turned reflective; their moment of conflict was past. But, Nat thought, it would return; it was inevitable. "You just came up from the concourse?" he asked.

Giddings took his time. "Why?"

"Because somebody was up in the building. I heard elevators." Nat paused. "Did those cops stop you?"

Giddings was frowning now. "They did."

"They stopped me too."

"And you're asking who else is in the building, and why? Maybe," Giddings said slowly, "you made it up. Maybe there isn't—" Giddings stopped, and turned. The light flashed off over the doors, and both men heard the sound of the elevator moving.

"I don't make things up," Nat said.

"This time," Giddings said, "I believe you."

They were silent all the way down to the empty concourse. Out in the plaza, Nat found the same black cop with his big Irish mate. "He and I," Nat said, pointing at Giddings. "Anyone else go in while you've been here?"

"One man," Barnes said. "An electrician. He said there was a trouble call."

"Who made it?" This was Giddings.

"I thought of that," Barnes said. He hesitated. "Maybe a little too late. Is it important, Mr. Wilson?"

"I don't know." Surely there could be no connection between the change-order copies in his pocket and the man who had gone into the building, because the change orders applied only to work in progress, and work was finished, or near enough. "He's riding the elevators," he said.

Giddings said, "Was he carrying anything?"

Barnes said, "A toolbox. And he was wearing his hard hat."

"Has he come out?"

"If he has," Barnes said, "it was by a different door." He hesitated. "And they are all locked."

3

FOR JOHN CONNORS, toolbox in hand, riding the elevators was a pleasurable business; slick, smooth-functioning machinery had always fascinated him. And if anybody was looking for him, as sooner or later they would be, sending empty cars up and down was probably the best way to confuse a search.

He was familiar with the building on ordinary workdays. But now, vacant and echoing, it was like an empty cathedral. He felt something great was about to happen, and thought of something he had heard once: "A few determined men changing the course of great events." He liked that. It had a grand ring. Determined men. Heroes. Electricity was the key. Connors remembered that

grid blackout a few years back, and how everything had come to a full stop and some people had even thought it was the end of the world. Now there would be panic, that was the thought to cling to.

He was no electrician, despite what he had told that cop, but he had worked in the building, and he knew in a general way how the power distribution was handled. On each of those electrical-mechanical floors was what is called a splicing chamber, and whenever he could, Connors had watched the subcontractor's men at work, peeling back the steel-wire armor encasing the electrical cables and then peeling back the vinyl jacket under that, and finally getting to the heart of the matter, the big inside wires that actually carried the current.

His first thought had been to attack the electrical installation that serviced the upper stories of the building, thereby isolating the Tower Room where the reception was to be held. He had in his toolbox an eighteen-inch wrecking bar and some stolen plastic explosive, and with them, he figured, he could stir up a considerable fuss and send sparks flying all over the place.

But the more he thought about it, the more he wondered, why limit his efforts to the top floors. Why not attack the basic underground installation where the power cables led in from the substation? All he had to do was stay out of sight. But just in case luck played him foul, it would be well to be prepared. He opened the toolbox and took out the wrecking bar. It was weapon enough.

THEY HAD BEEN setting up the platform for the ceremony in the plaza when Nat and Giddings came out of the building. Giddings looked at it with distaste. "Speeches," he said. "The governor congratulating the mayor and the mayor congratulating my boss, and one of the politicians saying what a great thing the building is for humanity—" He stopped.

"Maybe it is," Nat said. "You stay here and swear at it," he said.

"Where are you going?"

"Where somebody ought to have gone earlier," Nat said. "To see the right man about these changes." He walked off across the plaza.

In the interest of speed, he took a subway uptown to Grand

Central. He walked the two blocks along Park Avenue to the Architects Building, and rode the elevator to the tenth floor where the sign on the glass door read: Joseph Lewis, Electrical Engineer. The offices and drafting rooms occupied almost the entire floor.

Joe Lewis was in shirtsleeves in his big cluttered office, a small man, quick, sharp, direct. Nat tossed the change-order copies on the desk. One by one Joe read them swiftly, dropped them as if they were live things. He looked up at last, anger plain. "You issued these? Who in hell gave you the right?"

"I never saw them before this morning. My name, but somebody else wrote it."

"Then who?" Joe said. He tapped the papers with his finger. "Were these changes actually made?"

"We'll have to see. What I want from you is an order of priority. Which of these do we look at?"

"Every single one, even if you have to tear the building apart. Damn it, man, that electrical design is in my name."

"And ours. But which change do we look into first? Give us a list in order of importance and we'll get Bert McGraw's people on it. They are the general contractors."

Lewis sat down abruptly. "I'll tell you one thing. Bert McGraw wouldn't have had anything to do with this." He shook his head. "You try cutting corners on a Bert McGraw job, fishing for kickbacks, bribing inspectors—and you get your head handed to you on a platter."

Nat sat down too. "I had heard that, but I had no way of knowing whether it was true." It could put a different light on matters. The tale fitted what Nat knew of Bert McGraw. He could leave McGraw out of the puzzle. "Have you ever worked before with Paul Simmons?" he said.

"Ever since he married McGraw's daughter and McGraw set him up."

"Is that how it was? I never knew."

"Paul's a bright boy." Lewis stared thoughtfully at the change orders. "You think he might have put your name on these?" He shook his head. "It doesn't figure. Sooner or later these would turn up, and then everybody asks, 'Who benefits?' The electrical subcontractor is the obvious man: he gets his bid price for doing substandard work; money in his pocket. But it's too obvious. And why does he need it anyway? He's got a going business and Bert McGraw is his father-in-law."

"So," Nat said, "nobody else had any good reason to issue change authorizations in my name. Dandy. Will you have that list made out for me? First things first. No matter how deep we have to go, it's got to be right."

NAT WALKED uptown into Central Park. At once his pace slowed, his mind seemed to ease, and he began to notice his surroundings. Here there were trees and grass and bare rock. Oh, there were no vistas such as he had once known, no distant mountains, no clear dry air to breathe, no real silence. But it was better than the city streets, and his thoughts ran more easily here. The change orders could have been issued merely to discredit him. Why? Nat had no idea. He stopped at a vending wagon and bought a bag of peanuts. Then he sat down on a rock.

It was a pretty damn big assumption that nobody *would* try to booby-trap him. Seven years ago, he had come, in effect, out of nowhere, the mountain West, with no friends here in the big time, no letters of introduction. And he had walked in with his portfolio and had come back every day for four days until he got to see Ben Caldwell. He had walked out with a job any number of young well-recommended architects would have given their eyeteeth for. He probably had stepped on toes, then and since.

But suppose the immediate motive was for profit: reducing the quality of material and workmanship, thus increasing the profit margin between cost and payment for someone. Who? Paul Simmons was still the obvious candidate. But if Simmons had all going for him that Joe Lewis had mentioned, why would he take the chance of exposure? Nat had no answer.

The remaining possibility was that the changes were aimed, not at him and not at profit, but at the building itself. Did that make any sense?

Unfortunately, it did. In a world where violence seemed to be the norm, sabotage of a building was far from impossible.

432

BERT MCGRAW was in his office high above the street. His windows looked out at the city's buildings, a number of which he had had a hand in constructing. Usually he enjoyed the view. But now he was not sure, because sticking up in the center of the skyline was the World Tower, and what Giddings had been telling him and showing him about that structure was enough to curdle a man's enthusiasm even on as bright and shining a spring day as this.

McGraw glared at the copies of the change authorizations on his desk. He looked again at Giddings. "Just what do we *know?*" McGraw demanded. "Only pieces of paper, and not even originals."

"You're fancy-footing, Bert," Giddings said. "Those are honest copies of hanky-panky that's been going on under your nose and, yes, mine as well. How many of the changes were carried out I don't know yet. How serious they are I don't know yet. Why the changes were issued I can only guess."

McGraw heaved himself out of his chair and went to stand at the windows. Time was when he might have taken a thing like this in stride, or near enough. Now it was like a sneak punch to the kidney, and the world he looked out at suddenly blurred. It was not the first such experience, and it worried him.

"You're overweight," his Mary had told him, "and overworked, and you aren't as young as you were, Bert McGraw. Once upon a time you could spend all night drinking and being a terrible grand fellow and come home bright as a daisy, almost. But not anymore."

The world swam back into focus. McGraw turned away from the windows. "Did young Nat Wilson actually sign them?"

"He says no," Giddings said. "And I don't see why he would stick his neck out."

McGraw returned to his chair. "All right," he said. "At the least what we've got is confusion. On the face of those papers, that great beautiful building isn't up to specifications, and that puts a foot in the door for all sorts of trouble."

"And work," Giddings said. "Walls will have to be opened up; circuits checked out." He shook his head.

"We'll do what has to be done," McGraw said sharply. Then his belligerence disappeared. "It isn't that I'm thinking of." Was he being superstitious, as Mary, bless her, sometimes said he was, the bog Irish in him coming out? "You've seen it yourself," he said. "Little things go wrong on a job, accidents happen. . . ." He spread his hands. "And sometimes, it's as if, God help me, some kind of bad spell has been laid on and not even a priest's blessing can lift it. Do you know what I mean, Will?"

Giddings was thinking again of Pete Janowski walking off the steel at the sixty-fifth floor. "I know what you mean," he said.

McGraw sighed heavily. "Why the changes were issued you can only guess?" he said. "All right, guess away."

"You aren't going to like it," Giddings said.

"Be damned to that." It was honest anger the old man felt now, deep and strong. "We've been diddled, you for the owners, me for myself. I want to know who and why."

Giddings shrugged. "The changes are all electrical. With what I've seen, all the changes call for lower quality material or simplified circuitry. What does that say to you?"

There was no hesitation. "That somebody was trying to save money," McGraw said. He heaved himself out of his chair again and walked to stare at a blurred world through the windows. Over his shoulder he said, "And the man who saved money, you're saying, are you not, is the man who holds the electrical contract?" As before, the world swam slowly back into focus. McGraw turned. He kept his hands behind his back lest they demonstrate the tension that was in him. "Paul Simmons, my son-in-law—it's him you're pointing the finger at, is it?"

"I told you I was just guessing. And, I told you you weren't going to like it."

"No," McGraw said in a new, quiet voice, "I don't like it. I don't like you thinking it, and I don't like thinking it myself." He brought his hands into view at last, fingers spread and hooked, and he studied them for a long time. When he looked at Giddings again, his face was almost gray. "We'll find out, Will," he said. "If I have to pick him up with these two hands and bend him until he breaks, we'll find out. I promise you. In the meantime—" The words stopped suddenly as if the old man had forgotten what he was going to say. He rubbed one hand wearily along his jaw.

"In the meantime," Giddings said as if he had seen no lapse, "I'll try to find out what has to be done."

McGraw lowered himself into his chair. He nodded. "You do that, Will. And let me know." He took a deep breath. His voice was strong again. "We stand behind our jobs. We always have."

The old man sat motionless in his big chair long after Giddings was gone. The temptation was to refuse to believe that someone near, someone in the family, had transgressed. Besides, he was proud of his son-in-law. For one thing, Simmons was what used to be called a gentleman—not McGraw's breed of alley cat at all. The fact that his daughter Patty fitted right into Paul's circle was a further cause for pride.

McGraw and Mary still lived in the house in Queens that McGraw had bought with the earnings from his first sizable construction job thirty years ago. Paul and Patty lived in Westchester, only a few miles but an entire culture away. You dream that your children will have it better than you did. And when it happens, you get down on your knees and thank the good Lord. Now, did he just pick up the phone and call his son-in-law a cheat and a thief? He pushed at the copies of the change authorizations with one big hand. They rustled like dead leaves.

It couldn't have happened, McGraw thought, not on one of his jobs, not under Giddings's nose, or Nat Wilson's. And how about the inspectors? Bought? Or simply diddled by the bogus changes? Oh, there are tricks galore, and McGraw had encountered them all.

The telephone on the desk roused the old man, and he stared at it with distaste for a moment before he picked it up.

"Mrs. Simmons is calling," his secretary said.

Patty couldn't know, McGraw told himself. And neither did he know yet for *sure* that Paul was the kind of scum who would foul up an honest job. "Hi honey," McGraw said into the phone.

"You wouldn't like to buy me lunch, would you, Daddy?" Patty's voice was young, fresh, enthusiastic. "I'm at Grand Central, and Paul's tied up with a business appointment."

"And none of your friends are available," McGraw said, "so

finally you think of your old man." Just the sound of her voice counteracted some of the mental pain.

"That will be a day," Patty said. "You know I would have married you myself if it hadn't been for Mother. Come on, Daddy."

"All right, honey," McGraw said. "I have a phone call to make. You get a table at Martin's. I'll be along shortly."

McGraw pushed the intercom button and signaled his secretary: "Get me Paul Simmons, Laura."

When she got back to him she said, "Mr. Simmons is busy on the phone. I'll try again in a few minutes?"

Reprieve? Nothing of the sort. "Let me talk to his secretary." When the new voice came on, McGraw said, "Tell Paul that I want to see him in my office at two o'clock sharp."

The secretary hesitated. "Mr. Simmons has a rather full schedule, Mr. McGraw. He—"

"Honey," McGraw said, "you tell him to be here."

IN HIS OFFICE Paul Simmons, on the phone, was saying, "I've booked a table and I've told Patty I had a business engagement, so I do think you owe me your company at lunch."

"Do you, indeed?" Zib Wilson said. "I was expecting a call from Nat." Not quite true: she had been hoping for a call from Nat. "But," she said, "I suppose he's all involved with the Tower opening. Come to think of it, why aren't you?"

"I'm not wedded to my work the way your loving husband is. Lunch, my sweet. Over the first drink I'll tell you how much I love you. Over the second I'll tell you in whispers what I'm going to do about it."

"It sounds fascinating." There were piles of manuscripts on her desk, and the August issue of the magazine could not be locked up until she had one more piece of usable fiction. On the other hand, a sandwich at her desk did not appeal. "You've convinced me," Zib said. "Where? And when?" She jotted down the address. "Got it," she said. "*Ciao.* And I'll pay my share. As usual." Funny, she no longer even thought about Nat and what his reaction would be if he knew she was straying from the fold.

GOVERNOR BENT ARMITAGE, down from the state capital for the Tower opening, met Grover Frazee for an early lunch at the Harvard Club on Forty-fourth Street.

Over his martini the governor said, "The corporation reports you've been sending out haven't really said much, Grover. How are rentals going at the Tower?"

It was a troublesome point. "Rentals," Frazee said, "are going as well as can be expected under the circumstances."

The governor could smile like a Disney wolf, white fangs showing. "Words that say exactly nothing. You'd have made a splendid politician. Rentals are not going well. Tell me why."

"A variety of factors—" Frazee began.

"Grover. You are not addressing a formal stockholders' meeting. You are talking to one interested stockholder in the World Tower Corporation. Prospective tenants are staying away in droves? I want to know the reasons. Too much space available? Rentals too high? Money tight? Uncertainty in the business community?"

Frazee hesitated. The governor was a self-made man, and there were times, as now, when he set aside his jovial front and allowed you to see some of the force that had carried him almost to the presidency of the United States.

"All of those reasons," Frazee said. "Things will change. The Trade Center is feeling the same pinch."

"The Trade Center," the governor said, "is Port Authority. For them a less than full building can be tolerated almost indefinitely. We are a private corporation, and I keep thinking of the Empire State Building sitting half-empty during the Depression."

Frazee said nothing.

"What it means," the governor said, "is that we seem to have picked a poor time to build our shining great building, no?" He finished his drink. "I promised myself two martinis," he said, and crooked his forefinger at a waiter. "Cost overrun in construction?"

There at least Frazee was on solid ground. "No," he said. "We've held very tight to estimates. Careful design, careful planning."

"All right. That's a plus." The governor smiled suddenly. "An unexpected plus. It gives a little room for maneuver. We can afford to take a little smaller income on our rentals, no?"

437

"We have published our rate schedule," Frazee said stiffly, "We have signed leases on the basis of those rates."

"Good-oh," the governor said. "Now where you think it expedient, let our agents sign some leases at a little less than our published rates and suggest to the tenants that they would do well to keep their mouths shut about it."

Frazee opened his mouth and closed it again carefully.

"You're shocked?" The governor beckoned the waiter again. "We'll order," he said, "while I still have a little martini left. It's going to be a dull afternoon." He consulted the menu, gave his order and leaned back. "There are a lot of marbles involved, Grover," he said. "Maybe you don't care about yours, but I do care about mine. Gentlemanly ethics are all very well, but we built that building to make money. Let's get on with it."

5

PAUL SIMMONS was already in a small booth in the rear of the restaurant when Zib arrived. He rose as she came toward him smiling, skirt short on regal legs, long hair gleaming, unbrassiered breasts jouncing gently. She slid into the booth with her usual grace. "I shouldn't be here," she said, and brushed the long hair back with both hands. "I ought to be going through piles of slush to try to find a piece of fiction we can use without too much shame." She wrinkled her nose in distaste.

"So I am all the more flattered." Paul beckoned the waiter and ordered martinis. Then he leaned back and smiled at Zib. "When am I going to see you again?"

"You are seeing me again."

"Not the way I want to."

Zib smiled. "You always run true to type," she said.

"There are times when I wonder what my type is. Once," he said, "I thought I was a pretty average sort of fellow—prep school, college, then probably some corporation where I could serve my time without too much strain."

Zib watched him steadily. "And?" Her voice was quiet.

The drinks arrived. Paul lifted his in salutation and sipped slowly. "You haven't met my father-in-law, have you?"

"Nat speaks of him."

"They're not unalike. Bert's a brawling two-fisted Irishman—"

"Nat isn't. Nat is a lamb, sometimes too much of a lamb." Zib frowned. "Don't look at me like that. He is."

"The last thing I want," Simmons said slowly, "is a quarrel."

"Then don't say things like that. He's my husband."

Simmons nodded. "So," he said, "we'll stick to Bert McGraw, my revered father-in-law."

"You're afraid of him, aren't you?"

He sipped his martini. "Yes." He had no wish to appear heroic; there was more to be gained by appearing to throw himself on Zib's mercy—an approach he had used before with success. "You and I," he said, "are anachronisms. We were raised to believe that all men were gentlemen and all women ladies. No cheating, no gouging, life played strictly by the rules."

Zib nodded. "Go on."

"I think kids today see it more clearly than we ever did. They say that the people we look up to, or call successful, have not always played by the rules."

"Your father-in-law?" Zib said.

"Exactly. Bert is a street-fighter in a gutter neighborhood. He's in a tough trade, and he gets along fine."

Zib looked across the table with fresh interest. "And you don't?"

He shrugged, modest now. "I stagger along." His smile was appealingly wry. "With Patty pushing me every step of the way."

In a sense, he thought, he had been accurate when he said that he wondered what his type was. He had always had a chameleon's ability to blend into his surroundings, with his brains, technical competence, and charm, but sometimes it seemed to him that an essential ingredient had been left out, a hardening agent perhaps, and he had never coalesced into a firm recognizable entity.

"I like Patty," Zib said.

"You're welcome to her."

Zib studied her martini. She looked up. "I don't really know you at all, do I? Sometimes I wonder if I really know anyone. Do you ever get that feeling, that you're—locked out?"

"Frequently." Paul gestured to the waiter for another round of drinks. If he was going to face Bert McGraw, he thought, he wanted inner support.

"What you said about Nat," Zib said, "that he was not unlike Bert McGraw—what did you mean?"

"He's a character out of the Wild West, and every now and again it shows. 'When you say that, smile, podner!'"

Zib shook her head. The long hair covered her face. She brushed it back angrily. "You're wrong. I told you. He's a lamb and I wish he weren't." Because if he weren't, she thought, I wouldn't be carrying on with you, or anybody else. So, in a sense, it was Nat's fault. Comforting thought.

"Sweetie," Paul said, "let me tell you something. Don't ever push him too far. Now, let's order."

PATTY was at a table for two at Martin's when Bert McGraw walked in. Martin himself, menus in hand, scurried up in greeting and led the way across the restaurant. McGraw bent to kiss his daughter, then he sat down. His bourbon on ice was waiting. He tasted it, sighed, and smiled at the girl. "Hi, honey."

"You look peaked, McGraw."

"Maybe I am, but seeing you makes it better."

Patty was smiling too. "Liar. You're tired. After the World Tower, you need a rest. Take Mother away. Take that trip to Ireland you've always talked about." Patty paused. "Why haven't you ever done it, Daddy?"

Why, indeed? "There's never been the time."

"That isn't the reason."

McGraw smiled. "You're a smart whippersnapper. All right, I'll tell you the reason, honey. It's because Ireland is a dream to me, and I'm afraid the dream would be damaged if I actually went there." He finished his whiskey.

Patty smiled fondly. "I believe it all but one part," she said. "You, afraid? Of anything? Never?" She shook her head.

There were times when his feeling of closeness to her equaled, in different ways even surpassed, his feeling of closeness to his Mary. "Afraid of many things, honey," McGraw said. "Afraid from the moment I first saw you that one day you would go away, as you have. I don't know how mothers feel about their sons who marry, but I know how a father feels about his daughter." He forced himself to smile. "The finest man in the world isn't good enough."

"Do you think Paul is the finest man in the world?"

How do you answer that, McGraw? "I've known worse," he said aloud. Have you? After your talk with Giddings?

Patty's smile was gone. "I wonder if you mean that."

"I said it, didn't I, honey."

Patty said, "I know you're a very fine poker player, Daddy, but I don't see how; sometimes you're so transparent. I always thought you liked Paul. What happened? Is it bad?"

"Bullied by my own daughter," McGraw said lightly, "I don't know, honey. There may be—things to do with the World Tower."

"What kind of things? Shenanigans? Paul? But how—" She said quietly, "He could, couldn't he? I've heard tales of kickbacks—"

"I don't know anything for sure, honey. And I'm not going to bad-mouth a man until I do know."

Fresh drinks arrived. McGraw made himself sip his slowly. What he needed, he thought, was not a drink in a glass, but a bottle, as in the old simple days with his friends.

"Yes, Daddy. I wish I'd known you then."

Good God, was he talking aloud? He noticed that his hand was unsteady as he set the glass down.

"Let's order a meal," he said.

It was as if Patty had not heard. "I'm leaving Paul, Daddy. Or, I was. But if he's in trouble this isn't the time to walk out, is it?"

"I don't know, honey. I don't know what your reason is." McGraw hesitated. "Do you want to tell me?" He knew she did or the subject would never have been brought up.

"The reason," Patty said, "is the usual sordid reason. Or maybe it isn't usual these days. Maybe to most people a little wife-swapping doesn't matter. But it does to me."

McGraw's fresh anger was under tight control. "It does to me, too, honey. And to your mother. Do you know who it is?"

441

"Zib Wilson. I guessed it first from Paul's change of attitude toward Nat and Zib during construction of the Tower. We saw them a lot socially."

"Does Nat know?"

"I haven't asked him."

"Maybe," McGraw said slowly, "if you'd had children."

"We can't, Daddy. That's another part of it. Paul had a vasectomy. He didn't bother to tell me about it for a long time, but there it is." Patty picked up the menu. She smiled brightly. "As they say, so what else is new? I think some food for you, McGraw. Unless you're going to drink your lunch?"

If only we could take on their problems, he thought, their pain! "You sound just like a nagging wife," he said.

"And you, Daddy, sound . . ." She stopped. Tears appeared. She got Kleenex out of her purse and swabbed her eyes viciously. "Oh, damn!" she said. "Damn, damn, damn! I wasn't going to cry!"

"Sometimes," McGraw said, "it's that or break something. I'll order for you, honey."

ZIB TOOK A CAB from the restaurant back to the magazine. In her office she plumped down in her chair, kicked off her shoes, and ignoring the pile of manuscripts, stared at the wall.

She did not for a moment really believe what Paul had said about Nat: that he was a character out of the Wild West she would do well not to push too far. On the other hand, how well did she really know her husband?

She had lived in married intimacy with him for almost three years now. Nat emptied his pockets carefully each night and hung up all of his clothes. He squeezed the toothpaste tube from the bottom instead of the top. He slept soundly and did not snore. And although he was not one to sing in his morning shower, he was cheerful over breakfast. His morning run in the park and his walks to and from the office plus a regimen of daily floor exercises kept him in splendid physical condition. He was even-tempered and did not swear at waiters or cab drivers. He was punctual. He looked with approval at pretty women but Zib would have wagered heavily that looking was as far as it went. Their own sex life was pleasant.

442

Where in all that was the character Paul Simmons pictured? Could she actually imagine Nat in the outraged-husband role confronting her with the fact of her infidelity and, if Paul were to be believed, taking retaliatory action? Nonsense. If there was one quality Nat lacked, it was aggressiveness. She remembered pointing out to him one night that she'd never seen him lose his cool.

"It happens sometimes," he had said.

"I don't believe it." And then, groping for words to clothe the idea, "Respect," she said. "That's the thing that counts. How can you respect somebody who doesn't have a trace of bastard in him?"

Calmly, "Or bitch?"

"Right. In this world either you push or you get walked on."

"It's a big-city attitude."

"This is a big city. Why did you come here?"

"To find you."

"Be serious."

"All right." Nat was smiling again. "Because Ben Caldwell was here, and I wanted to work with the best. Simple as that."

"And you have." Zib nodded. "When the World Tower is all finished, just another big building, then what?" She hesitated. "Back to your mountains?"

"Possibly. Probably. Will you come with me?"

"I'd be out of place. As much—" She stopped.

"As much as I am here?" He shook his head, smiling again. No trace of temper, Zib thought now. Never a trace of temper. Oh, not emotionless; not that. With her he could be a passionate man, lover. But other times, in ways Paul had hinted? No way. Paul was wrong. That was all there was to it.

Then why the small, nagging doubt? Answer me that, Elizabeth.

6

BERT MCGRAW was back in his office after lunch, and Paul Simmons, clearly uncomfortable, sat low in one of the leather visitors' chairs. He looked at his watch. "Two o'clock," he said, "on the dot." He paused and, daring, added, "As specified."

"I had lunch with Patty," McGraw said. He had himself under control, but for how long, he had no idea.

"I was busy for lunch," Paul said. "Business is good."

"Is it now?" Deliberately the old man picked up the change-authorization copies, and with a sudden flipping motion scaled them to land accurately in Paul's lap. "Have a look."

In the big office only the faint whispering of the papers in Paul's hands disturbed the silence. Paul said at last, "So?"

McGraw was watching him. "So did you make those changes?"

"But of course."

"Why *of course*?" The old man's voice rose.

Paul scratched an eyebrow. "Why wouldn't I make the changes?"

"Because," McGraw said, "you're not some dumb working stiff. If somebody says, 'Do this,' you don't just do it without question." The old man was holding tight to the arms of his chair.

"All right." Simmons's voice had a faint edge. "Most times if somebody says, 'Change this,' I want reasons. But when Ben Caldwell, or his anointed disciple Nat Wilson give me the Word, then I tug at my forelock and say, 'Aye, aye, sir,' and the change is made. Not for me to question why. Does that answer it?"

"Don't be flip with me, young fellow. You're sayin', are you not, that it was Nat Wilson himself who signed those changes?"

Paul's face showed surprise. "I never thought different."

"And," McGraw said, "because the changes, as far as I've seen, stand to save you quite a bit of money, then you had even more reason not to question what was handed you, is that it?"

"You once suggested that the teeth of gift horses are best not examined." Paul tapped the papers in his lap. "If this was the way they wanted their building wired, and as you say, I saved money by doing it their way, why should I raise a fuss?"

McGraw said slowly, "Nat Wilson says he didn't issue those changes."

Paul's face altered, but he said merely, "I see."

"And what, damn it, do you see? Will Giddings doesn't believe Wilson issued those changes, either. Neither does Ben Caldwell."

"And what do you think, father-in-law?"

"What I think," he said slowly, "would call down penance in

444

confession." He was looking straight at Simmons now. "I'm thinking that the knave-or-fool judgment applies. You're carrying on with the man's wife—"

"Patty told you that?"

McGraw sat silent.

"O.K.," Paul said at last. "That's how it is. I know you can't understand it—"

"That I cannot. Nor can I forgive." The black fury was rising. "I'm an old-fashioned working-class fool, and you're young, bright, educated, decently bred, and all—and the stench of you is in my nostrils like the stench of something dead that's been out in the sun too long."

"Look," Paul said, "I've taken enough—"

"You haven't begun to take," McGraw said. "Move from that chair before I'm done and I'll break your back." His breathing was audible now. "Why would Nat Wilson issue those changes? Tell me that. They gain him nothing."

Simmons took a deep breath. "Nat Wilson resents me."

McGraw was frowning now. "Why? Because you're carrying on with his wife?"

Simmons nodded. It was better, he thought, not to speak.

"I don't believe it," McGraw said. "I know the man. If he knew you were sneaking behind his back, he'd brace you with it and take a few teeth out of that Pepsodent smile. He—"

"And he is playing with Patty," Paul said.

McGraw opened his mouth. He closed it again, but it reopened despite him. No sound emerged. His face had lost its color and his breath came now in great gasps that were not enough. His eyes protruded as he tried to make a gesture with one hand, and failed. He slumped in his chair still gasping.

Paul got up quickly. He stood for a moment indecisive and then walked to the door and threw it open. To Laura outside he said, "You'd better call an ambulance. He's having a heart attack."

GROVER FRAZEE took a cab back to his Pine Street office after his lunch with the governor. He had known Armitage a long time, and in the usual sense of the words they were, he supposed, good friends. But in the governor's world, and in Frazee's too, friendship had very little to do with business. If a man produced, you backed him; if he failed, you did not. "You're the man in charge, Grover," the governor had said, "which means that you get the brickbats as well as the bouquets."

Frazee had just returned to his office when the desk phone buzzed. He opened the switch. "Yes?"

"Mr. Giddings to see you. He says it is urgent."

First Armitage, now Will Giddings obviously with another kind of brickbat; there are times when they seem to come at you from all sides. "All right," Frazee said. "Send him in."

Giddings came straight to the point, explaining about the change authorizations.

"I want to call off the dedication this afternoon," he said, "I don't want people up in the Tower Room."

"Why? Because the lights might go out?"

Giddings nodded. "Something like that," he said. "I can't be sure. That's why I want time."

"I don't see how we can call off the arrangements, Will. Invitations went out months ago and were accepted by people who might now otherwise be in Moscow or London or Peking. They have put themselves to some trouble to appear here for what amounts"—Frazee smiled—"to a launching, Will. When a ship is launched the work is not completed, either. But the launching ceremony is a gala occasion that one simply does not call off at the last moment. What kind of trouble concerns you so much?"

Giddings lifted his big hands and let them fall. "I don't know. All I'm asking is time to find out how serious those things are. Is that too much to ask?"

Frazee picked up a gold pencil and studied it thoughtfully. What if there were some kind of electrical failure during the reception in the Tower Room. Would it not, by showing up flaws within the building, give him more time to find tenants, perhaps by following the governor's cut-rate suggestion, and in a sense, shift the blame to McGraw and Caldwell, contractor and supervising architect, for the delay? Frazee put down the pencil. "I'm afraid we cannot cancel

447

the arrangements, Will. We cannot make the building a laughing-stock."

Giddings stood up. "You're the boss. I hope to hell you're right and I'm wrong." As he went out the door he said. "I think I'm going over to Charlie's Bar on Third Avenue to get drunk."

Frazee was convinced that his own thinking was sound, but another opinion would be a good idea. He got Ben Caldwell on the phone. "These—things," Frazee said. "I don't even know what to call them—papers changing design—are they important?"

There was no hesitation. "We will have to see."

No trace of anxiety, Frazee thought with relief. "Will Giddings wants me to call off today's opening. What do you think?"

"Public relations is not my line, Grover."

"No," Frazee said. "Of course not."

There was a short silence. "Was that all?" Caldwell said.

"That was all." Frazee hung up and reflected that one thing was settled: there was no need to change plans.

ASSISTANT FIRE COMMISSIONER Timothy O'Reilly Brown was tall, redheaded, and intense, with a low boiling point. He did not know Nat Wilson, but he knew Wilson's boss, Ben Caldwell, by reputation, and everyone in the entire city knew his World Tower building. Nevertheless, "What you're telling me," he told Nat now, "is a purely internal matter. I've no desire to mix into it. You and Bert McGraw and the owners can straighten it out."

"You know better than I do, of course," Nat said, "but aren't fire regulations sometimes relaxed when a special event has to go through on schedule?" He was being as tactful as he knew how. It was uphill work.

"No."

"Never?"

"You heard me."

Tact be damned. "*Most* firemen, fire inspectors, are honest, just as most cops and building inspectors and most contractors are honest." He paused. "But some aren't, and you know that too."

Tim Brown said, "I don't know what kind of shenanigans you're trying to pull, but the door is right behind you. Out."

448

Nat made no move. "Suppose," he said, "just suppose—"

"I said out!"

"Think of the stink there'd be if you tried to put me out and something did happen at the Tower building." He paused. "It would look like Assistant Commissioner Brown had his fingers into something, wouldn't it?"

Tim Brown had half-risen in his chair. He sat down now. The nightmare of every public official, of course, was the possibility of being accused of neglect of duty. He hesitated.

"I'm not accusing anybody," Nat said. "But what I am saying is that maybe those electrical changes reduce or even eliminate the designed safety factors, and *if* certain leniencies in fire regulations were allowed in order not to stop this scheduled opening, then if anything were to happen, there might be hell to pay."

Brown opened a drawer, got out a pack of cigarettes, shook one loose, broke it in half and threw it angrily into the wastebasket. He tossed the package back and slammed the drawer shut. "That's fourteen today I haven't smoked," he said. He made himself sit quietly. "What do you want me to do?"

"It's your department," Nat said, "and I'm just guessing, but I can think of a dozen things your people *might* have overlooked, knowing that the building isn't really occupied and knowing too that today's doings can't be postponed." He paused. "Pressure in the standpipes, floor hoses in place, fire doors operable and not blocked, sprinkler systems and stand-by generators checked out."

Brown smiled wearily. "We try. We work with the building inspectors, and the cops too—"

"And another thing," Nat said. "There are cops in the plaza. I assume that's because somebody is worried about something. So am I," he added, "even if I don't know what." He was thinking of the blinking elevator lights, the soft whirring of the high-speed cables as somebody moved around in the empty building.

"These days," Brown said, "with nuts throwing bombs or shooting into crowds for no reason at all, everybody is always worried about everything." He sighed. "All right. I'll see what I can find out and I'll see that the building is as well covered now as a building that size can be."

"A building that size," Nat said thoughtfully. "Despite every safety factor we design into it—and every possible threat we anticipate—it's still vulnerable, isn't it?"

"Yes," Brown said, "the bigger they are, the more vulnerable they are. You just don't think about it."

"I'm thinking about it," Nat said.

He walked back to the Caldwell offices. Ben Caldwell had already left for the ceremonies at the Tower building. Nat went into his own office and sat down to stare at the drawings thumbtacked to the wall.

He told himself that he was being frightened of shadows as, one time when hiking alone on a windswept mountain slope high above timberline, he had come across the largest bear tracks he had ever seen showing plainly the long front claws that spelled grizzly. Black bears usually would not bother you if you left them alone. But the big fellow, *ursus horribilis*, played by no rules except his own, and his temper was short. When you hunted grizzly, you never, never fired unless you were above him; otherwise, he would get to you. Nat had had the feeling that he wanted to look in all directions at once, and that night in his sleeping bag every rustle of wind in the stunted Alpine growth sounded an alarm.

He never saw the bear, but he never forgot it. Now, in his silent office, he thought, I never saw the man in the building, either. Maybe he is harmless, but I don't for a moment believe it.

He put through a call to Joe Lewis. "Anything yet?"

"We're not magicians," the electrical engineer said. "Some of those changes we're going to have to put into the computer and see what happens."

Nat decided to call Will Giddings, but there was no answer at Giddings's telephone at the Tower building. Nat called Frazee's office. Frazee has already gone to the festivities. "Can't have a program without the MC," his secretary said. "Anything I can do?"

"Giddings," Nat said. "Do you know where he is?"

"Charlie's Bar on Third Avenue." She gave the address.

"If he calls in," Nat said, "tell him I'm looking for him."

"Shall I tell him why?"

"He'll know," Nat said.

IN THE YEARS he had known it Third Avenue had changed. What once had been neighborhood was now impersonal shops and apartment buildings, sidewalks filled with strangers. Like himself. Charlie's Bar was a throwback: swinging doors with the name etched in heavy glass; heavy dark woodwork; the smell of pipe smoke and malt, and the sound of quiet male talk. It was a bar where customers were known, and a man could while away an afternoon. Zib, for all her Women's Lib, Nat thought, would come in here and immediately twitch to get back out again.

He found Giddings at the bar, a shot glass of whiskey and a full mug of beer in front of him. He was not drunk, but there was a glint in his eyes. "Well, well," he said, "look who's here."

Nat gestured at the drinks on the bar. "I'll have the beer, but not the shot. Let's take a booth. I've talked with a fellow named Brown downtown."

"Tim Brown?" Giddings was alert now.

Nat nodded. He accepted the filled mug of beer, reached for his pocket.

Giddings said, "No. On me." Then he slid down from his stool, and led the way, drinks in hand, to the corner booth.

The beer was good, cool, not icy, soothing. Nat drank deep, and set the mug down.

"Why Tim Brown?" Giddings said.

"We've designed-in safety devices that ought to function immediately if something goes wrong. But suppose the safety device has been bypassed? Or it isn't functioning because the fire department or the inspectors let it go just for now?"

Giddings shook himself like a dog on a hearth. "Maybe," he said. "But if you went to Tim Brown, you're thinking fire. Why?"

"The electrical changes," Nat said. "You can fuse steel with a hundred and ten volts. I've done it: a knifeblade shorted out an electric toaster. We bring power into that building at thirteen thousand eight hundred volts, not a hundred and ten—"

"You're thinking of whoever it was riding the elevators? But why? Tell me, man, for the love of God, why?"

"I'm an architect," Nat said. "I also know horses and mountains and I know *things*. I don't think I know much about people. But

451

if somebody can't get anybody to pay attention to him and decides that, say, a bomb is the only answer, where does he plant it? In a place that gets lots of attention."

Giddings picked up the shot glass and set it down again untouched. "You've flipped," he said. And he added, "I hope."

"I hope so too." Nat felt calmer now, almost resigned. "That building of ours is the biggest. And today everybody is looking at it." He pointed to the color-TV set behind the bar. The picture was of the World Tower Plaza, the police barricades, the temporary platform now partially filled with seated guests. Grover Frazee, a carnation in his buttonhole, smiled and extended his hand as more guests mounted the platform stairs.

"You didn't want the opening," Nat said. "Neither did I. Now I want it even less. Where, incidentally, did you find those change orders, Will? Where are the originals?"

Giddings turned the empty shot glass around and around on the tabletop. "I don't know. And that's the stupid, simple truth. What I got in the mail yesterday was an envelope of copies. No note. No return address. Just a Grand Central Station postmark."

7

THE BUILDING was equipped with closed circuit television that could scan every floor. But on this day, because the building was not yet open to the public, the security desks were unmanned and the television systems were dead. The point had been argued, but economy had won. The World Tower, it was said, was no Fort Knox with gold piled high. Not yet.

But even today, as for many months since the building's skeleton of structural steel had begun to be fleshed out, the computer center in the basement was manned. Here at the semicircular desk facing the rotating spools of tape and the rows of instrument dials, one man watched over the health of the great structure.

Floor 125, the Tower Room, in anticipation of the flood of reception guests, each human a walking heat machine, was being cooled two degrees below normal.

452

Elevator 35, local, floors forty-four to fifty-four, was shut down for repair; it showed dead on the panel.

In the sub-basements, automated systems functioned, motors hummed softly, massive standby generators waited. The pressure of the electric current from Con Edison held steady. From the step-down transformers, all voltages were within normal limits.

The man in the padded swivel chair facing the great panel could relax. His name was Henry Barber and he lived in Washington Heights with a wife, Helen, and three children. He was thirty-six years old. He never became any older.

Mercifully, he never knew what hit him: the blow from the wrecking bar shattered his skull; he was almost instantly dead.

John Connors stood for a few moments studying the blinking lights of the control panel. Then he left the quiet room and went on down the stairs to the sub-basement where the electrical cables entered the building from the nearby substation. There, door closed, he sat quietly, from time to time glancing at his watch.

IN THE PLAZA the band played "The Star-Spangled Banner." The building was prayed for and blessed by ministers of three faiths. Grover Frazee, as master of ceremonies, introduced the speakers. The governor spoke. He praised the building's purpose. Mayor Bob Ramsay spoke in favor of the brotherhood of man. Senator Jake Peters praised progress. Congressman Cary Wycoff spoke of the benefits the building would bring to the city.

The invited guests flowed through the door and into two express elevators for the less-than-two-minute trip to the highest room in the tallest building in the world, where the bar was set up, candles lighted, canapés set out, champagne chilled and ready.

8

IN THE TOWER ROOM, amidst the talk and laughter and the quiet accompaniment of piped-in-music, Governor Bent Armitage, drink in hand, was saying to Grover Frazee, "I have nothing against holy men, *per se*, but some of them do go on and on."

"Would you care to have that quoted to the state electorate?" Frazee said. He felt better, easier, more relaxed than he had all day; congratulations were coming in now from all sides. Giddings had depressed him; there was no denying it. But now he looked contentedly around the room, "Might cost you votes," he said.

"You know," the governor said, "I'm not sure I'd give a damn. I have a ranch out in northern New Mexico. There's a trout stream, and from the ranch house porch a view of thirteen-thousand-foot mountains that never lose their snow." He too looked around the crowded room. "The ranch looks better and better all the time." He smiled as the mayor walked up. "Ah, Bob," he said.

"I thought it went quite well," the mayor said. "Congratulations, Grover." Bob Ramsay was fifty-seven years old, in splendid physical shape, in his second term as mayor of the great city and loving every minute of it.

"Your remarks on the brotherhood of man laid them in the aisles, Bob," the governor said. Baiting Bob Ramsay was as easy as shooting fish in a rain barrel. "Where's your good lady?"

"Over by the windows." The mayor's voice was fond.

The governor felt suddenly sentimental. "You've been married how long, Bob?"

"Thirty-five years."

"You're a lucky man."

"I am." He glanced in his wife's direction.

"And who is that with her?" the governor said.

"One of your supporters, a cousin of mine. Her name is Beth Shirley." The mayor was smiling now. "Interested?"

"Lead me to her," the governor said.

She was tall, this Beth Shirley, with calm blue eyes and auburn hair. She nodded acknowledgment of the introduction and then waited for the governor to set the conversational pace.

"All I know about you," the governor said, "is that you are Bob Ramsay's cousin and you vote the right ticket. What else should I know?"

Her smile was slow, matching the calm of her eyes. "That depends, Governor, on what you have in mind."

"At my age . . ." the governor began. He shook his head.

454

"I don't think your life has stopped yet." Beth's smile spread. "Don't disappoint me, please."

"You know, I think the last thing I want in this world is to disappoint you." It was, he decided, the old goat in him coming out. "And," he added, "if that sounds ridiculous, why, let it."

Talk swirled around them, but for the moment they were alone. "Your ability to laugh at yourself," Beth said, "is one of the things I've always admired in you."

"Tell me more," the governor said.

"Bob Ramsay cannot laugh at himself."

"Then he ought not to be in politics. The President of the United States can't laugh at himself either, and we're all the losers for it."

"You might have been President. You came close."

"In the West they have a saying that close only counts in horseshoes, and then you have to be damn close," the governor said. "I had my shot at the presidency. There won't be another, and that's that." Why was he thinking so often today of that trout stream winding through the foot of the meadow, and the scent of evergreens in the high clear air? "Do you know the West?"

"I went to the University of Colorado."

"Did you! Do you know northern New Mexico?"

"I've skied and ridden in the mountains."

The governor took a deep breath. "Do you fish?"

"Only trout fishing. In streams."

"I was married once," the governor said. It seemed a perfectly natural thing to say. "A long time ago."

"I know."

The governor's eyebrows rose. "How do you know?"

"Your *Who's Who* entry. Her name was Pamela Brown, and she died in 1950. You have a married daughter, Jane, who lives in Denver. She was born in 1946—"

"Which," the governor said, "can't have been much after your birth date."

"Is that a question?" Beth was smiling. "I was born ten years earlier. And I was married once too. It was a disaster. I had been warned, and I got what they told me I would—a thirty-five-year-old son instead of a husband."

"I'm sorry," the governor said. "Or maybe I'm not. I like it the way it is, your standing here talking to me." He saw Grover Frazee making his way toward him. "Brace yourself. We are about to be interrupted. . . . Hello, Grover."

Frazee said, "I want to talk to you, Bent."

"You are talking to me." The governor's voice was unenthusiastic. "Miss Shirley, Mr. Frazee. Grover's is the steel-trap mind behind the World Tower project."

"I'm serious," Frazee said. "We have a problem." He looked at Beth. "I'd rather—"

"I'll leave," Beth said.

The governor caught her arm. "I'd never find you again." He looked at Frazee. "What's the problem? Spit it out."

Frazee hesitated. "We have a fire. Somewhere on a lower floor. Oh, it isn't much, but there's a little smoke in the air conditioning and Bob Ramsay and the fire commissioner are on the phone, so I'm sure it will be cleared up in no time."

"Then," the governor said slowly, "why tell me, Grover?"

Ben Caldwell walked up, small, almost dainty, precise. "I heard the question," he said to the governor. "Grover has heard that there may have been certain irregularities in the building's construction. He is worried."

"And," the governor said, "you're not?"

He wastes no time in non-essentials, Beth thought.

"I see no cause for worry. I know the design of this building, and a small fire . . ." He shrugged.

The governor turned to Frazee. "I'd say take the fire commissioner's judgment. If he thinks it prudent to evacuate this room promptly, then, see to it, no matter what kind of press—"

It was then, without warning, with, some said later, an almost convulsive shudder of the entire great building, that the lights went out, the softly humming air conditioning stopped, the music was silenced, and all conversation was stilled. Somewhere in the room a woman screamed.

The time was 4:23.

THE FIRE sending the smoke into the air-conditioning ducts was small, and normally would have been quickly extinguished.

It was in suite 452, fourth floor, southeast corridor. The suite, already rented, was being decorated. Cans of oil-base paint and paint thinner were on the floor beneath a plywood board resting on two sawhorses, which the painters used as a table.

Oily rags igniting in spontaneous combustion were later believed to have started the blaze. A gallon of paint thinner apparently exploded and threw burning liquid in all directions.

The overhead sprinklers came on, but the plywood board protected the heart of the fire for a time while it gathered strength; and a fire of paint thinner, like flaming gasoline, merely spreads on the water and continues to burn.

Downstairs on the central computer-control panel a warning light showed, but there was no one to see it and the air-conditioning ducts in suite 452 continued to bring in a fresh supply of air to provide oxygen for the flames. New paint on the walls caught fire. More paint-thinner cans exploded from increasing heat. The air conditioning stepped up its efforts to control the temperature, thereby bringing in more oxygen.

Smoke began to seep through the entire system and at length reached the Tower Room.

At this point, there was no real danger. An automatic alarm sounded in the firehouse two blocks away. Within less than three minutes fire trucks were on the scene, working their way through the plaza. The thinning crowds began to gather again, hampering the firemen's work. Police, Shannon and Barnes among them, moved back the barricades to the edges of the plaza. A kind of order was restored.

ON THE TELEVISION SCREEN in Charlie's Bar, the camera had begun the incredibly long climb up the building's face, floor after floor, the whole foreshortening as the angle steepened.

"Beautiful damn thing," Giddings said. "I hate to admit it to you, but it is. And tomorrow we'll run down those damned change authorizations. I've talked with Bert McGraw and he says he'll do whatever, and what Bert says, Bert does." He was feeling almost friendly. "Even if you do get funny ideas sometimes, Nat Wilson, by and large you know your trade. You—" Giddings stopped suddenly. The TV camera now had reached the tower.

"What's that smoke?" Nat asked. "Just there. Below the tower."

"Air-conditioning exhaust," Giddings said. "Somewhere there's smoke inside, and that means—Where do you think you're going?"

Nat was halfway out of the booth. "To the job," he said. "Are you coming or are you going to sit there enjoying your drink?"

IN THE CENTER of the plaza a battalion chief with a white hat directed operations through a bullhorn. Hoses snaked across the pavement. Water was gathering in puddles on the concourse.

At the barricade, Patrolman Shannon said, "Nobody allowed through." And then, "Well, what do you know? It's you again."

Patrolman Barnes said to Giddings and Nat, "Orders. I'm sorry."

A new siren sound wailed up the street, a black limousine, red light flashing. Assistant Fire Commissioner Brown was out before the car stopped. His stiff-legged stride brought to mind an angry stork. He stopped in front of Nat. "Were you just guessing, or did you know this was going to happen?"

The question would be asked again and again, Nat thought. "Does it matter now?" he said. "We're here to do what we can."

"All right," Brown said. "Come on." He walked straight to the battalion chief. "What's the story?"

"It started on the third or fourth floor." The chief shrugged. "It had a start, too much of a start."

Giddings said, "Sprinklers?"

The chief nodded. "They help contain most fires. This one they didn't."

"And that," Nat said, "means what?"

"When it's all over, I hope, we may be able to find out," the chief said. "Sprinklers just make some fires worse. Electrical fires, gasoline fires." He raised his bullhorn. "More hose! Move it in!"

Giddings said to Nat, "You said electrical fire was a possibility."

"Third floor, fourth floor . . ." Nat shook his head. "They're not mechanical floors."

Brown said to the chief, "Shall we bring the brass down from the Tower Room in the express elevators?"

"It's a hell of a walk," Giddings said, "in case you're thinking of getting them down any other way. That building core where the elevators are is safe as anything can be."

They felt, then, the sudden explosion almost beneath their feet. Sound, dull and distant, came a moment later. The puddles on the concourse rippled gently. The interior lights were suddenly dead.

Brown looked at Nat.

Nat said, "The guts of the building are down there, the primary power that makes it live, thirteen thousand eight hundred volts."

The battalion chief raised the bullhorn and sent men scurrying down into the sub-basements.

"I'm not an electrical engineer," Nat said, "but if somebody monkeyed with those big transformers, oh—" He was silent, motionless, staring into the concourse.

"If the standby generators function," Giddings said, "we'll at least have power for the elevators."

Brown said quietly, "And if they don't?"

"Then," Nat said, "you've got a Tower Room filled with people a hundred and twenty-five floors above a fire. If it gets out of control—"

"It won't," the battalion chief said.

"It very well might. That was an explosion," Nat said. "Bomb? Maybe. But what about an enormous short in a primary circuit? How long does it take with that kind of power to overheat wiring —particularly if it's substandard wiring?"

"Substandard?" The chief looked from one man to the other.

"We don't know," Nat said. His voice was quiet, almost resigned. "I haven't heard a standby generator starting up."

A fireman came stumbling out of the nearest concourse door. Once in the open air he stopped, retching helplessly. He wiped his mouth with the back of his hand. "Bad down there," he said to the chief, the words almost incoherent. "Like a ship's engine room —burning." He was seized by another retching spasm. "We found one man," he said. "Fried like bacon. And at the computer panel there's another one—dead."

459

An ambulance attendant led the fireman away.

Brown looked at Nat. "What about that substandard wiring?"

"What he means," the chief said, "is that besides a fire in the sub-basement and another on the above-grade floors, we may have a hundred potential fires from wiring that burst its insulation."

"It couldn't happen," Brown said.

The battalion chief looked at him. "Yeah. I know. None of this could happen. But maybe, just maybe it has."

Brown looked again at Nat. His meaning was plain.

"What do we do now?" Nat said. "We toss ideas to Joe Lewis, the electrical engineer, and we try to figure out some way to get those people down. You keep doing what you can, and we'll try to think. What else is there to do?"

9

EVEN WITH THE fluorescent lights dead there was ample light coming through the tinted windows in the Tower Room, and the candles still burned. The governor said to Ben Caldwell, "What does it mean? No power at all?"

"I don't know," Caldwell said.

"You're the architect. Find out."

Beth Shirley, listening to the governor take command in this moment of crisis, found it difficult to control what she felt—like a schoolgirl with her first sudden crush. What was that old song from *South Pacific*—"Some Enchanted Evening"? She put her hand gently on the governor's forearm.

"It's all right," the governor said immediately. "We'll get it sorted out, whatever it is."

"I know you will, Governor."

"My name," the governor said, "is Bent." He favored Beth with a swift grin. Then, to Grover Frazee who had not stirred, "Where is the fire commissioner? And Bob Ramsay? You said you had a telephone. Lead the way."

They crossed the broad room, on all sides conversation buzzing, Beth on the governor's arm, Grover Frazee leading the parade.

Someone said, "What is it, Governor? Can you tell us?"

"We don't know yet. But we'll find out, and when we do, you'll be told. That's a promise." He grinned. "Not a campaign promise." The remark got a small murmur of amusement.

It was a pleasant office abutting the building's core, dimly lighted now by two candles. The mayor was at the desk, telephone at his ear. He nodded to the governor and said into the phone, "I want a report from Assistant Commissioner Brown in person, is that understood?" He hung up.

Frazee said. "What do we do? Do we clear the room?" He spoke to the mayor and to the fire commissioner who stood large and solid beside the desk chair.

"Before we do anything," the governor said, "we find out where we stand, how it looks from outside. And there are some things we can do up here while we wait. Are the elevators operable? There ought to be standby power, shouldn't there?"

"There sure as hell ought to be," the fire commissioner said, "but I haven't seen any indication of it."

"There are fire stairs, aren't there?" the governor said.

"Two sets." The fire commissioner nodded.

"All right," the governor said. "Grover, have Ben Caldwell check the elevators. You check the stairs. Oh, yes, and have those waiters start passing drinks again. We don't want a bunch of drunks, but we don't want panic, either." He looked down at the mayor. "It's your city, Bob. Objections?"

The mayor smiled faintly. "You seem to be in charge. Carry on." Senator Peters walked in as the telephone was ringing.

The mayor picked it up, spoke his name, listened briefly. "All right, Brown," he said. "I'll put the commissioner on. Give him your report." He paused. "The whole report, no punches pulled, is that understood?" He handed the phone to the fire commissioner.

Ben Caldwell walked in. He glanced around at the others and nodded without expression.

The governor said, "Where's Bert McGraw? He ought to have been here."

"McGraw," the mayor said, "had a heart attack."

The governor closed his eyes briefly. When he opened them

461

again, he said softly, "I always thought of him as indestructible."

"We're none of us getting younger, Bent," the senator said. "I haven't had any intimations of immortality for a long time. In fact, I had a funny vague hunch back in Washington today." He was silent as the fire commissioner cupped his hand over the phone and cleared his throat.

"Brown says," the fire commissioner reported, "that the fire isn't good, but the battalion chief thinks it can be controlled."

There was silence. Beth put her hand on the governor's arm. He covered it with his own.

"But the real problem," the fire commissioner said, "is down in the basements. And one of your men is there, Mr. Caldwell—"

"Nat Wilson," Ben Caldwell said, "I hope."

"And," the fire commissioner said, "Will Giddings, clerk of the works. They're both there. Near as they can figure some maniac got inside the building by pretending he was an electrician. They found him down in the major transformer room, fried to a crisp. Somehow he managed to short out everything, near as they can tell, but the smoke's so thick they can't know for sure what happened except that there isn't any power."

Ben Caldwell said, "The standby generators?"

The fire commissioner shrugged his massive shoulders. "There isn't any power," he said, "period."

Ben Caldwell lost none of his calm. "The elevators do not respond," he said. "I checked them all. But the stairs will be perfectly safe. The fire doors are for just that purpose. I suggest that we start sending everybody down the stairs, half on one side, half on the other."

The governor nodded. "With marching orders," he said, "and a dozen or so men on either stair to enforce them. No running. No panic. It's a hell of a long way down and there are going to be some who will have to be helped."

Grover Frazee was back, sweating. "The doors to the stairs . . ." he began, and the words ran down. "The doors—are locked."

The fire commissioner said, "They can't be. There's no way . . ." He shook his head, raised the phone, and spoke into it.

"Ben," the governor said to Caldwell, "you and the fire

462

commissioner go see." He looked at Frazee. "And you come in here and sit down and pull yourself together, Grover." He squeezed Beth's hand. "I'm sorry for all this, my dear."

MUCH LATER, bomb experts would assess the damage in the main transformer room and estimate the power of the explosive Connors had carried in his toolbox. Plastic explosive is safe to carry; it is brownish-gray putty-like stuff that can be dropped or pushed about without protest. To set it off a probe is inserted into its body and a small electric current sent through the probe.

The main transformers had been badly damaged, and although the explosion destroyed or distorted much material, Joe Lewis's computers—in a sense working backward from known results—did a creditable job of reconstructing probable cause: there had been a massive short circuit in the primary power. The resultant surge of uncontrolled power lasted only a matter of microseconds, but in that infinitesimal time it shot far beyond the cables designed to carry the voltage in safety, through the crippled transformers, and undiminished into wiring designed to transmit only such voltages as are required to light fluorescent fixtures or run electric typewriters. The result was immediate and catastrophic.

Defective wiring melted and in melting burst its insulation. In some instances there were further short circuits which, acting like arc welds, threw the enormous heat of an open electrical spark against wall material, soundproofing, insulation—all heat-resistant, but never totally fireproof.

Within the interior walls of the building, then, creeping fires developed. Some of these would die for lack of oxygen. But some would break into ducting, or burst into open shafts or corridors, gather force and fury, and roar on, consuming paint, woodwork, draperies, rugs, flooring. Overhead sprinklers, their fusible links quickly melted, would come on and for a time would stem the fires' spread. But too much heat generates steam in water pipes, which sooner or later burst, and then the sprinklers are dead.

The fires would be slowed here, slowed there; but from the beginning, as Joe Lewis's computers later showed, the outcome was never in doubt.

PATTY MCGRAW SIMMONS had always been frightened by hospitals. Now they had her father, Bert McGraw, in what they called the Coronary Care Unit, a room she saw only when the door opened occasionally, a room filled with dials and shiny cabinet-like things; and the bed her father lay in looked like some ancient torture rack with tubes and wires leading from it to him.

Oh, other people had heart attacks every day. But not Bert McGraw. Her first memories were of him, big and boisterous, shouting with laughter, treating Patty, as her mother said, "more like a bear cub, Bert McGraw, than like a tiny girl daughter. You'll break every bone in her body the way you fling her around."

The door to the Coronary Care Unit opened and a nurse walked out. Patty had her brief glimpse before the door closed again without sound. A proud lonesome old man lying helpless on a white bed. When you are young, Patty thought, they pick you up and brush you off and kiss you where it hurts; they are always there when you need them, and you take them for granted. Then their turn to be helpless comes along, and what can you do?

Mary McGraw, who had been located at last, came breathlessly along the corridor. Patty took her mother's hands, kissed her. "Mother, we've been trying to reach you all afternoon. He's in there." Patty nodded toward the closed door. "No one can see him. The doctor is a great heart man who'll tell me nothing. Sit down."

Mary McGraw said, "He had been complaining of shortness of breath. I told him he was overweight and overworked. Maybe—"

"You'll stop right there," Patty said. "Next you'll be working it into being all your fault, which it is not." Maybe it is at least partly mine, she thought; laying the burden of my troubles on him at lunch. And then a new thought occurred. "Paul was with him when it happened," she said. And where was Paul now?

Mary McGraw looked pleased. "I'm glad your Paul was with him. He and your father get along so well."

What point in saying otherwise?

Mary McGraw continued. "Maybe Paul can help your father so

that he doesn't work so hard. Paul is young and strong and doing so well—I just hope," she added, "that your father doesn't hear of the trouble they're having at the World Tower opening. He was to have been there, and he asked me, but I said no, all those important politicians just make me uncomfortable—"

"Mother," Patty interrupted. "What trouble are they having?"

"I heard about it on TV. There is a fire." Mary was silent for a moment. And then, suddenly, "Bert! Bert! Please!" in a soft, urgent voice.

"He's going to be all right, Mother."

"Of course he is." Quiet strength showed in her now. "You've been here a long time, child. I will stay with him now. You go have a cup of tea, go for a walk. Come back when you've rested a little."

"Mother—"

"I mean it," Mary McGraw said. "I'd rather be here alone for a bit. I'll say a few prayers for both of us."

Outside in the bright sunlight, Patty walked, and afterward had no memory of her route. But suddenly here was the great shining World Tower she had visited so often during its construction. It was crippled now, a helpless giant, like its builder. There were police barricades and people staring like ghouls, lusting for terror! Patty wondered if she was going to faint.

She made her way to the construction-site trailer office, not far from the Con Edison substation. Inside there were drafting tables and file cabinets, a few chairs, telephones, and the man smells Patty had known on construction sites since memory began, now somehow comforting.

Nat said, "Come in, Patty." He took her hand. "We heard about Bert. I'm sorry."

Giddings said, "He'll make out. He always has." And then, he said to Nat, "Those doors can't be locked! Unless—" He shook his head almost savagely. They could be blocked instead of locked. It's probably radio and television equipment for the mast. I've warned them about that, but they don't listen."

Assistant Commissioner Brown and three uniformed firemen stood by listening.

"So," Nat said, "we send men up each stairwell—"

"A hundred and twenty-five floors," Giddings said, "on foot?"

"In the mountains," Nat said, "you can climb about a thousand feet an hour on a trail. It's harder here because it's almost straight up. Say an hour and three-quarters, two hours. But, how else?" To Brown he said, "Give some men halligan tools and walkie-talkies and start them up." He nodded at the telephone at Brown's hand. "Tell them they're on the way."

He was suddenly aware once more of Patty's presence. "Have you seen Paul?"

"Not since this morning. Do you need him?"

"We need some information."

"I'm sorry," she said. "He was with Bert when he had his attack. But I don't know where he is now. Unless—" she stopped.

"Unless what, Patty?"

Everyone in the office was watching her, and all she could do was shake her head in silence.

Nat took her arm, and led her to a far corner. He kept his voice low. "Unless what? Where might he be?"

"You don't want to know." Her eyes were steady. "I'm sorry."

"I don't want to know any of what's happening now. Patty, if you have any idea where he is, then you've got to tell us."

She took a deep breath. "Maybe Zib knows."

The change in Nat was plain and deep. "Does that mean what I think it does?" His voice was quiet.

Patty's chin came up. "It means," Patty said, "that my Paul and your Zib have been, as they used to say, having an affair. Maybe she knows where he is. I don't."

Nat picked up a telephone and dialed with a steady hand. His face was expressionless. "Zib Wilson, please. Her husband here."

And now Zib's light classy voice, "Hi, dear. What's up."

"Do you know where Paul Simmons is?"

There was the faintest hesitation. "Why on earth would I know where Paul is, darling?"

"Never mind the why right now," Nat said. "I need him. Bad."

"Whatever for?"

Nat took a deep breath and held his temper firm. "We've got fires in the World Tower and a hundred people trapped on the

466

hundred and twenty-fifth floor. And I need information from Paul."

"Darling"—Zib's voice was the patient voice of a kindergarten teacher explaining to a backward child—"why don't you ask Patty?"

"Patty is right here with me. She said to ask you."

There was a pause. "I see," Zib said.

The temper broke. "If you don't know where he is, find him. And get him down here. On the double. Is that clear?"

"You've never talked to me like this before."

"It was a mistake." He hung up and stood staring at the wall.

11

IN THE OFFICE OFF the Tower Room the fire commissioner listened on the telephone, nodded, said, "Keep in touch," and hung up. He looked around the office. "The men have started up the stairs." His voice was expressionless.

The governor said, "A hundred and twenty-five floors is a long climb. We'd better try some things ourselves." He pondered for a moment. "Ben, you and the commissioner commandeer three or four husky waiters. Start working on one of those doors." He turned to the fire commissioner. "If we get a door open, we're in the clear, aren't we? A protected stairwell all the way to the ground?"

The commissioner hesitated.

The mayor said, "Speak up, man. Answer the question."

"We ought to be in the clear," the commissioner said reluctantly.

"You're dragging your feet," the governor said. "Why?"

"The men on the stairs," the commissioner finally said, "have walkie-talkies. They're—reporting smoke."

The office was still. "That means what?" the governor said.

The commissioner took a deep breath. "The first fire is contained. But what happened down in the main transformer room apparently started fires"—he spread both hands—"throughout the structure."

Grover Frazee waggled his head in denial. "A modern, fireproof building—that's ridiculous. Tell him, Ben."

Caldwell said, "Fire*proof*, no. Fire resistant, yes. Now, be quiet, Grover. Let's find out exactly where we stand." He pointed at the commissioner. "Call them back. I want to speak to Wilson."

Frazee said, "There. There's your proof. The telephone works, so we can't be out of electricity. Don't you see that?"

Caldwell said almost wearily, "Telephones have their own power source. There is no connection." He accepted the phone from the commissioner and pressed the desk speaker button. "Nat?" he said.

"Yes, sir." Nat's voice was hollow, echoing over the speaker. "We think, Joe Lewis, Giddings, and I, that a short sent a surge through the entire building. Wiring overheated and burned through its insulation and conduit."

"That," Caldwell said slowly, "could account for smoke in the stairwells?"

"We think so. The men on the stairs report that in places the walls are too hot to touch."

"The question here," Caldwell said, "is whether or not to try to break down the fire doors. If—"

"Are you getting much smoke through the air-conditioning ducts?"

"Not too much."

"Then leave the doors alone." Nat's voice was firm. "We got through to the Army," he continued. "You'll see a couple of choppers in a few minutes. I don't know what they can do, to be honest with you, but I thought they might have a look."

Caldwell smiled. "Keep thinking, Nat."

"And it might be a good idea to keep this line open."

Caldwell nodded. "I agree. I think that is all for now." He turned back to the room. "Comments? Questions?"

"Just one," the governor said. "How did all this happen?"

12

FROM THE START, the sheer magnitude of the World Tower had been frightening, but it was far more than that. The building had seemed to develop a personality of its own, as it took shape, and that personality was malign.

One day the front tire of a partially off-loaded truck standing perfectly still had blown out with sufficient force to shift the load of pipes, burying three men in a tangle of assorted fractures. On another day Paul Simmons had been standing outside the building talking with one of his foremen when Pete Janowski walked off the steel at floor 65. The man's screams ended abruptly with a sickening *thunk* that Paul, not ten feet away, would never forget. Was that the beginning of the end? Or that kid who kept bellyaching about the change orders coming through. He had been killed in the subway, fallen under the IRT express. Fallen?

"These things happen," McGraw had said that night at dinner with Paul and Patty in his small house in Queens. "I don't like them a bit better than you do, but they happen."

"It seems to me," Paul said, "that there are too many foul-ups on the Tower job, that's all. I've been waiting ten days for transformers. Today we found them. In Los Angeles, three thousand miles away!" Men standing idle, because each day the transformers had been promised; labor costs mounting. "We order cable. It's the wrong size. We check out an elevator installation, and the doors won't open because they weren't set right on the tracks."

"You sound like it's getting to you," McGraw said. His eyes were steady on Paul's face.

Paul made himself slow down. "It is," he said, "and it isn't." The actor's confident smile. "But you'll have to admit, there have been a lot of strange ones on this job."

"I'll admit it, boy. But I won't let it grind me under."

"It's almost," Paul said, "as if this were sabotage."

McGraw studied Paul carefully. "Are you trying to tell me something? Because if there is something on your mind, now, not later, is the time to bring it out."

"Nothing to confess," Paul said.

McGraw took his time. "You're part of the family, boy. But we're in a hard business, and we have a contract, you and I, and I'll have to hold you to it. You know that."

"I never thought otherwise," Paul said and the actor's smile never faltered.

FIGURES DO NOT LIE. And the figures he sat staring at the next day were Paul's own, computer-verified. They brought him a feeling of near-nausea.

He had been too close in his original bid. Weather had been against him. Material delays had thrown all labor-cost computations into chaos. Accidents had slowed the job, and there had been a larger than usual incidence of work rejected and thus done over. He, Paul Simmons, wasn't as good at this business as he had come to consider himself. He had had sheer bad luck.

The facts were that when he set percentage of the completed job against cost of the job so far, it was evident that he was not going to come out even financially alive, let alone showing a profit.

It was five o'clock. Distant sounds of traffic reached him from the street thirty stories below. He pushed back his chair, got up, and walked to the windows. He could see people hurrying along the sidewalks below. Going home? Happily? Reluctantly? Angrily? What difference? They are not a part of me; no one is a part of me. Not Patty, not Zib, nobody. I am me, and—what was McGraw's phrase—life has leaned on me this time and squashed me flat. And who cares, except me?

He walked back to his desk and stood looking down at the neat figures, impeccably aligned, like little soldiers marching along—where? To the edge of a high cliff, that's where—and then right over the edge. The sound of Pete Janowski's screams came to mind again, and the sickening *thunk* that ended them. Once again the nausea rose. He fought it down with effort.

The phone rang. It was Zib.

"You," Paul said, his eyes on the marching figures.

"That overwhelms me with its enthusiasm."

"Sorry. I was—thinking."

"I've been thinking too."

He and Zib, so much alike: her thoughts were of herself, his turned inward, too.

It was almost an effort to say, "About what?"

Zib's voice was carefully unconcerned. "I've been thinking that I'd like to be with you. Might you be interested?"

Sex was the last thing he was in the mood for now. Why couldn't

470

the silly woman have chosen another time? And yet, why not? Why not lose himself in her slim softness? What better answer? "The hotel in twenty minutes," he said.

NAKED, relaxed, "I'm supposed to be having dinner with a writer who suddenly arrived in town," Zib said. "Nat didn't even question it. There are benefits to being an editor."

Paul was staring at the ceiling. What if—

"Did you hear me, darling?" Zib ran her forefinger lightly down his chest. "Hmmm?"

"I heard."

"Then why so quiet?"

"I'm thinking."

"At a time like this," Zib said, "that is a hell of a thing to do." She sighed. "All right, so what are you thinking about?"

"Nat." Paul was thinking of one of Bert McGraw's favorite maxims: You don't dislike anybody quite as much as somebody you've done the dirty to.

Zib frowned. Her forefinger was still. "What about Nat?"

"Why," Paul said, and suddenly he was smiling, decision made. "I think he's going to do me some favors."

"You're mad." Zib paused. "Why should he do you favors?"

"Why? He won't even know he's doing them." He reached for her then, and she came to him willingly. "Any more," Paul said, "than he knows that he lends me his wife on occasion. Like now."

That had been many months ago, long before the Tower was completed.

13

NOW IN THE TOWER office the governor said wearily, "There isn't much for us to do except wait. Meanwhile, I promised a report."

Frazee said, "For God's sake! We don't know it's as bad as they say it is. Let's keep it here in this room until we do know."

"Grover"—the governor's voice was sharp and the wolfish grin showed his teeth in a near-snarl—"I made a promise. I intend to keep it. Those people out there have just as much right to all the facts as you have." He looked at Beth Shirley. "You don't have to come," he said.

"I wouldn't miss it."

Ample light was still coming through the tinted windows, but the waiters had lighted more candles around the big room. As the governor and Beth walked in conversation slowed, and then stopped.

The governor asked a waiter to bring a chair to the center of the room. The governor stepped up on it and raised his voice. "In my younger days," he said, "I was used to soapboxes. This will have to do." Always start on a light note. He waited until the murmur of amusement subsided. "This is the situation. . . ."

Beth looked around while the governor was speaking. Most faces wore masklike smiles, a few wore frowns of puzzlement, one or two of annoyance. The young congressman, Cary Wycoff, seemed tensed, holding down his anger with effort. His eyes never left the governor's face. Paula, Bob Ramsay's wife, tall, serene, was smiling as she had smiled through a thousand social events and campaigns. She caught Beth's eye and winked in a girlish gesture of intimacy. Obviously to her the situation was far from serious. Directly in front of the governor's chair were the UN's secretary-general and the USSR's ambassador to the UN, their faces expressionless.

The governor wound up his explanation. "Help is on the way but it is a long climb, so we must be patient." He paused. Had he said it all? He thought so. "This," he said, "is not exactly the way this reception was planned, as I am sure you are aware. But I, for one, intend to enjoy myself while I wait for matters to be brought back to normal."

"And if they aren't?" Cary Wycoff shouted angrily. "What if they aren't, Governor?"

The governor stepped down from the chair. "You are out of order, Cary." His voice was pitched low. "Justice Holmes made the point: 'The right of free speech does not carry with it the right to shout "Fire!" in a crowded theater'."

The congressman flushed, and the governor turned to look for

Beth. She came forward and took his arm. "A fine rousing speech," she said. "I will vote for you."

The governor was in no hurry to return to the office, and Beth understood that by his presence he was offering reassurance. Together they moved from group to group, pausing for introductions where necessary, and a few polite, apparently meaningless words.

To an aging actress: "There was a movie," the governor said, "well before your time, I am sure. It was called *King Kong* and it featured a gigantic gorilla who climbed the Empire State Building. I almost wish Kong would appear now. He'd be a diversion."

"You're sweet, Governor," the actress said, "but not only was it not before my time, I had a bit part in it."

To a network president: "Do you think your people are giving us good coverage, John?"

"If they aren't," John said, "heads are going to fall." He was smiling. "Isn't there, by the way, a battery-powered television set here we could use?"

"Good thought," the governor said. "I'll see about it. But not," he added quietly as he and Beth walked on, "for public viewing. Those on the ground will already have us doomed."

"Are we, Bent?"

Nothing changed in the governor's smile, but his hand tightened almost imperceptibly on her arm. "Frightened?" he said.

"I'm beginning to be."

"So am I," the governor said. "Just between us, I'd much rather be out in New Mexico with a fly rod in my hand and a cutthroat trout giving me a tussle." He looked down at her. "With you," he said. "And if that makes me selfish and cowardly, so be it." He was about to say more when he was interrupted.

"This is outrageous, Bent."

A tall, gray-haired, corporate-executive type, Beth thought; and almost giggled when her estimate was verified.

"Why, Paul," the governor said, "I'll agree with you. Miss Shirley, Paul Norris—*J*. Paul Norris. Outrageous is the proper word, Paul. Do you have any suggestions?"

"By God, somebody ought to be able to do something!"

"I quite agree." The governor's smile brightened. "And there you have your answer, Paul. The Army has arrived." He pointed to two helicopters banking into position to circle the building.

They seemed so free, Beth thought, close but distant, impossibly removed from this—this confinement.

The governor's hand tightened on hers. "There's our diversion," he said quietly. "Now we can slip back to headquarters."

Frazee had a double Scotch beside him in the office. He said, "You spoke to the populace, Bent? You told them the unpleasant facts and you placed the blame squarely where it belongs?"

"Where does it belong, Grover?" The governor perched on a corner of the desk. "That is a point I'd like cleared up."

Frazee waved one hand in a broad gesture of disclaimer. The drink was having its effect. "Will Giddings came to my office with a cock-and-bull tale I didn't begin to understand—"

"Not quite, Grover," Ben Caldwell said. "You were lucid about it when you phoned me." He turned to the governor. "There are change orders in existence authorizing certain deviations from the original design of the building's electrical system. They came to light only today, and we had no idea whether the changes had actually been made." He gestured at the candles lighting the room. "Now we have to assume that at least some of them were made."

The governor said, "You knew they were potentially dangerous, Grover?"

"I'm not an engineer! Stop trying to pin it all on me."

In crisis, Beth thought sadly, the jaunty, dapper Frazee was already smaller than life-size, and still shrinking rapidly.

"You asked me," Caldwell said, "if I thought we should call off the ceremonies. You must have understood a great deal of what Giddings told you."

Frazee's hand automatically reached for the drink. He drew it back. "You said there was no need to call the reception off."

"Not quite." Caldwell's voice was cold. "I said that public relations was not in my line. A very different answer. You—"

The governor broke in. "Ben, you are the technical man. Did you see the potential danger?" The question hung in the air.

"The answer ought to be obvious," Caldwell said at last. "I came myself. I am here, along with the rest of you." He showed an almost glacial calm. "No one could anticipate a madman down in the main transformer room. No one could anticipate the fourth-floor fire which by itself might not have caused more than small unpleasantness." He paused. "But taken together, along with the design-change orders which apparently were followed . . ." He shook his head. "A concatenation of errors."

"Leading how far?"

Caldwell shook his head faintly. "You are asking an impossible judgment from me, Governor." He looked at the fire commissioner. "Let's have a judgment from your people. Then let me speak again to Nat Wilson."

Assistant Commissioner Brown's voice came over the telephone's desk-speaker. "We're doing the best we can—" he began.

"Damn it," the commissioner said, "I know that you're doing the best you can, Tim. What I want to know is how does it look?"

Brown hesitated, "It doesn't look very good, to be honest with you. There isn't enough equipment anywhere that will reach up there, as you know," his voice became almost angry, "and, with the tower mast, there's no place for the army choppers to set down on the roof. Wilson here has tried to talk me into phoning the Coast Guard—"

"For God's sake, man, why?"

"They have guns that shoot lines out to ships in trouble: And he thinks maybe, just maybe . . ." The voice was silent.

"Put Wilson on." The commissioner nodded to Caldwell.

"Caldwell, here, Nat. What is your thinking?"

"Apart from the Coast Guard idea," Nat said, "I've got Joe Lewis trying to get power in from the substation, then maybe we can jury-rig something for one of the express elevators. We'll need some men—and Simmons." Nat's voice had changed. "Yes", he said, "I'm anxious to talk to Simmons. About a lot of things".

"All right, Nat," Caldwell said. "Thank you." He turned back into the room. "You heard it," he said.

The time was 4:59.

Thirty-six minutes had passed since the explosion.

THE MEN CLIMBING the interminable stairs could feel even through the fire doors the fever of the building's torment. Firemen Denis Howard and Lou Storr paused for a breather on the thirtieth floor. Smoke was not constant, only the heat, and at this level the air was clear. They took off their masks gratefully.

"Mother of God!" This was Howard. "Do you feel like one of those mountain goats?" He was catching his breath in great gasps.

"I told you to stop smoking," Storr said. "See what it did for me?" His breathing was at least as labored as Howard's. "I make it ninety-five floors to go. Let's get on with it."

THEY HAD CARRIED the charred body from the sub-basement covered decently with a stretcher sheet. The TV cameras followed the body's progress to a waiting morgue wagon where Patrolman Frank Barnes stopped the stretcher, raised the sheet, and had a long, careful look. He asked the morgue attendant, "Does he have a name?"

"There's a name inside the toolbox—John Connors."

Barnes looked at the blackened toolbox. "That's probably our boy, Mike. He was carrying it."

Barnes went off to find the police lieutenant, whose name was James Potter. The lieutenant listened, wrote Connors's name down in his notebook and sighed. "O.K.," he said. "It's a start."

"I could have kept him out of the building, Lieutenant," Barnes said. "I could have—"

"Frank, he didn't wear a sign saying he was a nut carrying explosives!"

Barnes rejoined Shannon at the barricades, feeling no better, while the lieutenant went to the construction trailer, where a conference was in progress. Patty was perched on a nearby stool.

Tim Brown was saying, "The gun shoots a line, and then what?"

"Breeches buoy."

Giddings was looking out of the trailer window. "To where?"

"North Trade Center tower. It's the closest."

All five men stared up at the soaring buildings. Tim Brown glared at Nat. "Swinging in a canvas bag with your legs sticking through, a quarter of a mile above the street, a quarter of a mile!"

Patty, listening, shuddered.

"All right," Nat said, and his voice was almost brutal, "which would you rather be—swinging in that canvas bag and scared half to death or cooked to a cinder by a fire that won't stop halfway?"

Tim Brown said almost explosively, "All right! We'll get Coast Guard people here."

Lieutenant Potter took out his identification folder and opened it to show his badge. "If one of you has a little time . . ."

"I don't know if I can be of any help," Nat said.

Potter looked at Nat's identification badge. "Architect," he read. "Wilson." He paused. "A man named John Connors. Ring any bell?"

Nat thought about it. He shook his head.

"He," Potter said, "is apparently the—charred one."

"The electrician?"

Potter's eyebrows rose. "You know about him?"

"The cops told me. The man was inside, riding elevators. I heard him. I never saw him."

Potter said to Nat, "The other dead man . . ."

"I don't know him," Nat said, "but I understand he was at the computer console."

Potter looked thoughtful. "Could he have—done anything to help? Is that why he was clobbered?"

"I'd say yes," Nat said. "Almost any kind of trouble would show up on the console. Trouble ought to be taken care of automatically, but just in case—he can override the automated systems."

Patty cleared her throat. "I don't mean to—interfere," she said, "but if Connors knew that the man at the computer console could possibly do anything before everything went dead—then doesn't that mean that Connors was familiar with how the building works?"

Nat was smiling now. "Good girl" He looked at Potter. "It means that Connors probably worked on the building, doesn't it? Mind you, I doubt that he was really an electrician. Unless he wanted to kill himself he'd have known better than to mess with primary power."

Patty said, "I'll call Daddy's office and have them see if Connors's name shows up on a crew list." She stepped down from the stool, glad to have something to keep her from thinking about the big helpless man in the hospital bed.

Tim Brown came in, his red hair rumpled. "The Coast Guard's sending some men and some equipment," he said. He shrugged angrily. "They don't think it will work. The nearest Trade Center tower is probably too far away to shoot a line into the Tower Room."

Nat's face was thoughtful. "We'll just have to see," he said.

PAUL SIMMONS was in the midtown hotel room when Zib arrived breathless, her color high. She glanced at the television set. It was dark. So he doesn't know, she thought.

Strangely, she felt almost calm. Resigned. "I have a message for you. You are wanted down at the World Tower Building."

She walked to the television, switched it on. A picture sprang into focus—the plaza, the fire trucks, uniformed men. Zib turned the volume down and the room was still.

"Nat called me," she said. "He has been trying to reach you. Patty is at the Tower and said I might know where you were."

"I see." Merely that. Paul was watching the silent picture on the television screen. "What's happening?"

"He said that fires have trapped a hundred people in the Tower Room, and he needs some answers from you."

"Trapped." Paul repeated the word, his eyes on the screen. "That means no elevators. No power." At last he looked at Zib. "And just what answers does he think I can give him?"

"He didn't say."

Paul wore a small, quizzical smile. "Was that all he said?"

"No. He told me to get you down there on the double."

Paul said, "Well!" He seemed a stranger, uninvolved. He glanced again at the screen. "There's nothing I can do there.

Nothing." He faced Zib again. "What's done, as Shakespeare might have said, is already done and not to be undone."

Zib said slowly, "Have you any idea what has happened? Is that it? I think—"

"I don't give a tinker's damn what you think." Paul's voice was cold. "You're decorative, and sometimes amusing, but thinking isn't your forte."

Dialogue straight out of the magazine, Zib thought. Escape fiction come alive. "You flatter me," she said.

"We agreed at the beginning—"

"That it was fun and games," Zib said. "Yes."

"Don't tell me you began to take us seriously?"

"No," she said. "There was never anything about you to take seriously." She glanced at the screen. "There is even less now." She faced Paul squarely. "You were the man on the job. I know that much. Paul Simmons and Company, Electrical Contractors. Did you skimp the work? Once you told me that Nat was going to do you favors, only he wouldn't know it. Was that what you meant?"

"Silly questions," Paul said, "don't deserve even silly answers." He walked to the television set and switched it off. "Well," he said, "it's been nice. Don't think it hasn't." He walked to the door. "I'll miss this hotel and its cozy atmosphere."

"Where are you going?"

"I think I'll see a couple of men," Paul said. "And then I think I'll go home." The door closed quietly.

It was unreal, incredible. Zib plumped herself down on the bed and dialed the construction trailer. Nat was there. Zib kept her voice calm, expressionless. "I gave Paul your message."

"He's coming down?"

"No. I'm—sorry, Nat. He said he's going to see a couple of men and then he thinks he'll go home. What are *you* going to do?"

"Have him picked up. Objections?" His tone dominated as Zib had never heard it before.

Zib shook her head in silence as Nat hung up.

He turned from the telephone and looked around the trailer. Assistant Commissioner Brown was there, and two battalion chiefs, Giddings, Patty, Lieutenant Potter, and himself. "I don't know if we can use Simmons or not, but I think we want him."

"If you want him, we'll get him," Potter said.

Giddings said, "More important, if Lewis has done his figuring, let's get some men on the job and see if we can get power to at least one of those express elevators."

Nat snapped his fingers. "We need Simmons's foreman, Harris, to lead them." He paused. "But we need Harris for another reason. Simmons didn't put those changes in with his own hands. Harris had to know about them."

Patty spoke softly. She was alone, but quite at ease in this man's world. With Daddy, she had sat through countless technical discussions. "There is somebody else who would have had to know about the changes," she said. "The inspector who signed them off. Who was he?"

In the silence Nat said again, "Good girl."

Giddings said, "I know his face. His name . . ." He was silent for a moment. "Harry," he said. "Harry. I don't know his last name, but we'll damn well find out and get him down here."

15

MAYOR RAMSAY came out of the office in search of his wife. He found her at the Tower Room windows, looking out over the river.

She smiled as he came up. "So solemn, Bob," she said. "Is it really as solemn an occasion as Bent indicated?"

"I'm afraid so."

"You will think of something."

"No." The mayor shook his head. "Any thinking will have to be done by the technical people." His smile was wry. "And any orders will come from Bent, not from me."

"It is your city, Bob."

"There comes a time," Ramsay said, "when you have to admit that others are better men than you are. I'm not in Bent's class."

Paula smiled gently. "You are the finest man I have ever known."

Ramsay stared out at the river almost hypnotically. "Bent

mentioned something today. He questioned the merit in building the *biggest* anything. Quality and need ought to be the criteria."

"But Bob, where have you strayed from that?" Paula said.

"I let the city stray. Is a building like this necessary? No. We have more office space than we can use. And I could have stopped it. Instead, I gave it every bit of help City Hall could give it, just to have a building all the world would admire."

"And will, Bob."

The mayor started to say something, then thought better of it. "Maybe," was all he said.

Paula said, "Thirty-five years is a long time, Bob. People get to know one another well. I know what is in your mind now." She smiled. "There are telephones. I think we might call Jill. She was going to watch on television. She will be worried."

"Good idea." All at once the mayor was smiling again, the boyish smile the voters knew so well. "We'll reassure her."

"That," Paula said, "wasn't quite what I had in mind."

"Now, wait a minute. There's no need to panic."

"Not panic, Bob, but isn't it time that we stopped pretending? Those helicopters out there—what can they do? The firemen Bent says are coming up the stairs . . ." Paula shook her head. Her smile was gentle, unreproachful, but it asserted denial. "I want to hear Jill's voice again. I want her to hear ours. I want her to know that we don't think she has failed, even with her divorce. I want her to know that we understand that we heaped too much on her because there were always cameras and reporters, and that from the beginning it was probably impossible for her, a child, to see the world as anything but sugarplum candy. Most of all, I want her to know what is true and always has been—that she is very precious to us, and that now that we're in this ridiculous predicament, it is she we are thinking of." Paula paused. "Those are the things I want to say, Bob. Are they—wrong?"

The mayor's voice was gentle. "Let's find a phone," he said.

SENATOR PETERS was a strange, earthy, complex man. He was a bird watcher of almost professional caliber, and his catalogue of birds to be found in the Washington tidal basin was standard. He read Greek and Latin with ease, and spoke both French and German. It was said that his repertoire of bawdy limericks was the largest in Congress. Wycoff found him leaning against a wall watching the room. "You're taking it calmly enough," the congressman said. There was accusation in his voice.

"What do you suggest?" the senator said. "A speech? A committee hearing?" His voice altered subtly. "Or should we call the White House and lay the blame squarely on this administration?"

Wycoff said, "You and Bent Armitage—you both treat me as if I were still a kid, wet behind the ears."

"Maybe, son," the senator said, "that's because sometimes you behave that way. Have you ever seen real panic?"

Wycoff said, "Have you?" He ought to have known better, he told himself; Jake Peters never waved an empty gun.

"I was in Anchorage in sixty-four," the senator said, "when the earthquake hit. You think of the earth as solid, unchanging, secure. And when even it begins to move under you, then there is no security left anywhere. Yes, I have seen panic. And I don't want to see it again. Particularly here."

"All right," Wycoff said, "neither do I. What do you suggest?"

"That I move away from this wall. I've been feeling it heat up. It's come along pretty fast. That probably means that heated air, maybe even open fire, is climbing in some of the shafts in the core." He glanced at his watch. "Faster than I thought. But I can't think of anything to do about it without making things worse. So let's relax and watch the people. Where do you suppose Bob and Paula Ramsay are headed so purposefully? For the johns?"

Wycoff smiled. "As good a guess as any. What do you want for an epitaph, Jake? 'Exit laughing'?"

The senator became serious. "No. I'd like to feel that I'd earned the proudest epitaph of all: 'With what he had, he did the best he could.' I think we might have a drink, don't you?"

IT WAS A NEAT little house in a Long Island suburb, green lawn, white petunias in bloom, an enormous television mast dominating the roof.

Mrs. Pat Harris answered the door in tight peach-colored jeans, matching sneakers, and a striped tank top. Her hair was in blue plastic curlers. She was young, attractive, and thoroughly conscious of it. "Well," she said, "this is a surprise, Mr. Simmons. You want to see Pat?"

"If I may." Paul wore his actor's smile and his easy manner.

"He's downstairs watching the World Tower opening on TV. You go on down. He'll be awful glad to see you."

I doubt it, Paul thought, as he went to the paneled game room. On the massive color-television screen fire trucks crowding the Tower Plaza looked the color of blood. The announcer was reporting, "The fire is spreading inside the building. This entire disaster is incredible. Every safety factor known to architects—"

The set went black and the sound stopped. From his chair Pat Harris said, "Welcome, boss. I figured you'd be along." He laid the remote control on the coffee table and jumped up out of the chair. "Drink?" There was faint hostility behind the words.

"I think a drink would be a good idea," Paul said.

He sat down and looked around. There was a bar, and a full-size pool table, a large sofa and matching chair, a card table with poker chips set out, a dart board, three darts in the bull's-eye.

"Nice place you have here," Paul said. He accepted his drink, nodded his thanks, tasted the mellow Scotch.

"Yeah." Pat Harris was a small man. His restless eyes watched Paul's face carefully. "Man works hard, he likes to live it up a little." Harris paused. "Just a working stiff. I do what I'm told."

"Do you intend to keep on doing what you're told?"

Harris lit a cigarette and then tore the match into bits, his movements sudden and jerky. "Funny, I was just thinking about it."

Paul said slowly, "And what conclusion had you come to?"

Harris leaned forward. "Like this, let's say you work for a guy. He treats you right, so you owe him, you know, something better than a kick in the teeth. On the other hand, a guy has to look out for himself. This is a dog-eat-dog world. You get yours, or you get nothing. So the way I see it," Harris said, "you balance one against the other and try to see what's—right."

"And," Paul said calmly enough, "how did you decide?"

Harris inhaled deeply and blew four large smoke rings in rapid succession. "I hear Bert McGraw's in the hospital. Heart attack. I hear he may not make it."

"I can't say," Paul said. "He had a heart attack, yes. Before the attack, however, he showed me some change orders. He asked me if we made the changes. I said yes, of course we made them, why should we not?"

Harris wiped his mouth. "Wow! Now I know you've flipped."

"The change orders had surfaced," Paul said. "I don't know how, but Will Giddings found them. No matter what I said to Bert, they were going to tear into the walls to see for themselves. So the only thing I could say was, yes, of course we made the changes. Look at the signature: Nat Wilson, Caldwell's fair-haired boy. Should we question word from on high?"

"You make it sound O.K., but I don't know." Harris walked across the room and back to his chair. "I'll level with you. You been a good Joe. Some I've worked for, I'd just like the chance to kick their teeth in, but you're O.K."

"Thank you," Paul said, and meant it.

"I'll tell you how it is," Harris said. "I got two things I can do. First"—he held up one finger—"I can go down to City Hall. I can say, 'If I'd of even guessed, I'd of told him to shove it.' You, I mean. 'But,' I can say, 'he's the boss and he says the changes are O.K.; the change orders are signed by the architect and who am I to argue?'"

There was silence. Paul said without expression, "Your only argument, Pat, was about how much it was worth not to argue."

"That's what you say," Harris said. "But I say I did argue and I can come up with three, four guys who'll say sure I did, but you told me everything was O.K., so I went ahead. And Harry, the inspector, signed the work off, so why should I wonder about it?"

Easy, Paul told himself, easy. "And what is the—other thing you can do?"

Harris moved restlessly. "You told McGraw we made the changes because we had the orders with Wilson's signature on them. O.K. I can say the same. I can say you and I talked about them, wondered about them, but when Caldwell's office says you do something, that's just what you do. That's the other way."

"A very good way," Paul said.

"A couple things, though. Harry the inspector for one."

"Harry won't cause any trouble," Simmons said. "Or if he does it will only be for himself. What else?"

Harris's face was expressionless, the face of a poker player studying his opponent. "You remember a kid named Jimmy?"

"No."

Harris smiled scornfully. "No, you wouldn't. He worked in one of my crews, went to engineering school at night. He didn't like the changes that were coming through. Especially the one taking out that primary-power safety-ground circuit. He said it was dangerous and he was going to talk to Nat Wilson about it. He wouldn't listen to me or Harry."

"I see," Paul said.

"He didn't get to talk to Wilson," Harris said. "He had an accident instead. He fell in front of an IRT express at rush hour."

"I see. But why tell me? Is your conscience bothering you?"

"I want to know," Harris said. "What's in it for me?"

"You've already had yours."

Harris shook his head. "Uh-uh. I got paid for doing a job. This is for something else."

Paul felt no outrage at the shakedown, merely determination that the bargain would be a good one. "How much?" he said.

Harris smiled. "Now we're getting somewhere."

Paul went up the stairs alone. Down in the game room the television set was again turned on. To Mrs. Harris who had taken out her blue hair curlers and now smiled fetchingly, "You have a lovely home," Paul said. "Pat is a lucky man."

As he drove away, a black-and-white police cruiser turned into the street. Paul watched it in his mirror. It parked at the Harris house and two uniformed policemen walked up to the door.

Paul drove on.

IN THE TRAILER Patty turned from the telephone and held out a slip of paper to Lieutenant Potter. "John Connors," she said. "He worked on the job months back. A sheet-metal man. He was fired. The union made no protest."

The firing was clearly justified or the union would have been up in arms, Nat thought.

"A sorehead," Potter said. "Maybe. But you never know." He tucked the slip of paper in his pocket. "We'll try to find out." He walked to the trailer door. "Good luck," he said, and was gone.

At the far end of the trailer a walkie-talkie came to life. "We've reached seventy-fifth floor," the tired voice of fireman Denis Howard said, "and it's getting hotter than the hinges, Chief. No smoke up here yet, but I hate to think what's happening beyond these fire doors."

"Play it cool, boy," the chief said. "If you can't make it, you can't make it." He turned to Assistant Commissioner Brown. "I'll not deliberately throw good men away in a lost cause," he said, "no matter who is up there. Inside the fire doors of that building we've worked men up twelve floors with hoses." The chief paused. "Near as we can tell, there are a hundred more floors each with their own fires, before the top is even in sight. Another thing"—the battalion chief looked at Nat—"that electrical genius of yours, Lewis. Drawing pretty pictures about stringing wires together to get an express elevator suddenly to work."

"You don't think so?" Nat said.

"No, I don't think so!" It was almost a shout. "But I'm willing to try anything that'd have the chance of a snowball in hell."

IN THE OFFICE off the Tower Room, the governor was saying, "Sooner or later we're going to have trouble, maybe panic." He spoke to the fire commissioner. "Just in case, I think we might have four or five of these husky waiters standing by."

"I'll take care of it," the commissioner said. He left the office.

"Grover, why don't you go out and mingle with your guests," the governor said to Frazee, "and, damn it, smile!"

"I'll go with him," Ben Caldwell said. They left together.

"And now," the governor said to Beth, "do you see how crafty I am? We're alone."

Beth said slowly, "Will there be a tomorrow, Bent?"

The telephone rang. "Armitage," the governor said.

"One stairwell is untenable, Governor," Brown's voice came on.

487

"The other may hold. My men aren't very optimistic, but they're still trying to reach you to get the door on that side open."

"Let's look at the odds," the governor said. "One stairwell is already out. What are the chances of all the fire doors on the other side holding long enough to get any of us down?"

Brown's voice was reluctant. "I'd have to say almost nonexistent, Governor. But there are two other possibilities that seem better. Maybe Wilson's electrical engineer can get an elevator running." He paused again. "And the other is that somehow we can get the fire inside the building under control before—" He stopped.

The governor's face was expressionless. "Then our chances are better staying here?"

"I—would think so." Brown hesitated. "There's one other chance, but it's wild. Wilson's idea. If the Coast Guard can get a line to you from the Trade Center roof, and rig a breeches buoy . . ."

"We'll go for anything," the governor said. He straightened. "But call your men back from the stairwell."

"Maybe," Brown said slowly, "maybe we'd better let them go on to you, Governor. Just in case. I'm only guessing about the odds."

"Call them back," the governor said. "There's no point in expending them in a lost cause."

It was, Brown thought, precisely what the battalion chief had said. He nodded acquiescence. "Yes, sir. But there's fire beneath two of them, Governor—they can't come back."

"We'll let them in," the governor said. "We'll give them a drink and some snacks." His voice turned serious again. "All right, Brown. Thanks for the report." He hung up the phone. With no change of expression, "You asked a question," he said to Beth.

"I withdraw it."

"No. It deserves an answer. I doubt there's going to be a tomorrow. And I'm sorry about that for many reasons."

Quietly, "I know, Bent."

"How can you know my reasons?"

Her smile was faint, but real. "I know."

The governor stared at her. "Maybe." He nodded. His broad gesture took in the office and the entire building. "I'm here," he said "out of vanity, and you always pay for that. I love the hurrah.

488

I might have been an actor." He smiled suddenly. "At any rate, there I am. Exposed," he said.

"I like what I see."

The governor was silent for a few moments. "Perhaps," he said, "with someone like you, the White House might not have been out of reach. . . . What might have been." He straightened. "I'd far rather stay right here, but I belong outside, moving around. . . ." He shook his head in apology.

"May I come with you?" She was smiling still as she stood up.

Together they paused on the threshold of the Tower Room, and looked around. It was as before: groups forming, flowing; waiters and waitresses passing trays; conversation, even occasional laughter, perhaps overloud. But it was now, Beth thought, like a party scene in an opera or ballet, designed to hold the audience's attention until the principals came out of the wings.

"Well, here we go," the governor said. He smiled then at the secretary-general who walked over to him carrying a champagne glass in an easy practiced manner. "Walther. I don't think I've apologized before for this—melodrama. I do now."

"But are you responsible?"

"Only indirectly." The governor left it at that.

The secretary-general said, "Have you noticed how quickly one's perspective changes? Only a little time ago I was concerned largely with budget, unrest in the Middle East, world environment. . . . But when survival is the problem, only the here and now are important. . . . I take it there is nothing new in our situation?" He nodded at what he saw in the governor's face. "I thought not. A suggestion. Mr. J. Paul Norris is, shall we say, on the point of explosion."

"I'll talk to him," the governor said.

J. Paul Norris, the tall, gray-haired executive type, glowered at them. "If somebody doesn't do something soon," he said, "I am going to take matters into my own hands."

The governor nodded pleasantly. "And do what, Paul?"

"I don't know."

"A splendid suggestion, entirely worthy of you."

"Now look here, Bent. I've had just about enough of you poking fun at me and the things that have made this country great. You—

"Among them, inherited wealth and position." The governor nodded. "I saw your name on a list not long ago, Paul. Your income last year was close to one million dollars, but you paid no income tax."

"Perfectly legal." A vein was beginning to show on Norris's forehead. "Absolutely within regulations."

"I'm sure it was, but a little difficult for a man earning ten thousand dollars and paying twenty percent tax to understand."

Beth wondered why in the world the governor was deliberately antagonizing the man.

"I don't give a damn about the man earning ten thousand dollars a year," Norris said. "He isn't worth consideration."

I see it now, Beth thought; it was pure diversion, waving a red flag to distract the man from the major problem.

"You know, Paul," the governor said, "our hypothetical ten-thousand-dollar-a-year-man doesn't give a damn about you either. He thinks you and your kind ought to have been ploughed under years ago. Ponder those sentiments for a time." And then, "But don't even think of creating a disturbance in this room, or I'll have you tied up like a Christmas turkey with a gag in your mouth." The governor showed his teeth. "Don't try me, Paul. I only bluff in poker." He and Beth walked on.

A waiter with drinks stopped them. "Thank you, son." The governor handed a glass to Beth, took one for himself.

"How about it, Governor?" The waiter kept his voice low. "They're saying that we're stuck here. For good. They're saying—"

"There is always 'they', crying doom," the governor said.

"Yeah. But I got a wife and three kids. What about them?"

"Boys," the governor said, "or girls?"

"What difference does that make? Two boys and a girl."

"How old?"

The waiter frowned. "One boy's eleven. That's Stevie. Bert's nine. Becky's just six. What're you giving me, Governor?"

"Becky is probably too young," the governor said, "but why don't you take Stevie and Bert to the ball game Saturday?"

"That's tomorrow."

490

"So it is. I may see you there. If I do, I'll buy you a beer, and a Coke for each of the boys. How about that?"

"I think you're putting me on, Governor. But I'll sure as hell take you up on it if I see you." He turned away, smiling.

"He understands, Bent," Beth said.

The governor added. "I was stationed in London during the blitz. When it came right down to the crunch, the people took it without complaint, and they rarely panicked. People like that man. People Paul Norris isn't fit to—live in the same room with."

"I agree." Beth's eyelids stung. "Maybe in the end I'll—panic."

"The end isn't yet." The governor's voice was strong. "And even if it does come, you won't panic."

"Don't let me, Bent. Please."

The time was 5:23. An hour had passed since the explosion.

16

IN THE TRAILER a telephone rang. Brown answered it. "Yes," he said, "she's here." He handed the phone to Patty.

"I thought you would be there, child," her mother's voice said. "I am glad. Your father would have been glad."

Patty closed her eyes. "Would have been?"

Mary McGraw said in a calm voice without tears, "He is gone."

Tears were close. Patty held them back. "I'll come up."

"No. I am going home, child."

"I'll come there."

"No." The voice was strange, taut and yet controlled. "I am going to have a nice cup of tea. And a good cry. Then I'll go to church. And you cannot help me with any of those." Mary paused. "I don't mean to turn away from you. It is just that right now I want to be alone. Your father would have understood."

Hesitantly, "I understand too, Mother," Patty said.

"God bless you, child."

Patty hung up slowly. She was aware of Brown and the two battalion chiefs waiting self-consciously for her to give them their cue. Strange, how easily she understood men like these, men Daddy had always dealt with; men unlike Paul. But I have no business being here, she thought. "My father is dead." She said it slowly, and then stood up. "I'll leave now."

"Sit down," Brown said. In silence he got out his cigarettes, chose one, snapped it in half and almost threw the pieces into the ashtray. "I am very sorry, Mrs. Simmons. Your father and I had our fights; he was a builder and by his lights I was a heckler, and we both had low flash points. But a better man never lived, and I am glad he is not around to see—this."

Patty said, "Thank you. I—don't want to be in the way." But I have no place else to go, she thought, the enormity of being wholly alone bore in upon her.

The walkie-talkie crackled. "We're at the Tower Room floor, Chief." Denis Howard's voice, panting and dull with fatigue. "The smoke isn't too bad yet. We'll try to get the door cleared."

"What's the matter with it?"

"There're big, heavy boxes, some marked 'Fragile, Electronic Equipment,' jammed against the door. Where *were* our people, letting a fire door be blocked like this?"

The battalion chief closed his eyes. "I sure as hell don't know, Denis. Tear the damn boxes apart." His voice was savage. "Get out of that stairwell and inside!"

Brown gestured wearily. The battalion chief handed him the walkie-talkie. "The governor has promised you a drink and some snacks," Brown said. "That ought to make your day."

There was no reply. The batteries in Howard's unit had failed from the mounting heat.

NAT WAS DOWN in the black bowels of the building, moving partly by feel and partly by the eerie light of firemen's head lamps, claustrophobic in his mask and afraid that each breath would somehow be the last, drenched by water from the big hoses and fighting through smoke almost as through a solid substance. Giddings and Joe Lewis and two electrical crewmen were somewhere near.

It was, he told himself, ridiculous that he should be down here. Joe Lewis was the electrical engineer; Giddings knew as much about actual placement of panels and circuitry as anybody. And yet here he was, unable to wait outside while they wrestled with the problem.

Lewis had said, "All we can do is bring in another cable from the substation, and hope that there's enough of the rising cable left to carry power to the elevator motors."

Nat was jostled suddenly by two firemen stumbling past with a hose. Nearby, one of the electricians, his voice muffled through a mask, said suddenly, "O.K. Give me a light, damn it!"

Joe Lewis, standing close, said hollowly, "Hurry it up." He began to cough. "A man can only stand so much of this."

"Then beat it," Giddings said. "We'll finish it off."

In the near-darkness Nat saw Lewis raise an arm and let it fall in a gesture of defeat. His coughing was deep, wracking. He turned away, stumbled, fell, tried to raise himself, and failed.

"Stay here," Nat said sharply to Giddings. "I'll get him out."

He levered Lewis over his shoulder and into a fireman's carry. Then half-walking, half-stumbling, he headed off into the murk.

Lewis's limp body was a dead weight. Nat stumbled onto the first stairs and laboriously began to climb. As in the mountains on a steep trail, the only thing to do was put your head down and concentrate on setting one foot in front of the other.

Once he stumbled over a hose and went painfully to his knees, was tempted to drop the body that hampered him—and managed to withstand the temptation. Get up, damn it, get up! He stopped on a flight of stairs to cough and cough again, and then lurch on in the blackness. And here at last was a door.

Out at last into the unbelievably sweet air of the plaza, freed from the mask—and here came men in white to take Lewis. Nat went toward the trailer. His legs were weak as he climbed the steps. One of the battalion chiefs grinned. "Like to join the Department?"

"Thanks much," Nat said. "But from here on I fight my fires in forests back home."

"Are you all right?" This was Patty, small, bright, concerned.

"Fine," Nat said. "Soon as I get my breath."

Brown said, "What about the elevator?"

Nat gestured wearily. "It may work. They're going to try."

Giddings came up the steps. Seeing him, Nat got some idea of how he himself looked. Giddings's face was white where the mask had been, his forehead black with soot. "A couple of chimney sweeps," Nat said, grinning.

"And sweeps," Patty said, "are lucky as lucky can be. We'll hold that thought." And pray for luck in all directions, she told herself.

"If the elevator does go," Giddings said, "we won't know it's gotten to the Tower Room unless they tell us. Better get on the horn." He and Brown and the two chiefs moved toward the telephone.

Patty said softly, "Nat. He's gone, Nat. Daddy. As big and strong as he was, he's—"

"I'm sorry," Nat took her small clean hands in his own and Patty made no effort to take them away. "I'm sorry," he said again.

Patty had caught her lower lip between her teeth. Her eyes were closed. When she opened them, they were bright. "I'm O.K." She paused. "I told Daddy at lunch about Paul and Zib. I told him I was leaving Paul and I had to give a good reason."

Nat squeezed the small hands again. "Of course." Had he been fooling himself all along that he and Zib had a real marriage?

"Paul saw him after that," Patty said. "Paul was there when he had his attack." She was silent, watching Nat's face.

"What are you saying, Patty?"

"Daddy being Daddy," Patty said, "he would have braced Paul with Zib—their confrontation is what killed Daddy." Her hands in Nat's were tensed. "Oh, I could kill Paul. So help me."

Nat said quickly, "Patty—" He stopped.

Brown was talking into the telephone, "You're sure? Yes, Governor. We'll hang on." He cupped his hand over the mouthpiece. "The elevator got there. They're working the doors open now. How about that? Now we can forget that breeches buoy nonsense."

Nat hesitated. "No," he said. "If the elevator works, fine. But let's have a backup, just in case."

WINDOWS in the northeast quadrant on the sixty-second floor were the first to shatter from heat. Heavy shards of the tempered, tinted glass sprang out from the building as if from an explosion,

494

glistened like icicles in their long fall, and crashed into the plaza.

Patrolman Shannon put his hand to his cheek and stared at the blood that instantly covered his palm.

Barnes whipped out his handkerchief. He wadded it against the long clean cut. "Hold it tight, Mike, and head for that ambulance. You'll need stitches."

"Do you think," Shannon said, "that there'll be a Purple Heart in it, Frank? I've always wanted to be a wounded hero."

"You have your wish."

17

THE OFFICE OFF the Tower Room was again the command post, and the governor dominated the room. "What is the elevator capacity?"

Ben Caldwell said, "Fifty-five persons is the rated load. Another ten, perhaps, could be squeezed in."

"They will be," the governor said. "Traditionally, women and children are first. Does anyone see a reason to flout tradition?"

"I do," Beth said. There was a silence. "You are the important people, the ones who need to be saved. Let's be practical."

Senator Peters said, "All right, my dear, let's be practical. We've had our time. We've influenced what events we could." The habit of oratory was strong. "You, not we, are the future of the human race. You see to it that there are children to replace us."

The governor said, "You are overruled, Beth." He looked around the office. He said to the fire commissioner, "Pete, see to it. The rest of you men help him. And hurry!"

Beth waited. "I'm not going, Bent. Not without you."

"Oh, yes, you are. Come here." He took her hand and placed it flat against the surface of the inner wall. She drew it away. "Hot, isn't it?" he said. "Not much more time, and I want you safe."

"I told you—"

"But I'm telling you." He lifted her chin and kissed her. "For once in my life I don't have any words to cover what I feel. And if that sounds unbelievable, well, this entire situation is unbelievable, but it has happened. Come along. I'll see you off."

She held back. "Will there be a second load? You? The others?"

"We'll count on it. First we'll see you safe." Together they walked to the door and there they stopped.

Someone shouted, "What the hell do you think you're doing?" There were other voices raised, and the sound of running.

"Wait here," the governor said and hurried into the big room. The scene had altered drastically. Like ants around an uprooted nest, everyone seemed to be in haphazard frantic motion.

"Hold it!" the governor shouted. "Hold it!"

Some of the movement stopped. Faces turned in his direction.

"What's going on?" the governor said. "They've worked a miracle down below, and sent us an elevator. It—"

"That is the problem, Bent," Senator Peters said. "The elevator is gone, and it has only one passenger. Can you guess who?"

The big room was still. I don't have to guess, the governor thought, I know. Aloud he said, "You tell me, Jake."

"Paul Norris," the senator said, "who else? J. Paul Norris."

The governor nodded slowly. He walked back into the office past Beth as if she did not exist, picked up the telephone, and flipped the speaker switch. "Armitage here," he said. "The elevator is on its way down. It has one passenger. I want him held."

Brown's voice said, "Yes, sir." And then, incredulously, "Just one passenger, sir?"

"That is what I said. I want the district attorney apprised of the fact that the man deliberately stole the elevator. If the district attorney can see his way clear, I should like the man to be charged with attempted murder." The governor paused. "Witnesses," he said, "may be hard to come by. Tell him that too."

Brown said, "We'll send the elevator right back. If we can."

The governor nodded. "If you can. I understand. You've done a superlative job, all of you. I want you to know that we appreciate it." He was staring thoughtfully at the telephone. "How long the telephone will last is anyone's guess, but I'm sure that somewhere up here there is a battery-powered radio. You can reach us through the city's radio station. We'll stay tuned to it."

The mayor stood in the doorway. "I'll find a radio," he said.

"The elevator is down, Governor." Brown's voice on the desk

496

speaker again. "The man inside—" Brown's voice shook. "He's dead, Governor. Burned pretty bad."

Nat Wilson's voice came on. "The heat in the core. There must be a blowtorch effect."

Ben Caldwell moved in past the mayor. "Masks, Nat?" he said. "Asbestos suits? Spray the inside of the car to cool it off—"

"No," Nat said. "One chance, and we blew it. We won't get that car up again. It's badly damaged and off its rails. We'll try another, but . . ." He left the sentenced unfinished.

Caldwell exhaled in a low whistle. "I understand."

Brown came on again. "We're still working the inside of the building floor by floor. Sorry, Governor. Eventually . . ." He paused. "What's left now," Brown said, "is that wild idea of Wilson's."

"Keep us posted," the governor said, and stood up with an effort. "Time for another report." He started for the door.

As before, the governor stood on a chair in the center of the big room. He waited briefly until all conversation had stopped. Then, "The elevator reached the concourse," he said. "The man in it was dead from the intense heat in the core of the building." There was silence. He had his audience now. "They are attempting to send us a second elevator, and if they are successful, there will be insulated clothing and breathing masks for those who ride in it."

There was hammering at the fire door on the far side of the room, and firemen Denis Howard and Lou Storr lurched through. Each carried a halligan tool, a long, heavy bar, hooked at one end, canted at the other. Their masks hung around their necks. In each face there was a bone-weariness plain to see.

"We thank you for coming," the governor said.

A voice called from the crowd, "Can we use the stairs?"

"Tell them," the governor said to Denis Howard.

The fireman took his time. "You can use them," he said. "But you won't reach the bottom or anywhere near the bottom." He held out his hand. It trembled. "See that? There used to be hair." He ran his hand wearily over his face. "And I used to have eyebrows."

The room was still.

"I promised you both a drink," the governor said. He looked at a nearby waiter. "See that they have them. Then show them to the office." He looked around at his audience. "It is not good," he said. "But neither is it hopeless. I can't tell you more."

Cary Wycoff raised his voice. "I demand to know how all this happened? Who is responsible?"

The governor waited while the low murmur of agreement ran its course. Then, in the silence, "I suggest, Cary, that you appoint a congressional committee to look into the matter. I will be happy to tell it all I know." He stepped down from the chair, offered Beth his arm, and walked back to the office.

Inside, he dropped into the desk chair. "I think of myself as a patient, reasonable man," he said to Beth. "But right now I would cheerfully strangle Cary Wycoff. And my one great hope is that I live long enough to spit on Paul Norris's grave."

Beth said, "If Norris had *not* stolen the elevator—"

"True," the governor said. "None of you would have reached the bottom alive. But that changes nothing."

"I understand, Bent."

He caught her hand and pressed it to his cheek. "Do you believe in an afterlife, my dear?"

"I think so."

"I have gone through the motions of worship just as I have gone through the other forms of conventional behavior. If I could pray and mean it, I would pray to believe that you and I will meet again somewhere."

"We will, Bent."

"Beside a celestial trout stream? I think that would be my choice." He dropped Beth's hand and sat up straight as the two firemen and the fire commissioner appeared in the doorway. "Come in," the governor said. "Sit down. Let's consider the possibilities."

18

ONE PART OF Patty's mind had retreated into its own secret place to mourn, while the other part concentrated on the tension that filled the trailer. After talking to Ben Caldwell, Nat had come back to stand near Patty and stare at the tormented building. He said,

498

"The way they used to design them, big buildings were so fire-resistant that the city actually reduced fire department coverage in high-rise areas." He looked at Patty. "Did you know that?"

Patty shook her head.

"Thick walls," Nat said, "thick floors, windows that opened—you could get in and out. A fire could be contained. Now—core construction is more economical. You can concentrate elevators, escalators, pipes, ducts, wiring, all the unproductive items, in a central shaft. That leaves more rental space. But when a fire breaks out, a big one like this . . . ." He shook his head.

"That blowtorch effect you talked about on the phone?" Patty said. "Like a chimney?"

One of the battalion chiefs said, "With a fire like this, temperatures in the core can be so high that firemen can only work five minutes at a time." He looked at Nat. "Blowtorch, you call it. More like a blast furnace." He pointed up toward the building's top. "If we get anybody out of there alive, it'll be a miracle."

Assistant Fire Commissioner Brown's voice angry on the telephone said: "Yes, we want them in here! On the double! You think this is some kind of charade?" He slammed down the telephone and waved his bony fists in helpless rage. "The cops couldn't see what the Coast Guard had to do with a fire in a building."

Patty touched Nat's arm. "Is all this really Paul's doing?" Her voice was quiet. "Daddy said he wasn't sure."

The change-order copies were still in his pocket. Nat took them out, and put them on the drafting board. He watched Patty glance at them. She said at last, "I'm not an engineer, but I do know a little." She was watching Nat's face. "Your name on all of these, but you didn't sign them, did you?"

"How do you know that?"

"Not quite your style," Patty said. "Somehow I just know that." She looked down at the papers. "One of Paul's talents, imitating handwriting. Tell me," she said then, "what is the name for a woman who turns against her husband?"

"Admirable." Small and indomitable, Nat thought; willing to face facts squarely even when they hurt.

"I wish I could believe that."

"You have my word for it," Nat said.

"Now," a new voice from the trailer doorway, "what seems to be the trouble and what do you think we can do about it?" He was a big man, massively calm—Chief Petty Officer Oliver, United States Coast Guard. He listened while Nat explained, and together they went outside to stare up at the north tower of the Trade Center.

The chief looked around the plaza at the writhing hoses and shouting firemen. He squinted aloft again, measuring distances with his eye, and slowly shook his head. "I doubt if it can be done."

"You've got guns," Nat said, "and line—no?"

"We've got it all," the chief said.

"The distance isn't that great." Nat's voice was urgent, almost angry. "So it takes half a dozen tries. One line into that Tower Room is all you need. We'll have that whole bank of windows broken out. You'll have a target the size of a barn."

"Here on the ground," the chief said, "the wind is calm. Up there—fifteen hundred feet—blowing merry hell. See that smoke, how it lays out straight? That's what we'd have to shoot a line into. Still, we'll give it a try."

For the first time on this disastrous day, Nat felt a glimmering of hope. It was hard to keep triumph out of his voice. "We'll give you firemen and cops," he said, "anybody you need to go up to the Trade Center roof with you and help you do your thing. I'll see that the Tower Room windows are broken out and men are standing by to catch a line." His thoughts were flowing now. "My boss, the boss architect, is up there. He'll find structure strong enough to take the breeches buoy line. Then—"

"We'll try," the chief said. "That's all I can promise." He smiled suddenly. "But it'll be the damndest gut-busting try you ever saw." The smile spread. "And, who knows?"

THE GOVERNOR took the call and promptly sent for Ben Caldwell and the fire commissioner. Nat explained the plan over the speaker phone.

"We'll start on the windows when you give the word." Caldwell said. "But it's a long way. Nat, from that Trade Center roof."

"All we can do is try. The gun shoots a weighted projectile carry-

501

ing a light messenger line. When you get the line, you haul it in on signal. They'll have secured the heavier line to it. Two lines, actually; the heavy one to carry the load of the breeches buoy, and the smaller line that pulls the breeches buoy across to you and then back down to the Trade Center roof." He paused.

"Understood," Caldwell said.

"You're probably way ahead of me," Nat said, "but I'll go through it all anyway. Make the heavy line fast to structure that will take a hell of a load. And I'd suggest that where the line goes through the window frame you make damn sure all the glass is gone. We don't want the line cut or frayed." Another voice spoke in the background. "Wait a moment . . ."

There was a brief silence, then Nat's voice came again. "They've cleared the plaza. You can start on the windows."

Caldwell looked at the fire commissioner. The commissioner made a circle of thumb and forefinger and hurried out.

Nat's voice said in a different note, "If this doesn't work . . . we'll think of something else. That's a promise. All for now." He clicked off.

From the big room came the sound of breaking glass and a growing murmur of voices. The governor heaved himself out of his chair. "Show time," he said. "Let's bring somebody up to date."

NAT TURNED AWAY from the phone and began to gather the change-order copies. "We'll want the originals of these," he said to Patty. "If we can find them."

Patty said automatically, "Paul's office files."

Nat thought about it. "You're probably right. We'll have them picked up. I'll talk to the police." He was gone only moments.

"How do you explain Paul?" Patty said when he returned. "I mean, I know these things happen. But Paul?"

He understood her need to talk about it. "You know him better than I do, Patty."

"Do I?" Patty shook her head. "I don't think I do."

"Maybe," Nat said, "there isn't very much there to know."

Patty's glance was shrewd. "You never thought so, did you?"

"He and I are entirely different. I'm a country boy."

"That's a pose."

Nat smiled faintly. "Maybe. But down deep it isn't. An air-conditioned duplex apartment overlooking the East River, a house in Westchester or Fairfield, a yacht on the Sound or a membership in the Racquet Club—these aren't living to me; they're ridiculous attempts to make an artificial existence bearable."

Patty's smile was gentle. "What is it you want, Nat?"

"I'm an architect. Maybe that's it. What I want above everything else is space, room to move around in, distances you can see, mountains that make you feel small—"

"Room to breathe?"

Nat looked at her. "You do understand, don't you?"

"I've never been out in your country," Patty said, "and I'd probably be out of place—"

"Not you." Nat had said the same to Zib once, but for wholly different reasons. "You're—real," he said now.

"I'm flattered."

"You're like your father in a lot of ways. When Bert said something, you didn't have to look it all over for booby traps. He said just what he meant."

From the far end of the trailer Brown said, "They're on the roof." A walkie-talkie was speaking hollowly. "Oliver wants the word when they're ready in the Tower Room." Brown held out the phone to Nat. "You'd better take over."

19

PAUL SIMMONS parked his car in the basement of his Manhattan office building. He started for the elevators and then changed his mind and walked out to the street and into a nearby bar. It was dimly lighted and deserted. Paul tried not to look at the color television screen on which the World Tower seemed to writhe in smoke. He paid for his drink and carried it to a booth.

So the cops had picked up Pat Harris. It now seemed likely to Paul that under pressure the story Harris would tell would not be the one they had agreed on down in the game room, but the one he had threatened Paul with: Harris had questioned the change orders, but Paul Simmons had told him to do what he was told. So maybe Harris came out of it not very bright, but not culpable.

Harry Whitaker, the building inspector with his hand conveniently out—what about him? In panic? Probably. Paul maneuvered out of the booth and went to the public telephone.

Harry's wife answered. Harry came on and snarled, "Yes?"

"Simmons here."

"I've been trying to get you," Harry said.

"Now you have me," Paul said, "what do you want?"

There was a significant pause. "What do you think I want, Mr. Simmons? I want to know what to do."

"About what?" The stupid oaf was obviously trying to think.

"Look, Mr. Simmons, haven't you seen on TV what's happening? At the World Tower? There're fires, and people trapped up in that Tower Room, and there's no power in that whole building!"

"So?"

"You've got to be kidding, Mr. Simmons. I mean, you and I know what must have happened. There's no other way. A primary short that wasn't grounded—I mean, what else could it be?"

"I don't know what you're talking about," Paul said.

Harry's breathing turned audible. "Look, Mr. Simmons." His voice, lower, was carefully controlled. "You paid me. You know you did. You told me everything would be all right, and once everything was buttoned up, who would know that we'd cut a few corners? You never told me anything like this could happen. I mean, there's two dead guys already, and what if they can't get those people down out of the Tower Room?" The voice took on a new urgency. "If they can't get those people, Mr. Simmons, that's— murder! What do we do? That's all, tell me what we do!"

"I wouldn't know," Paul said.

"Look, you paid me!"

"I paid you nothing. I don't know what you've dreamed up."

"You paid me!" The voice was out of control now. "You paid me! How do you think I took that Florida vacation?"

"It did seem a little odd on an inspector's salary."

"So that's the way it is." Harry's voice was almost resigned.

"O.K., Mr. Simmons. My name's on all the sign-offs. I'm the guy they'll come looking for. And you know what I'll tell them?"

"Tell them what you please."

"I will! I'll tell them what you paid me, down to the last penny! How you told me nothing could happen and I believed you!"

"But you have no witnesses, no proof. 'Harry' they'll say, 'aren't you making this up to save you own miserable neck?' And what answer will you give them to that?" Paul hung up, walked back to his booth, and sat down heavily.

Nat Wilson, he thought, Giddings, Zib, Pat Harris, and now Harry Whitaker; yes, and Patty herself, hadn't she gone over to the other side?

So where did that leave him?

He had told Bert McGraw that he had not questioned the change orders because they bore Nat Wilson's signature. Let Harris and Whitaker say what they chose, nobody could prove anything. Or could they? If there was a real stink, as there probably would be, a special inquiry into the fire, there was little doubt that the files of Paul Simmons and Company would be subpoenaed. So? Face it, Paul told himself, the files were entirely too revealing. Any competent cost accountant could detect that up to a certain point in the World Tower job, Paul Simmons and Company had been floundering, but that in a remarkably short time the ratio of costs to payments had taken a sharp reversal. And it would be no trick at all for Nat Wilson to tie the sudden change in fortunes to the issuance of the first of the change orders. Simple as that. Nat Wilson again.

Paul looked idly now at the television picture. The camera was focused on the north face of the Tower Room, a close-up with a long-range lens. They were breaking the windows out. Glass shards fell like shining hail. It was, Paul thought, merely a picture on a screen. He returned to a study of his drink.

The files were bad, but still they proved nothing. He had followed the change orders, and because of the changes his fortunes had improved. People might suspect that there was a causal relationship indicating hanky-panky, but they couldn't prove it. Still it would be well to check. And one question remained: Where had the copies of the change orders come from?

He went to the telephone again, and called his office. It was very late, but his secretary answered breathlessly.

"Ruth, honey," Paul said, "you sound uptight." A warning bell rang faintly in his mind. "Anything wrong?" At least she would tell him the truth, stick with him. After all they had had together. Not so much since Zib, but what difference? A good-looking chick, Ruth, really stacked, *and* bright.

The breathless voice calmed a little. "It's just that—you *have* seen what's happening down at the World Tower, haven't you?"

"I've seen."

"And," Ruth said, "you know about Mr. McGraw's heart attack?"

"That, too."

"He's dead."

"I'm sorry to hear it." Paul smiled. He bore the old man no particular malice, but it was better, far better this way.

"Where are you, Paul? Are you coming to the office?"

That warning bell again. "Why? Have there been calls?"

"No calls," Ruth said. "It's just that—I want to see you."

"Is there anybody there?"

"Nobody but me." Ruth's voice sounded puzzled.

Paul let his breath out slowly. Just jumpy, he told himself. "O.K.," he said, "I'm coming up. Get out the World Tower files. I want to look through them." He paused. "O.K.?"

"Of course." Good looking, *and* bright. "I'll have them waiting."

"That's my girl," Paul said. He walked out to the street.

The receptionist was long gone. In Paul's office Ruth was waiting, and on his desk were the World Tower files.

"Hi, honey," Paul said, and closed the door. Then he stopped and stared at the two men who had been standing behind it.

"This," Ruth said quite calmly, "is Mr. Simmons. These gentlemen have been waiting for you, Paul."

The room was still. "John Wright, District Attorney's office," one of the men said. "We've impounded your World Tower files. And we'd like you to come downtown with us to answer a few questions." Wright's voice hardened. "Maybe more than a few."

Paul looked at Ruth. Her face was expressionless. He looked again at the two men. "By what authority—"

"We have a search warrant, Mr. Simmons," Wright said.

Paul looked at the pile of file folders. "You won't find anything—"

"Wrong, Mr. Simmons, we already have found a great deal. The originals of some highly suspect change orders, for example."

Paul's mouth opened. He looked at Ruth.

"They weren't destroyed, Paul," Ruth said. "I thought it better to keep them. That way I had them to make copies to send to Mr. Giddings." Her voice was perfectly calm, modulated. "I was sure he would be interested."

In the silence, "You bitch," Paul said.

The girl smiled then. It was a pleasant, satisfied smile. "Perhaps," she said. And then, "You see, I don't like being used, Paul. I don't think many women do."

20

COAST GUARD RATING KRONSKI walked to the low parapet at the edge of the flat Trade Center roof. He put both hands on the structure and cautiously leaned forward to look down. Hastily he backed away. "Chief," he told Oliver, "you can't even see the ground! I never been this high in my life!"

"You've been in an airplane," the chief said.

"But I ain't no paratrooper." Standing back from the roof's edge, Kronski studied the row of broken windows that was the face of the Tower Room. At his feet was the rifle-like gun to fire the projectile which would carry the light messenger lines now neatly coiled and ready in tubs. "You got to be kidding, Chief," Kronski said. "That far, in this wind?" He shook his head. "No way."

Privately, Oliver agreed. It was even farther than he had estimated—maybe six hundred feet—and the wind was blowing half a gale. "I didn't ask your opinion, Kronski," he said. "Let's get on with it."

Kronski picked up the rifle and loaded it carefully. "Suppose we do get a line there, Chief?" he said. "An' we get a breeches buoy rigged." He looked squarely at Oliver. "How'd you like to take a ride from there to here, up this high, in this wind?"

"Get on with it, Kronski."

Kronski nodded. He raised the gun to his shoulder and aimed high. Into the walkie-talkie, Oliver said, "We're firing the first try."

"O.K." Nat's voice. "They're standing by in the Tower Room."

The light line rose shimmering from the gun's muzzle. It grew in length, light as a contrail in the sky, glistening in the late sun. Rising still, it reached in a graceful climbing arc for the broken windows, until it was level with the tip of the communications mast itself. Then it began to fall, but even before its head dipped beneath the level of the distant windows, they knew they had failed.

Kronski cursed.

"Try again," the chief said. "We're not giving up yet."

THE GOVERNOR stood well back in the Tower Room, his arm around Beth. Together they watched the line rise shining and clean and bright, and for a moment there was hope.

Ben Caldwell's artist's eye first measured the failure. "Start thinking of something else, Nat," he said. It was a whisper, no more, but the senator heard it.

"Hopeless?" Senator Peters said quietly.

"Probably," Ben said, "with that rifle. I think some of the shore stations have cannons, but how accurate they are . . . ." He shrugged. "Getting a line aboard a ship the size of a freighter is one thing; all you have to do is land it somewhere across the deck. Getting it into these windows from that distance . . . ." He shrugged again.

Grover Frazee, drink in hand, watched as if hypnotized, and when the line dipped sharply and disappeared beneath the windows his lips began to move without sound, and the look in his eyes was not quite sane.

Someone in the big room had turned on a radio Bob Ramsay had found. Rock music blared to a heavy beat. "This is not the time for that kind of thing," Mayor Ramsay said. He, too, had watched the reaching line plummet out of sight beneath the windows. "I'll put a stop to it."

"Leave it, Bob," the governor said. "These people are scared to death. Let them do their own things." His arm tightened around Beth's waist. "I'll get back to the phone. . . . You?"

508

"I'll go with you," Beth said. "I—don't want to be alone."

On the phone, "Sorry, Governor," Nat's voice said. "It was a long shot. The chief is giving it another try, but . . ."

"Understood," the governor said. "The elevators are out of the question?"

"Too much heat," Nat said. "Distortion of the rails."

To Beth the office seemed small and crowded. Howard and Storr, the two firemen, had come in along with Ben Caldwell and Grover Frazee and the fire commissioner. Beth had the insane feeling that she could smell fear.

The governor had turned from the telephone. He said to Howard, "You're sure the stairs are out of the question?"

"For a fact," Howard said. He looked at Storr, who nodded agreement. "We're better off here, which isn't saying much."

"And what do we do here?" Grover Frazee said. "Just wait, knowing what's going to happen?" He stood up suddenly. "Well, I'm not!" His voice was rising.

In the doorway Mayor Ramsay said, "Sit down, man! Start behaving like a responsible adult."

"You ought to have been a Boy Scout leader," Frazee said, and started for the doorway. "Don't try to stop me."

"We won't," the governor said, and watched Frazee disappear around the corner.

The office was still. Beth opened her mouth, closed it again without a sound. The fire commissioner stirred uneasily. The mayor said, "We should have stopped him, Bent."

"I'll take the responsibility," the governor said.

Fireman Howard said, "He'll never in this world get down."

"I am aware of it." The governor's face showed strain. "In areas of public concern I will take a stand. But what a man chooses to do, unless it directly affects others, is not my concern."

The telephone made noises. The governor flipped on the speaker switch that all might hear. "Armitage here."

Nat Wilson's weary voice said, "The second shot was no better than the first, Governor. It wasn't much of a hope from the start, but we gave it the best try we could."

"Understood," the governor said. "We appreciate the effort."

"Brown wants to know if his two men reached you safely."

"They did, but did the other two get back?"

There was a pause. Brown's voice came on the speaker. "I'm sorry to say they haven't, Governor. They're on about the fiftieth floor. There's fire in the stairwell beneath them."

"Then send them back up, man."

"There is fire above them too, Governor."

The governor's eyes were closed. At length he opened them. "Brown, I want a complete report prepared of this comedy of errors. You will put together—" He stopped at the sudden hush out in the big room.

Someone screamed, screamed again.

"Hold on." The governor jumped from his chair and rushed to the doorway. "God!" he said. "God in heaven!"

Someone had opened the fire door in answer to hammered knocks. Grover Frazee stood framed in the doorway. Most of his clothing had burned away. He was burned bald and blackened, his eyes were merely dark holes in the torment of his face. His teeth showed white in a grin. Flesh from his upper body hung in ragged strips and the remaining leather of his shoes smoldered. He made one wavering step forward, arms partially outstretched, a bubbling sound deep in his throat. And then all at once he collapsed face forward into a huddled, blackened heap. He made one convulsive shudder, and then no further move and no sound.

The great room was silent, in shock.

The governor said quietly. "Cover him up."

21

ONE BY ONE the building's defenses collapsed.

Within the building's core a thousand vertical crevices turned into chimneys, carrying heat up, and reaching down to suck in more fresh air, first to generate and then to support combustion. Heated air rises; superheated air rises more quickly. Heat is transmitted by conduction as well—through steel structure, paneling, tiling, flooring, wiring, piping, and curtain walls. A fire once well begun

becomes almost self-sustaining, raising temperatures above combustion levels, causing materials to ignite spontaneously.

Word had spread. Around the world it was known that in the richest country on earth in the newest, tallest building man had ever conceived, a peacetime catastrophe was in the making, and all the king's horses and all the king's men were helpless to cope.

Not quite.

THEY HAD COVERED what was left of Grover Frazee with a white tablecloth and left the body where it had fallen. The fire door was again closed, but to everyone in the room it was clear now that doors were only temporary protection. The fire would break through in time. Unless . . . .

"They are trying to contain the fire in the lower floors," the governor said. He was again standing on the chair. "That is our best hope." He had almost said *only* hope.

When he had stepped down, he took Beth's arm. "A drink," he said, "and somewhere to talk. I am tired of grinning to show how confident I am."

With me, Beth thought, miraculously he did not have to dissemble. Together they walked to the bar, and then carried drinks to a deserted corner. The governor swung two chairs companionably close and they sat, their backs to the room.

It was Beth who broke the silence. "Thoughts, Bent?"

"I'm thinking of waste. Regretting it. Hating it. Shaking my fists at the sky in childish futility."

"When I was a child," she said, "and being punished, confined to my room, I used to try to think of what I would most like to do, concentrate on that. What would you most like to do, Bent?"

Some of the tension perceptibly flowed from him. "Retire from politics. That ranch out in New Mexico—"

"Just that, Bent? Nothing more."

"No. You make me really look at myself. I would hate total retirement. I am a lawyer; I'd like to find out how good I am at it."

"You would be good at anything you decided to do."

"But the fishing would always be there," the governor said, almost as if she had not spoken, "and I would see to it that there

512

was always time for it. And, since I am painting a picture of Utopia, you would always be there too."

There was total warmth in her. "Is that a proposal?"

Without hesitation, "It is."

"Then," Beth said slowly, "I accept."

NAT WALKED DOWN the steps of the trailer to stand on the plaza and stare up at the immensity of the building. Until she spoke, he was unaware that Patty had followed him.

"What will happen to all those people, Nat?" Patty's voice was intense. "Will they . . ." She left the question unfinished.

"They're hauling hose in and up," Nat said, "a floor at a time. Every step is a fight."

"But what is burning? That's what I don't understand."

"Everything. Some of the offices are leased. Furniture, carpeting, paneled doors, are the first to go. And that raises the temperature to the point where tiling and plaster will melt, until things you wouldn't believe combustible start to go too."

"What are you going to do, Nat, when all of this is over?"

Nat shook his head in silence.

"Will they rebuild?"

"I hope not. Human pride affronts the gods." He paused. "Let's go back in."

"Have you thought of something?"

"No. But I can't stay away any more than you can." A new thought occurred: "What if you were not Bert's daughter," he said, "but just—married to somebody involved?"

"To you? Would I be down here at the building?" Patty nodded emphatically. "I would."

"That's what I thought," Nat said slowly, and wondered at his sudden pleasure.

PAULA RAMSAY walked up to the governor and Beth who still sat in a corner of the Tower Room. "I'm sorry to interrupt," she said, "but what's happening behind your back . . ." She shook her head. "I'm afraid I'm old-fashioned."

The governor nodded, expressionless. "With the exception of

Paul Norris and Grover," he said, "they've all done splendidly, so far. What can we expect?"

"Cary Wycoff is making a speech."

The governor cocked his head. He could hear the high-pitched, angry voice, but not the words. "He's probably saying that someone is to blame, and he is promising an investigation."

Paula smiled faintly. "You have it exactly right, Bent. Furthermore, people are swarming to the bar. One of the waiters is sitting in a corner by himself, drinking from a bottle."

The governor wondered if it was the waiter with three kids. He sighed and stood up. "What do you think I can do, Paula?"

"I am like Cary Wycoff, Bent," she said. "I think something ought to be done, but I don't know what. So I turn to you."

"I am flattered." The governor's smile sadly mocked himself and the entire situation. "I'd just as soon sit right here." He glanced down at Beth. "But I'll give it a try."

He passed Grover Frazee's body beneath a white tablecloth. The secretary-general stood looking down at the motionless shape. Slowly, solemnly he crossed himself. "Since my student days," he said, "I have prided myself on my freethinking. Now I find that early beliefs do not die so easily. Amusing, is it not?"

"It is not, Walther. I find it almost enviable."

The secretary-general hesitated. "I am beginning to understand that you are basically a kind man, Bent. It is sad that it requires a crisis situation before people come to know one another. Is there anything I can do to help?"

"Pray," the governor said without mockery.

"I have done that. If there *is* anything else, Bent—"

"I'll call on you." He walked out into the center of the room and looked around.

Paula had not exaggerated. The bar was doing a thriving business; a group had gathered to hear Cary Wycoff's speech; it *was* the waiter with three kids who was sitting by himself drinking; in the far corner the radio was playing rock, and some were maneuvering in spastic gyrations. Smoke was leaking from the air-conditioning ducts now, but it was not yet oppressive. The governor sneezed.

Mayor Ramsay nearby said, "Well, look at that!"

One of the younger dancers, female, was carried away. With a single motion she stripped her dress over her head and threw it from her. She wore minibriefs and no brassiere.

Senator Peters said, "It's getting hot in more ways than one."

Ben Caldwell joined the group around Bent. "More smoke," he said. "Until we broke out the windows, this was a more or less sealed system."

Nearby, Cary Wycoff shook his fists above his head as he glared at the governor's group. "Have you all gone mad? Standing around at a tea party! Don't you even understand what's happening?"

"I quite understand that you are having a temper tantrum, Cary," the governor said. "Are you going to hold your breath until your face turns blue?"

Cary got himself under control with effort. "We've listened to you." His voice was calmer now. "We've behaved like ladies and gentlemen—"

"All of you," the governor said, "except Paul Norris and Grover Frazee. They wanted action. You saw the results. Is that what you have in mind, Cary?" His voice was cold and hard.

Someone in the group behind Cary said, "There has to be some way! We can't be trapped here like rats!"

"And," Cary shouted, "that silly gesture of shooting a line over from the Trade Center tower. Everybody knew it couldn't work!" There was a general murmur of agreement.

The governor waited until it subsided. "I am open to suggestion," he said. "We all are."

The blaring rock music stopped suddenly. The almost-naked girl continued her ecstasy, but the other dancers turned to listen.

A quiet voice came from the crowd. "What is your assessment, Governor?"

"I won't try to fool you. It's grave, but not hopeless—yet. If there is any change, I promise to let you know." He turned away, and walked back past the covered body without a glance.

Beth was waiting with Paula Ramsay. "We heard," Beth said, She was smiling gently. "That was well done, Bent."

"The next time," the governor said, "isn't going to be so easy."

515

CHIEF PETTY OFFICER OLIVER had served twenty years in the Coast Guard, on shore stations and aboard cutters, in tropical waters and in Arctic ice lanes. He had helped fish men from burning oil-covered water and plucked them from foundering vessels; and sometimes the men he had gathered in had been dead. He had learned the long hard way that some operations were impossible. But still part of him rebelled against failure.

Kronski said, his voice weary, "So we shoot another line?"

"No." The chief could not countenance sheer waste either. He stood staring across the gap. Finally, he raised the walkie-talkie. "Oliver here. Come in, trailer."

Nat's voice came on immediately. "Trailer here."

"It's no good," the chief said. His voice was heavy with disappointment.

"I see." Nat kept his voice expressionless. Another idea gone bad. Think! Holding the walkie-talkie in one hand he pounded softly on the table with the other. "Hold it a minute, Chief."

Something was crawling around in the back of his mind, and if he could get it out in the open—damn it. *Another* idea gone bad, he thought suddenly. That was the key. Another idea—but what if two of them were taken together? Into the walkie-talkie he said, "We had a chopper up there early on, Chief, and they couldn't find any place to land." He hesitated. "But what about getting the chopper to take you and your gun over close enough to the building for you to shoot a line into the Tower Room? Then it could haul the line back to the Trade Center roof. Might that work?"

There was a long pause. Then, in slow wonderment, the chief said, "I'll be damned. Call in your whirlybird." He grinned at Kronski. "You're going for a ride, son. Just don't get airsick."

22

BEN CALDWELL supposed that a majority of people in the room still entertained some hope although he no longer did. How deep the eventual damage to the building's structure was going to be he could not begin to estimate, but long before the damage was complete, everyone in this room was going to be dead. He had resigned himself to that. And it did not bother him because a large part of himself had already died.

This was his building, his vision, his soaring dream. In New York, in Los Angeles, in Chicago, in Pittsburgh, his monuments would stand long after he was gone. But this building had been his masterpiece, and it was now beyond redemption.

In the far corner the heavy rock beat once more blared from the radio. The almost-naked girl danced on, her eyes closed, the world shut out.

The governor came out of the office, found a chair and climbed upon it. He raised his voice. "I promised news if and when there was any. Now I want your attention."

The singing died away. Someone turned down the radio.

"They are going to try again to get a line to us. This time—"

"Another sugar pill to keep us quiet!" Cary Wycoff's voice shrill with anger, tinged with terror.

"This time," the governor's voice carried above Cary's, "they are going to try to shoot the line in from a helicopter." He beckoned to the fire commissioner. "Have some men stand by to pounce on the line when it comes through the windows. Then—"

"When?" Cary shouted, "You mean if! And you know good and well it isn't going to happen."

From the crowd there was a low, angry murmur.

Bob Ramsay shouldered his way through to tower over Wycoff. "Easy, Cary. Everything has been done—"

"Give that to the voters, not to us. We're here to—die, man! And who's responsible? That's what I want to know. *Who?*"

"I'm afraid we all killed Grandma." Senator Peters raised his voice for attention. "Ever since I've known you, Cary, you've had more questions than a tenement has rats. But damned few answers, only reactions, and infantile ones at that."

Cary took a deep breath. "You can't talk to me like that."

"Why not?" The senator's smile was unpleasant. "By your standards, I'm an old man, but don't let that bother you if it's violence you're thinking of. In the neighborhood I grew up in a ten-year-old kid would eat you for breakfast."

517

Cary was silent, indecisive.

"All of you" the senator said, "simmer down. The governor is trying to tell you what to do. Now, listen!"

Suddenly the governor was smiling. "I've said it all." He pointed. "Look!"

They all turned. A helicopter was swinging toward the bank of broken-out windows, the staccato sound of its engine growing louder by the moment.

INSIDE THE CHOPPER, Kronski thought, boats, even small boats in heavy seas, moved with some kind of rhythm. All this chopper did was buck and jump. How did the chief think he could even hit the building, let alone the windows?

His stomach was bucking and jumping, too. He swallowed hard and breathed the cold air in deeply.

He could see faces massed to one side of the Tower Room staring at the chopper as at a vision.

The pilot looked at Kronski. There was question in his eyes.

"Closer!" Kronski roared. "Closer, damn it!"

The pilot nodded shortly. He moved his control stick as if it were a fragile thing. The building moved toward them. The faces inside were plainer. The bucking and jumping increased. "Close as I'll go!" the pilot said. "Shoot from here!"

Kronski raised his gun and tried to take a sight. One moment he was looking at the gleaming mast of the building, and the next moment what he saw was a row of intact windows below the Tower Room. He raised his voice in a great shout: "Can you, please, hold this thing still?"

FROM INSIDE the room they could see Kronski's strained face. The gun he held, fired. The fragile line shot twisting into the room, crashed against the far wall, and collapsed in a writhing tangle on the floor.

The fire commissioner and three waiters pounced on the line and held it tight.

The helicopter lurched quickly away, paying out line as it went. Someone cheered. It was contagious.

518

23

THE TELEPHONE hooked on his shoulder and the walkie-talkie on the desk in front of him, "So far, so good," Nat said. "They've made the messenger line fast inside the Tower Room. The chopper pilot is working back towards the Trade Center roof."

Tim Brown said, "God be praised!" He took out the half-empty cigarette package and in sudden decision threw it into the wastebasket. "I'll never have a better reason for really quitting."

Patty sat quietly on a stool, watching, listening.

"What is involved?" the governor was saying on the phone. "I have never had to ride in a breeches buoy, so I know nothing about it. Can a woman ride safely alone?"

"You stick your legs down through two holes," Nat said. "You're inside a kind of sack. All anybody has to do is close his eyes and hang on." His voice was solemn. "But you do have a couple of things to work out, Governor. Who goes in what order—"

"Women first. We decided that earlier."

"Governor. The round trip, Trade Center roof to Tower Room and return, is going to take a little time. Say a minute. You have a hundred people up there, maybe half of them women. It's going to take the better part of an hour just to get the women across, and another hour for the men. That's a lot of waiting, and you'd better have the exact sequence."

The governor said, "Senator Peters has anticipated you. He is preparing numbered lottery slips."

"Good. And somebody to enforce the sequence?" Nat said.

"That too is in hand. Two hours is your estimate?"

"Maybe less," Nat said. "But slow and easy is the only way."

The walkie-talkie crackled. "Oliver to trailer," it said. "We've bent on the heavy lines. We'll pay them out as they haul in. When all this heavy line is out, they're going to have a lot of weight to haul. More, because of the windage."

"Will tell," Nat said. "Hang on, Chief."

He spoke into the phone. "All set, Governor. Tell your men to haul away, and be prepared for a load. Good luck."

"Thank you, young man." The governor's voice was tinged with anxiety. "You will continue to stand by the phone?"

"Yes, sir."

"Bless you," the governor said.

Nat laid the telephone on the blotter and leaned back in the desk chair. He caught Patty's eye. She smiled. "You did it. You promised a new idea and you came up with it. I'm proud of you."

"It isn't over yet. Not by a long shot."

One of the battalion chiefs said, "If they're already getting smoke up in the Tower Room . . . . Two hours is a long time."

Time, Patty thought. Within its framework those who waited in the Tower Room would live or die. She was reminded of her vigil in the hospital. She wondered how her mother was bearing up.

The telephone crackled. Nat picked it up. "Yes, Governor?"

"I'm having a list prepared of names and addresses of everyone up here. We'll read it to you—just in case."

"Yes, sir." Nat cupped a hand over the phone. "We need someone to take down names," he said to Brown.

Patty slid down from the stool. "Let me." Nat watched her, smiling approval.

On the walkie-talkie a voice said, "Oliver to trailer. They've got the line over there. I want to make damn sure they tie a decent knot; a bowline is what I'd like. If that end pulls loose while somebody is between the buildings . . ." He left the sentence unfinished.

Nat said, "There are two firemen up there, and probably some ex-Boy Scouts as well." He could not stifle entirely a triumphant sense of gaiety. "I'll see to it, Chief. Hold on."

He picked up the phone, spoke to the governor and returned to the walkie-talkie. "Bowline it is," he said. "Rest easy, Chief."

"Then tell them to haul away on the breeches buoy line. We're ready at this end." There was triumph in the chief's voice too.

THE BUILDING's structural steel began to glow. Lesser materials melted or vaporized. On floor after floor, superheated air burst out of the core into open corridors and turned instantly to great, leaping flames. The heavy tempered-glass windows shattered and threw out their shards to rain down on the plaza. Aluminum panels

521

curled and melted, the skin of the structure peeling away to expose the sinews and the skeleton beneath.

From the ground, the line dangling between the two buildings could hardly be made out. When the breeches buoy swung loaded for the first time from the Tower Room and began its descent to the roof of the Trade Center, it seemed that the canvas bag and the woman it contained were hanging free, suspended by nothing more than faith, defying gravity in a miraculous attempt to escape the rising blast-furnace heat.

HER NAME WAS HILDA COOK, and she was starring on Broadway in the new musical *Jump For Joy!* She was twenty-nine years old, wearing a mid-thigh dress tucked up now above her waist. Her long, shapely legs dangled through the breeches buoy and she clung to the edges of the canvas bag with the strength of the hysterical.

She had stared unbelieving at the number on the small paper slip she had been handed from the empty punchbowl, and had squealed. "It can't be!" Her voice was shrill. "I'm number one!"

The secretary-general was conducting the drawing. "Someone," he remarked, "had to be. My congratulations, young lady."

They had carried the heavy line on which the breeches buoy rode, through the window and up to the ceiling where one of the firemen had broken through with his halligan tool to expose a steel beam around which they had bent the line. Ben Caldwell had made the point: "Unless we go to the ceiling the line will rest on the windowsill and we will not be able to get the breeches buoy into the room. I, for one, would rather get into the bag inside than climb out the window to get to it."

Three men manned the lighter line attached to the breeches buoy itself, and Hilda Cook, swinging free within the room, said, "Easy, guys. I'm already scared spitless!"

As she rode through the window and away from the building's protection, wind buffeted the bag, the heavy line began to swing, and Hilda felt she was falling. She screamed and closed her eyes. "And it was just about then, darlings," as she told it later, "that I wet myself. I really did. I'm not ashamed to say it."

The wind was cold on her legs and it wailed through the pulleys above her head. The rocking, swinging motions became wilder as she approached the center of the span.

"I thought I was going to die, I really did. I screamed for the damned thing to stop! But there was no way. No way! And when I was a kid I didn't even like roller coasters!" She may have fainted; she was never sure. "The next thing I knew, I was in Heaven! I mean the swinging had stopped, and the howling of the wind, and the biggest, strongest man I ever saw, darlings, just plucked me out of that canvas sack like I was something in a grocery bag. And he set me on my feet and held me up or I would have gone flat on my face. Was I crying? I was bawling like a baby and laughing at the same time! And the big man said, 'O.K., lady. It's all over now.' I still dream about it and wake up trying to scream!"

NAT WATCHED from the trailer doorway until the breeches buoy had returned to the Tower Room and emerged again. "Just over a minute," he said. "At that rate . . ." He shook his head and walked back inside to pick up the walkie-talkie. "Trailer to Oliver."

"Oliver here."

"Nice going, Chief. But it's going to take a long time. How about a second line, two breeches buoys working at once?"

"No dice. At the angle we work from, we couldn't get the lines far enough apart through those windows. In this wind they'd be sure to foul each other." His voice was calm, but tinged with regret. "We'll have to do the best we can."

Nat nodded. "I know you will. Thanks, Chief." One hour and forty minutes, he thought; that's all we need. An eternity.

24

POLICE LIEUTENANT JIM POTTER, notebook on knee, sat with his captain and the chief inspector in the quiet office. "John Connors," he said, "Caucasian male, thirty-four. Widower. No children. Occupation: sheet-metal worker when he worked, which hasn't been very often recently." He paused. "A history of mental disturbance commencing three years ago."

The captain said, "What happened then?"

"His wife died in jail. In the drunk tank."

The chief inspector said, "She was an alcoholic?"

"No. She was a diabetic. She had collapsed and was lying on the sidewalk. So they tossed her into the drunk tank, and without medication she died."

"Didn't she carry some kind of identification?" the captain said. "Something to say she had diabetes?"

"Maybe." Potter's voice was bitter. "And maybe nobody bothered to look. The investigation wasn't very thorough. Connors was the only one who cared much, and he went off his rocker."

The chief inspector let his breath out in a sigh. "O.K.," he said. "So he did have a grudge, and so he wasn't playing with a full deck of cards, why the World Tower Building?"

"I'm no shrink," Potter said. "But the World Tower Building was the last real job he had. He was fired. There's a connection, but maybe you have to be loony to see it. All I know are the facts."

IN SLOW, ALMOST INTERMINABLE succession, the women were helped into the canvas bag. Almost without exception their eyes were wide with terror. Some cried. Some prayed.

Paula Ramsay was number twenty-two. "I don't want to go," she told the mayor as they waited for her turn. "I want to stay with you."

The mayor shook his head. "I want you to go. I would rather have you safe than anything else in the world. And Jill needs you."

"Jill is a big girl now. We agreed on that." Paula looked around. "Where is Beth?"

"In the office with Bent."

"I thought," Paula said, "that she was ahead of me."

The mayor could not remember when last he had lied to his wife. "I wouldn't know." He stared out of the window as the breeches buoy began its trip back from the Trade Center.

The secretary-general said, "Number twenty-one, if you please." There was no answer. He repeated the call.

"Hey," somebody said, "that's you. Here's your ticket."

The half-naked girl stopped dancing. She shook her head as if to clear it. "I thought I was to be last girl out, number forty-nine." She giggled, and lurched toward the loading window. "Here I come, ready or not."

She was lifted into the canvas sack. Someone tossed her dress into her lap. Only then, realizing her nakedness, she began to cry. "What am I doing?" Her voice was almost a scream. "I—can't—"

"Lower away!" the fire commissioner commanded. "Hang on, sister, and you'll be home free before you know it."

The girl's shrieks were lost in the whistling wind.

The mayor took his wife's arm and walked with her toward the loading window. They stood quietly, holding hands, as the breeches buoy reached the Trade Center roof. They watched the chief lift the girl out of the canvas sack. Then he gestured toward the Tower Room and the breeches buoy began its return journey.

The mayor's wife watched its approach. "Bob."

"Yes?"

She turned to look up into the mayor's face. "You can't put thirty-five years into words, can you?" She closed her eyes as the breeches buoy swung through the window and halted, swaying gently.

"Number twenty-two, if you please," the secretary-general said.

Paula opened her eyes. "Good-bye, Bob."

"Au revoir," the mayor said. He was smiling gently. "Your words to Jill remember? Give her my love."

THE SENATOR knocked and walked into the office. The governor was in the desk chair. Beth was perched on a corner of the desk, long slim legs crossed and swinging gently.

"Come in, Jake," the governor said.

"I don't want to intrude."

"Nonsense. Sit down."

The senator sat and stretched his legs wearily. "Anything new?"

"I phoned down the lists," the governor said. "And then"—he smiled—"I indulged myself by calling my daughter, Jane, in Denver. I charged the call to the executive mansion telephone.

That will give the auditors pause. Anyone you want to call, Jake? I'll let the taxpayers pick up your tab too."

"No one," the senator said. "Do you ever doubt yourself, Bent? Wonder just what in hell use you've been to anybody?"

"Frequently."

"I mean it," the senator said. "When you're a kid just starting out—for me that was back in thirty-six, just elected to Congress— you look around and see the big ones, the important ones, the man in the White House, the cabinet officers. You study their style because they're what you want to be." His smile was wry.

"So," the senator went on, "you learn your role. Then you're a comer in your forties, beginning to carry some clout. You reach fifty, sixty and you've come a long way, but you aren't *there* yet. Do you know what I mean?"

"You're never *there*," the governor said sadly. "There's always something just over the next hill, and when you reach it"—he spread his hands in a gesture of dissolution—"what looked so bright from a distance, is only sunlight on smoke."

"And you wonder," the senator said, "just when you'll make the step that puts you where you've always wanted to be so you can relax." He shook his head "The answer is—never. You don't realize it until you face something like—this. And suddenly you see that all your life, chasing, has been so damn futile!"

"But fun," the governor said. "Admit that, Jake. You've had just the hell of a time outsmarting, outarguing, outstaying the rascals who got in your way. Would you change it?"

"Probably not. And that's the stupidest part of all."

"And," the governor said, "you have the gall to admit that you enjoyed it all, but still find it futile? When you leave a restaurant filled to the brim with a good meal, do you spend your time regretting that you couldn't eat everything on the menu?"

"As a philosopher, Bent, you're no Santayana, but you may have made a point or two worth considering. I'll ponder them outside." He stood up. At the doorway he flipped his hand in a vague gesture. "By the way, number twenty-one just went off." He spoke directly to Beth. "The naked chick. She thought—"

"I'm number forty-nine," Beth said, and made herself smile.

526

The senator hesitated, then waved again as he walked out.

"And that," the governor said, "leaves us alone again for a moment at least." He smiled up at Beth. "So pensive?"

"All the things you said to him," Beth said slowly, "could apply as well to you, couldn't they?"

"Probably. But the difference is that when you say them to yourself you don't necessarily believe them."

"I think I understand, Bent. I hope I do."

"There have been times," the governor said, "when I have done things I am not particularly proud of, or allowed them to be done, in order to achieve an end I thought worth the compromise."

"I think you are a good man, Bent, in the best sense of the word."

The governor took her hand. "Now tell me, since you're speaking so frankly, what number did you draw, twenty-one?"

25

ONE BY ONE Chief Oliver called down the names of those safely across, and Patty checked them off on the complete list. Nat stood outside the trailer's doorway. Squinting upwards, he could make out the loaded breeches buoy on its journey down to the Trade Center roof. Idly he wondered who was in the breeches buoy on this trip. He went inside. "How long do we have?" he said to Patty. "How many are we going to have time to get out?"

"Maybe all of them," Patty said. "I hope." She studied Nat's face. "You don't think so?"

Nat shook his head in silence.

IN THE TOWER, the fact of the breeches buoy had allayed many fears. There was still some singing, and some praying, and a few people drinking or dancing while each waited his turn for deliverance. Of all the people in the Tower Room, only a handful understood and accepted that catastrophe was inevitable.

Ben Caldwell understood and accepted; simple arithmetic sufficed: One hundred and three persons had drawn numbers. The round trips of the breeches buoy averaged very close to one minute. One hour and forty-three minutes, then, would be necessary to evacuate the Tower Room. With heat in the building's core already sufficient to distort steel elevator rails, would the Tower Room remain a sanctuary for one hour and forty-three minutes? No.

So be it.

With far less technical knowledge the governor nevertheless understood and accepted the situation. "The need is for haste," he said to Beth, "but we can't hurry." It was becoming hotter in the office. The temptation was strong to hammer his fist on the desk in sheer frustration. He stifled it.

Mayor Ramsay appeared in the doorway. "Paula has gone," he said. "I watched her land safely—if that's the word." She had turned to wave. He paused, remembering. "Thank God for that."

The governor said, "I'm happy for you, Bob."

Beth was smiling. "I'm glad," she said.

The governor said, "What is your lottery number, Bob?"

"Eighty-three." The mayor's voice was expressionless.

The governor smiled. "I'm eighty-seven."

"It isn't fair!" Beth said suddenly. "There are people out in that room who aren't worth any part of you! Of either of you! And what is Senator Peters's number? I'll bet it's high too!"

"Easy," the governor said. "Easy." He stood up, took off his jacket, and loosened his tie. He sat down again and began to roll up his sleeves. He smiled at Beth. "It's probably cooler out in the big room," he said, "but for now, at least, I prefer it here." He paused. "Unless you disagree?"

Beth hesitated and then shook her head slowly. "I'm sorry, Bent."

"They're behaving very well, so far, Bent," Bob Ramsay said. "Even Cary Wycoff is defused, for the moment at least."

The last-moment rush to the lifeboats, the governor thought, or the inevitable jamming of the exits when flames appeared. He well understood that in sudden panic terrible things could happen. "But it might be just as well, to have barricades set up? Some of those heavy tables surrounding the loading area with room for only one person at a time to come through?"

The mayor nodded. "And the opening guarded against gate-crashers. Yes, I'll see to it."

"Is there going to be trouble, Bent?" Beth asked.

"We'll try to anticipate it." The governor picked up the phone and spoke into it. Nat answered instantly. "Everything," the governor said, "is going beautifully, young man. You and the Coast Guard have my thanks. It is orderly now, but when the pressure starts to build, and people begin to understand that there won't be time for everybody . . . ."

"Yes, sir," Nat said. "I've been thinking about that too."

"Good man." The governor waited.

Nat said slowly, "We have the leverage, or the chief on the roof has, and maybe he'll do what I say."

The governor was nodding. "Which is?"

"We can issue an ultimatum," Nat said. "At the first sign of trouble we can put it that unless the process stays orderly, we'll shut the entire operation down, because slow and easy is the only way it can work. One mistake can spoil it for everybody."

"And can you make the ultimatum stick?"

"If we have to," Nat said, "we will."

"You may have to. For the moment, that's all. Bless you for standing by." He leaned back and closed his eyes.

"Bent," Beth said. She hesitated. "Oh, Bent, why does it have to be like this?"

"I wish I knew."

"It's ridiculous," Beth said, "and I know it, but I can't help asking: Why did we meet here and then have it—like this?"

The governor was smiling faintly. To that particular question he did not have the answer.

CARY WYCOFF sipped a glass of plain soda slowly while he watched the heavy tables being maneuvered into position around the area where the breeches buoy came in through the window. It was perfectly obvious what the purpose of the tables was: entrenched privilege throwing up barricades to keep out the barbarians. Himself. And he resented it with fierceness.

The lottery slip in his pocket was number sixty-five, which meant that fifteen males would go before him to safety. Bent Armitage, Bob Ramsay, and Jake Peters, he was willing to bet, would be among them. Oh, they would not be the first three; they were too canny for that. But they would be close to it.

Cary resented the women going first too. He had fought hard for women's rights, but he did not really believe in them. Women were created weaker, altogether less useful members of the community except for the one function which they never let you forget they alone could carry out. He, Cary Wycoff, was a far more valuable member of society than any of the women in the Tower Room. He should, therefore, have preceded all of them to safety. But the stupid electorate who thought with their stomachs and kept sending him back to a very pleasant life in Washington, would not see it that way. So there it was. Let the women go.

The men now; that was different. He was not going to stand idly by and watch fifteen—fifteen!—others go ahead of himself. Armitage and Peters, those two in particular, had always treated him at less than his real worth. Cary had another sip of soda while he thought about it. "I'll show you," he said softly. "You won't get away with it this time."

NAT PUT DOWN the phone after his conversation with the governor. He was conscious that Patty watched him, frowning. "You heard what I said?" he asked.

Patty nodded. "Would you do it? Stop the whole—operation?"

Nat said merely, "We'll see what the chief says." He picked up the walkie-talkie. "Trailer to Oliver." And then, "How's it going, Chief?"

"Slow. Steady. Number twenty-two was Mrs. Robert Ramsay. Twenty-two across in"—he paused—"twenty-three minutes flat. Best we could hope for."

"Better than I was afraid of," Nat said. "But when the pressure really begins . . ."

"Trouble you mean? Important people, aren't they?"

"That," Nat said, "doesn't mean that some of them won't—panic." He told the chief what he had said to the governor.

"Then the way I see it," the chief said calmly, "first sign of trouble, you let me know and we hold the breeches buoy right here until they line up again and stay in line. That way we may not get them all out, but we'll get some.

"I couldn't agree with you more, Chief."

Nat laid the walkie-talkie down on the desk and walked once more to the doorway to look out over the plaza. It was a dismal scene. The light was smoky gray, the air soot-filled, acrid. Firemen swarmed in the plaza—the perimeter of the area was an almost solid mass of fire equipment parked cheek-by-jowl, engines and pumps throbbing.

The entire plaza floor was a lake now. Cascades of water poured back out of the building, down the concourse steps—like spawning ladders for salmon.

Never again, Nat told himself. Never again a fire like this in a building this size. Correction: Never again a building this size.

He heard a telephone ring in the trailer, and Patty's voice saying, "Yes. He's here." And then, expressionless, "Nat."

She was holding the instrument out to him. "Zib," she said.

ZIB HAD LEFT the magazine office at the usual time, taxied home, and hurried into a scented bath. Luxuriating in the suds, feeling the tensions flow away, she told herself that everything was going to be all right. She had turned her back on Paul Simmons, hadn't she? Nat must have seen that from her telephone call telling him that Paul was not coming down to the building. At heart Nat was a lamb. He hadn't really meant to speak so harshly to her. He couldn't have. Not to her.

She sank deep in the tub, closed her eyes, and stroked one smooth, sudsy shoulder with her hand. What was that commercial on TV? "If he doesn't feel the difference, he has no feeling." Nat would be tired when he got home. But not too tired.

She got out of her bath dried herself, and applied scent sparingly to throat, breasts, and belly. Then she put on her light-weight full-length white robe Nat liked especially, and the heeled mules he had given her, and went into the living room to put music on the record player. It was then that she decided to call the trailer office.

ON THE PHONE, "Hello," Nat said.

And what had she thought to say, anyway? "Hi." And she added inanely, "I'm home."

Nat heard music in the background. Beguiling. "I guessed that."

"Darling, how is it going? I mean—"

"Great. Just great." Through the open doorway Nat looked again at the plaza. He raised one hand to wipe at his forehead and saw the grime on his palm.

Zib said, "I—tried to watch on television. I—couldn't." She paused. "It's a mess, isn't it?"

"Understatement. Did you want something?"

The hesitation in her voice was un-Ziblike. "Not really. I came home and—" She stopped, her voice now uncertain. "Will you be coming home?" She could not bring herself to add the word, ever.

Nat was conscious that Patty was watching him. He tried to ignore her and could not.

"Darling, I asked a question."

"I don't know the answer." Nat hung up.

Zib put the phone down slowly as the tears began.

THE GOVERNOR was on the phone. "Only two more women to go. Then we start the men." A faint warning was plain in his voice.

"O.K.," Nat said. "I've talked with the chief. He agreed that at the first sign of disorder he'll hold the buoy on the Trade Center roof until people line up again. If anybody doubts that, get him on this phone and I'll tell him."

"As long," the governor said, "as the telephone line remains in service."

"That's another thing, Governor," Nat said. "We'll get right through to the city radio station. If the phone goes out we'll go on radio to you. But you won't be able to reach us, so if there's trouble, just flutter a handkerchief at the window and the chief will call down to me. O.K.?"

There was a short silence. "O.K.," the governor said. Another silence. Then, "You think well, young man. You have done a superlative job. You have the gratitude of all of us . . ." Pause. "Just in case the opportunity to tell you in person doesn't arise."

26

THE LOWER FORTY FLOORS were now in shadow. Most of the windows had broken out from the heat and smoke poured through the empty frames. Through the smoke, the building itself was faintly incandescent, and in the distorted air currents caused by its radiation the entire structure seemed to writhe.

THE GOVERNOR walked back to the office and sank into the desk chair. He felt suddenly old, and tired beyond mere fatigue. It was as if in Beth's presence he had spent these past few hours in the spring of eternal youth, knowing that it could not last, and yet hoping. Now Beth was gone, the last woman out safely. At the final moment the governor had not been able to watch.

He thought about what it had been with Beth. Given other circumstances in which choice was as free as choice ever was, the governor thought that Beth would have gone willingly, if not eagerly with him to the ranch in high New Mexico. Dream stuff, pure and simple. And not to be.

Feeling sorry for himself, wasn't he? Well, why the hell not? Down in the streets behind the barricades were a thousand people, maybe ten thousand, who were going home when the show was over to do whatever they chose before they went to bed, knowing that they were going to wake up in the morning.

Face it, he told himself as he had told the senator, you've had just a hell of a good time. And what would you change if you had it to do over? Probably not a single bloody thing.

Except Beth. Maybe, he thought, if he had tried harder he might have found her or someone like her before it was too late.

Beth. At least she was down safe. He hoped. He wished now that he had stayed to watch, just to be sure. Well, it was easy enough to make sure.

He flipped on the telephone's speaker switch. "Armitage here," he said. There was no answer. He punched the disconnect buttons, punched them again. There was no sound. The phone was dead. And now, he thought, we are truly alone.

THE HEAVY LINE stretching from Tower Room to Trade Center roof supporting the weight of the breeches buoy was nylon, strong, flexible, flawless nylon. It was secured around a ceiling beam in the Tower Room, and the knot that secured it, a bowline, had been tied under the firemen's watchful eyes.

Because with nylon even a bowline, the queen of knots, has been known to work loose, the firemen had taken the added precaution of bending the bitter end of the line into two half hitches around the standing part. The half hitches showed no signs of slipping, and unless they did, the bowline had to hold.

But the beam around which the line was bent was steel, a part of the building's structure, major support for the communications mast that rose still shining in the waning sunlight.

Steel conducts heat well.

And nylon melts.

THE TELEPHONE on the desk in the trailer made noises. Nat picked it up and spoke his name. The sound of his voice in the instrument was all wrong, it echoed. Like the governor, he tapped the disconnect buttons, tapped them again, and yet a third time. The dial tone sounded suddenly in his ear.

He dialed the Tower Room office number, dialed it again, and then hung up. "That's that," he said. "Their line's gone."

The building's systems had collapsed one by one. There was something of finality in the death of the telephone. He dialed again the number he had already called once, the city radio station. He was answered immediately. "World Tower Plaza," he said "Their phone line has gone. You're the only way we can reach them."

"We'll hold this line open. When you give the word, you'll talk right on the air."

"Thanks," Nat said. "We'll stand by." He laid the phone on the desk again, and picked up the walkie-talkie. To the chief on the Trade Center roof he said, "Telephone's out. If you get a signal, call me. I'll get on the radio."

"Will do," the chief said.

Nat leaned back in the chair and looked around the trailer. Tim Brown was there, one battalion chief, Giddings, and Patty.

"You heard it," Nat said. He lifted his hands and let them fall.

It was then that the walkie-talkie came to life. "Roof to trailer." In the sudden silence, Nat picked it up. "Trailer here."

The chief said, "Something white is waving. You'd better get on the air. I have the breeches buoy and I'm holding it."

Nat took a deep breath. "Here we go," he said and reached for the phone.

27

WITHOUT WARNING, and by one of those freaks that were so much a part of this disastrous day, the air-conditioning ducts suddenly belched out quantities of hot acrid smoke. And that, like the pulling of a trigger, apparently set off the panic.

The radio, tuned to the city station, played quiet music. The women were gone now, and there was no more dancing.

In a corner, Rabbi Stein, Monsignor O'Toole, and the Reverend Arthur William Williams spoke quietly together. In the loading area behind the table barricades, Harrison Paul, conductor of the city's symphony orchestra, allowed himself to be hoisted into the breeches buoy and swung out through the window. He tried to keep his eyes closed, but the temptation was too great, and looking down on the city from this terrifying and almost unsupported height made him violently sick. The storm music from Beethoven's "Pastoral" symphony thundered through his mind as he clung desperately to the swaying canvas bag, positive that he would be killed. When at last he reached sanctuary, and the chief and Kronski together lifted him out of the breeches buoy, he dropped to his knees to kiss the Trade Center roof.

He was the first man out, and for a time it appeared that he would also be the last.

The waiter with the three kids was sitting on the floor now, still nursing his bottle of bourbon. The number of the lottery ticket in his pocket was ninety-nine. He had decided that his chances of getting out safely were just about those of a celluloid dog chasing an asbestos cat through Hell. He did not particularly enjoy the bourbon, but he thought that if he passed out he wouldn't mind so much what he was powerless to prevent.

The two firemen, two waiters, the fire commissioner, and the secretary-general were behind the table barricades. One of the waiters testified later that although you could feel tension building, everything seemed under control. "Until," he added, "the smoke hit us."

Cary Wycoff was talking with a dozen men, only one of whom, another waiter, was later identified: Bill Samuelson, at various times longshoreman, semi-pro footballer and professional boxer.

It was hot and getting hotter. The waiter from the barricaded area told it like this: "It was funny. The wind coming in from the broken-out windows was cold, and my hands were almost numb. But my feet were hot and the rest of me felt like I was standing in a hot room in the gym. Heat all around us, but still the cold wind, and that was what was so—funny, if you see what I mean."

Ben Caldwell and the Soviet ambassador were talking together about the architecture of Moscow and the nostalgia that always struck the ambassador whenever he saw in this alien land a *zwiebelturm*, the onion-shaped tower of eastern European design.

Senator Peters was at the west bank of windows, quietly watching gulls over the river and the harbor.

The governor was still alone in the office with the dead telephone and his thoughts. He could hear faintly the music on the radio, but other than that the big room outside was quiet.

"So solemn, Bent." Beth's voice from the doorway. She stood quietly, a half-smile on her lips, awaiting his judgment.

The governor stared at her in wonder. "Something happened to the breeches buoy?"

Smiling still, she shook her head.

The governor raised his hands, and then dropped them. It was near-disbelief that he felt, colored by joy and sorrow. "You didn't go," he said. "I couldn't watch."

"I saw." She walked slowly forward.

"I tried to phone to see if you were—safe. But the line is dead." He roused himself from near-apathy. "I wanted you safe." His voice was stronger, some of its old assurance regained.

"I know." Beth had reached the desk now. She perched on it as before, long legs swinging gently. She held out her hand, and the governor took it, held it tight.

"You should have gone, damn it."

"No, Bent." There was calmness and serenity in her voice, her manner. "I told you I was not going to make believe anymore. I gave up my place. Even if I wanted to, there is no taking it back. When you step out, you go to the end of the line."

"Damn it—"

"Bent, listen to me." Her fingers squeezed his. "These past few hours for the first time in my life I have felt that I was—doing something useful, not very much perhaps, but far, far more than I have ever done before."

"All right," the governor said, "so you've learned a few things while we've been trapped here. Then take that knowledge and go."

"There is another reason, Bent. It is not the kind of thing one says, and is believed. But it is true." Her hand now quietly rested in his. Her eyes were calm on his face. "It is that I would rather be here with you, than be outside—alone again."

From the overhead air-conditioning duct a puff of black smoke appeared, spread, and settled slowly. Neither noticed it.

"This is where I want to be. Dear Bent—"

It was then that the sounds of strife broke out in the large room, voices raised in angry shouts, the din of furniture overturning.

The governor shoved his chair back and stood up. "Stay here," he said and hurried through the doorway.

It was a scene from Bedlam played in a haze of black smoke. One of the barricade tables was overturned and men were forcing it aside, opening a passage, tearing at one another like animals. As the governor looked, the fire commissioner grabbed the first man through by the top of his jacket front, drew him close, and drove his fist against the man's mouth. He released him and reached for another.

A waiter in a white coat, a large, muscular man—it was Bill Samuelson—crowded through the gap, slammed two punches into the commissioner's belly, and pushed him aside to fall.

Cary Wycoff stood near the overturned table, free of the mêlée, his voice raised, screeching, and as the governor trotted across the room Senator Peters, a candlestick in his right hand, poked Cary in the middle with it, doubling him over, and moved on to slam the candlestick against the big waiter's head. The man dropped like a pole-axed steer.

Madness and confusion. Someone punched the governor's shoulder; behind the punch was the contorted face of the network executive. All the governor could think of was a fear-crazed sheep.

More smoke burst from the ducts, choking, blinding. The governor raised his voice. "Stop it! Stop it, I say." He was shouting into a whirlwind. He lowered his head and charged.

An elbow bashed his cheek. He pushed on through. Here was the heavy line coming through the window. Here was the window itself. He clung to the line with one hand and leaned as far out as he could to wave his handkerchief again and again. Then he pulled himself back inside and tried to make his way out of the scramble. Somewhere, somewhere that radio still played music. The governor homed in on it as on a beacon.

He saw it sitting on a nearby table, and as he lunged for it, the table overturned. The radio skittered across the floor, playing still. Someone slammed into the governor's side and he went down on all fours, and then with all of his strength dove forward and got the radio into his hands. Holding it tight against himself, he worked out of the mêlée, and then, temporarily away from the struggle, he held the radio high and turned the volume full on.

Music was suddenly silenced. And then, a giant's voice, Nat Wilson's voice, roaring into the confusion: *"Now hear this! Now hear this in the Tower Room!"*

There was a pause. Some of the sound of struggle was stilled.

"In the Tower Room hear this!" the voice blared again. *"This is Plaza Trailer Control. I don't know what's happening up there, but until it stops the breeches buoy will remain on the Trade Center roof. Is that clear? I repeat: Until there is order again, the breeches buoy will not return to the Tower Room. If you read me, wave something white from the window."*

The great room was silent. All eyes watched as the governor walked to the loading area, the radio still in his hand. He passed

538

it to the senator, took a tablecloth from a nearby table and, leaning out as before, waved it vigorously.

The silence held.

"*All right,*" Nat's voice blared suddenly, "*All right! Now resume your drill. Is that understood? Resume your drill or the entire operation stops. We're doing everything we can to get you all out alive. If you cooperate, we may succeed. If you don't, nobody gets out. Is that understood? Nobody!*"

The governor looked around at the bruised and bloody faces. "Any comments?"

There was no reply.

"*Is that understood?*" Nat's voice roared.

The governor leaned out the window again. He waved the tablecloth. There was a pause for transmission from rooftop to trailer.

Then, "*O.K.,*" Nat's voice said. "*The breeches buoy is coming back. But*"—the voice paused—"*at the first sign of more disturbance it stops again.*"

The senator turned down the radio's volume. Music began once more to play.

The secretary-general said quietly, "Number fifty-one, if you please, number fifty-one."

One of the waiters not involved in the disturbance moved forward. He had his slip of paper held tight in both hands.

"Number fifty-two," the secretary-general said.

Fireman Howard said, "What's your number?"

The secretary-general smiled. "It is sixty. There are eight more ahead of me."

"And I'm one of them," Howard said. "Fifty-eight."

The secretary-general smiled again. "My congratulations." He paused. "It has been a pleasure working with you."

"Maybe," Howard said, "we can have a drink together on that when all this is over."

"I will look forward to it."

The senator walked over to Cary Wycoff. He still held the candlestick in his hand.

"The next time, Cary," he said softly, "I will crack your skull. You can believe that."

SHE WAS SITTING still where the governor had left her, perched on the corner of the desk, her calm blue eyes seeming to smile.

This, the governor thought, was how he would always remember her. Always? Always. Through eternity.

"You are leaving now," he said. He saw objection forming in her face and he attacked it immediately. "Yes," he said. "You are going. Because, my dear," he said, "it is my wish, my plea."

"Bent—" She stopped. Her eyes no longer seemed to smile.

"I will not end a long life with an act of selfishness," the governor said. "Come along."

They came out of the office holding hands. The big room was subdued now, spiritless. The radio played quietly; no one listened.

To the secretary-general, "Number forty-nine was overlooked, Walther," the governor said. "Here she is."

The secretary-general smiled at Fireman Howard. "I was wrong," he said. "There were nine ahead of me."

Beth said, "Oh, Bent!"

"Good-bye, my dear." The governor hesitated. He smiled. "Some day catch a trout for me." He turned away then and walked back to the empty office.

"SIXTY-ONE!" The fire commissioner's voice. "Sixty-two . . . Sixty-three . . . Sixty-four."

Cary Wycoff started forward. The senator stepped in front of him. "I'm number sixty-five," Cary said and held up his slip.

The senator merely glanced at it. He nodded and stepped back. "You would be," he said.

WITHIN THE GIANT STRUCTURE the heat continued to rise.

"Seventy-six!" The fire commissioner's voice was hoarse from smoke and strain. He coughed with a deep retching sound.

The senator looked around the great room. Over by the fire door the white tablecloth marked Grover Frazee's remains. In a nearby chair an elderly man was slumped, head back, mouth and eyes open. As nearly as the senator could tell, he was no longer breathing. Ben Caldwell lay in the center of the floor where he had apparently collapsed. He made no movement.

The waiter on the floor held up his bottle offering a drink. He had a silly grin on his face.

"Thanks, anyway," the senator said, "but I'll wait a little." His voice sounded strange, heavy. He straightened himself with effort and walked toward the office.

The governor was in the desk chair. He looked up, smiled, and coughed. When the coughing had stopped, he said, "Sit down, Jake. Let's have a talk."

TOGETHER the chief and Kronski hauled the man out of the breeches buoy bag. "Hold him up," the chief said, and added, raising his voice, "Oxygen over here!" He waved at the Tower Room windows and slowly the breeches buoy began its return trip.

"Seventy-seven," the chief said. He spoke into the walkie-talkie. "Name of Bucholtz. He'll need ambulance care."

He stood waiting, his eyes on the Tower Room windows, while Kronski paid out the breeches buoy guideline.

Here on the Trade Center roof, in the slanting rays of the sun, the evening chill worked its way into a man's bones. Kronski stomped his feet and beat his hands together.

The chief showed no signs of discomfort. "Over there," he said, "they have heat enough, and to spare." And then, "Look!" For the first time his voice rose. "Look there! It's coming out empty!"

The breeches buoy swung through the window. No hand held it back. Of its own weight it began the careening slide down the immense curve, faster, faster, swinging, swaying like a mad thing.

"That's done it!" The chief pointed. Like a snake the heavy supporting line slid through the window, its end whipping from the weight of the knots that still held, the line itself melted through from the heat of the beam it had been tied to. It fell endlessly.

"Stand clear!" the chief said, and jumped aside himself as the heavy line lashed viciously against its fastening on the roof. Then he strained to see through the Tower Room windows. He held out his hand. "Binoculars." In silence he studied the room through the glasses and then let them dangle from their lanyard around his neck. He raised the walkie-talkie. "Roof to trailer."

"Trailer here." Nat's voice.

541

The chief's voice was expressionless. "The line has parted. You'll find the breeches buoy somewhere down below. It's empty."

Nat cursed softly.

"It doesn't matter," the chief said. "I can't see any movement over there. I think it's all over." He paused. "The best we could," he said. "It wasn't enough."

The time was 8:41. It had been four hours and eighteen minutes since the explosion.

Later

THEY walked in silence in the evening chill, block after block, without destination, each deep in thought. They stopped at last almost as at an inaudible signal, and turned to look back.

The tip of the great tower caught the last of the day's light. Below, the structure glowed in gathering darkness. Like an ember after the leaping flames have died, it no longer seemed to writhe.

"The chief said it," Nat said. "The best we could do and it wasn't enough. Maybe it wasn't the best we could." His voice was low-pitched, savage. "Maybe—"

"It's done," Patty said. "Leave it there, and go on."

"On where?"

"Just on," Patty said gently. "Ahead, not back. There is no turning back. It's all—behind us."

They began to walk again. Together.

Richard Martin Stern

"The story told in *The Tower* is a disaster that I am afraid could happen. I hope it never does."

Clearly Richard Martin Stern knows what he's writing about. "I have worked on construction jobs," he goes on to say, "and I knew, even before starting to write, some of the problems, risks and opportunities for chicanery in any large construction project. I began my research by picking the brain of an architect friend and borrowing his books, among them one on the legal pitfalls in the practice of architecture in which actual examples of shenanigans are lovingly told. I studied texts on building construction, with special emphasis on electrical installation. I was lucky enough to get a master schematic of the basic wiring of an existing skyscraper much like my imaginary Tower."

The book, which has been purchased by Warner Brothers for a film, is the fifteenth novel in which Mr. Stern has drawn on his rich and varied life as a Harvard graduate turned odd-job man, engineer, and later full-time writer. His colourful career has taken him to Europe and the Caribbean, but home for Richard and his wife is now Santa Fe, New Mexico.

Some of the research for *The Tower* Mr. Stern could do on his own doorstep. It was a Santa Fe neighbour, a retired rear-admiral, who instructed him about breeches buoys. And his physicist friends at the Los Alamos Scientific Laboratory advised him on such matters as heat transference and the action of explosives.

Even so, as Mr. Stern asserts, "A story is people, not merely a mass of data; and the main problem in the book was to make the building itself a character of almost equal importance to the humans involved."

How well he has succeeded in this his breathless readers will surely testify. The death of the Tower matters. It is a warning to city planners the world over.